Far

A History of the Planet Venus
in Fact and Fiction

edited by Brian W. Aldiss
assisted by Harry Harrison

Panther

Granada Publishing Limited
Published in 1971 by Panther Books Ltd
3 Upper James Street, London W1R 4BP

First published in Great Britain by
Macdonald & Co. (Publishers) Limited 1968
Copyright © Brian Aldiss and
Harry Harrison 1968
Made and printed in Great Britain by
C. Nicholls & Company Ltd
The Philips Park Press, Manchester
Set in Linotype Times

Acknowledgments

LAST AND FIRST MEN, by Olaf Stapledon. Copyright ©
1930 by Methuen & Co. Ltd., London. Reprinted by
permission of the publishers.

PIRATES OF VENUS, by Edgar Rice Burroughs. Copyright
© 1932 by Edgar Rice Burroughs, Inc. Reprinted by permission of Edgar Rice Burroughs, Inc. and of Ace Books,
Inc.

PERELANDRA, by C. S. Lewis. Copyright © 1940 by The
Bodley Head Ltd. Reprinted by permission of the publishers.

ALCHEMY, by John and Dorothy de Courcy. Copyright ©
1950 by Avon Periodicals Inc. Reprinted by permission of
Forrest J. Ackerman and the authors.

THE MAN FROM VENUS, by Frank Paul. Copyright ©
1939 by the Ziff-Davis Pub. Co. Reprinted by permission
of the Ultimate Publishing Co.

THE CITY ON VENUS, by Henry Gade. Copyright ©
1941 by the Ziff-Davis Pub. Co. Reprinted by permission of
the Ultimate Publishing Co.

UNVEILING THE MYSTERY, by Willy Ley. Copyright ©
1955 by Galaxy Publishing Corporation. Reprinted by permission.

EXPLORING THE PLANETS, by V. A. Firsoff. Copyright
© 1964 by V. A. Firsoff. Reprinted by permission of the
author and Sidgwick and Jackson Ltd.

THE BIG RAIN, by Poul Anderson. Copyright © 1955 by
Astounding Science Fiction. Reprinted by permission of

The imaginary travellers to these worlds of the sky have always carried with them their terrestrial ideas.

Camille Flammarion, Popular Astronomy

Contents

Foreword

ON 18th October, 1967, a complex piece of hardware weighing 2,439 lbs. settled down on the surface of the planet Venus. A new story had begun; we cannot foresee how that story will continue, how long it will last, how it will end, or even what the plot is going to be about.

But, equally, a story has ended. It is a long story, because man has been telling himself it for many centuries: the story of a fair imagined Venus. The last hundred years of that story are related here.

Venus, Earth's "Sister planet" ... An unsatisfactory sibling she has proved at last. And even to the imagination there has always been something cheating about her. She has been teasing, ambiguous, hiding herself near the sun, disappointing – a close relation who has yet stayed distant, blank-faced.

Her name is most beautiful. And yet: the Cytherean landscape, under the thick oppressive Cytherean cloud banks, must be uglier than anything Earth can offer. Venus just has not come up to expectations.

Section I

Clouded Judgements

A CENTURY ago, they were arguing about Venus. Since the facts in the case were in short supply, there was plenty of room for this to be a good religious argument.

However much that particular religious argument seemed like a new thing to those strange vanished Earthmen, the Victorians, it was an old one to Venus. She had been confused with religious promptings from time immemorial.

The planets, the wanderers, were known to earliest men, and in the Pleistocene evenings and dawns, Venus must have been a familiar and reassuring sight. The stars were real spectacles in those days, and remained so until man invented gunpowder and filled the sky with bigger and better – if briefer – stars of his own.

To the eye, our two nearest planets, Venus and Mars present very different sights. Mars is red and sullen. Venus is silver and elusive. What more natural than that the one should be identified with masculine war gods and the other with goddesses of love?

The Venus we know comes from the Mediterranean. She was a goddess of garden fertility, worshipped in Rome at quite an early date. Later, however, she was identified with the Greek goddess of fertility, Aphrodite. Behind Aphrodite are shadowy and Semitic figures, pre-hellenic deities – in the words of the anonymous contributor to this volume: "worshipped girls and duskier hags, Ishtar and Astarte."

13

The combination of Roman and Greek goddess was a powerful one. This goddess of love was worshipped in Greece principally on the island of Cythera. From this comes the adjective Cytherean which will be used here, since such adjectives as "venereal" and "venal" have been pressed to other uses. "Venusian" is a barbarism and, although it will probably conquer, should not be permitted to triumph over a lovely word like Cytherean all at once.

To the Ancient Greeks, the planet Venus was two stars: Phosphorus, the Morning Star, and Hesperus, the Evening Star. So even then she had two natures; and today we know that, bright though she may look from Earth, Venus is a dull world, shrouded under a clouded and oppressive atmosphere. But Pythagoras, five centuries before Christ, realised that the two stars were one, and Homer speaks of Venus as Callistos the Beautiful. Cicero used the two names for it again: Vesper, the evening star, and Lucifer, the morning star; of all these titles, it may be Lucifer that will seem the most accurate to the men who eventually stand in armoured pressure suits upon the Cytherean surface.

For the Romans, Lucifer, of course, held no reference to the fallen archangel ruling in hell; it simply meant "Light-bearer", being a translation of the Greek Phosphorus; but in view of what we have now learned about our neighbour, the mis-application is a fruitful one.

When we come to the Bible, the obscurities are such that even the Italian astronomer Schiaparelli, who devoted a whole book to Old Testament astronomy, cannot entirely clear them away. In the Book of Job, the Almighty, growing vexed, unleashes a pretty formidable pride of rhetorical questions at Job, among which some of the astronomical ones are, "Canst thou bind the sweet influences of Pleides, or loose the bands of Orion? Canst thou bring forth Mazzaroth in his season?"

Schiaparelli says that the sun, the moon, and Mazzaroth (or Mazzaloth) were the three principal stars for the Hebrews, so that Mazzaroth is most probably Venus, and that these stars also had particular religious significances in Babylon, where the goddess Ishtar is identified with Venus. In Mithraism, another religion from the East which at one time nearly overwhelmed Christianity, Venus was one of the spheres the dead soul passed through in its process of purification.

Other generations have held other beliefs, deifying Venus in their hopes, mixing her with shifting mythologies, co-opting her into astrology and alchemy. We have gone one better. We have landed what is now a load of metallic junk on her! Should we celebrate this success or mourn the death of the legends?

The Victorian concern over Venus – and the other planets of the solar system – gave the legends a new aspect. They were concerned with the Christian viewpoint. Were there people living on Venus? If so, what were they like? Were they Christian or heathen?

It was difficult to get a clear directive from the Church on the matter. Revealed Religion contained no doctrinal guidance about the inhabitants of other planets – naturally, since the whole concept of planetary bodies was recent compared with Christ's teaching. The invention of the telescope in the seventeenth century was instrumental in proving that planets are bodies enjoying day and night much like Earth, and that the Earth revolved round the sun with the other planets (the essence of the Copernican theory), rather than that the sun revolved round the Earth (the essence of the Ptolomaic theory). But the Church had accepted such ideas only reluctantly.

This gave the philosophers plenty of scope for speculation.

Galileo's telescope was not powerful enough to resolve Saturn's rings. It was left to Christian Huygens, working with a cumbersome air telescope, to determine that Saturn was not a jug with two handles floating in space. Huygens also wrote a treatise called *The Theory of the Universe, or Conjectures Concerning the Celestial Bodies and their Inhabitants*.

The Frenchman, Bernard de Bovier de Fontenelle, whom Voltaire called the most universal genius of his age, published his *Conversations on the Plurality of Worlds* in 1686. It was even more successful than Huygens' work, and went through many translations, including three English ones, which ran to many editions. From the start, the question of other living things on other planets fascinated everyone.

15

With very little to go on apart from the planetary name, Fontenelle believed that the Cytherean inhabitants devoted all their time to love in pleasant surroundings. Swimming, singing, dancing, feasting – these are happy standbys when a change is needed from love-making.

Emanuel Swendenborg, the seventeenth century Swedish philosopher and scientist, suspected Venus of harbouring giants.

It became fashionable to suspect life everywhere. As Sir David Brewster put it in the Eighteen-Fifties, "Just about the same time that the invention of the *telescope* shewed that there were innumerable worlds which might have inhabitants *requiring the Creator's care* as much as the tribes of this earth do, the invention of the *microscope* shewed that there were in this world innumerable tribes of animals which had been all along enjoying the benefit of the Creator's care as much as those kinds with which man had been familiar from the beginning."

It was precisely these tribes of animals that were about to enjoy, not just the benefits of the Creator's care, but the privilege of man's attention, as the increasingly dirt-conscious Victorians got busy on the problem of infection and immunity!

The idea of swarming populations was oddly attractive to the Western nations of last century, who saw that their new industrial power required workers and consumers in plenty. And they were not troubled by the population explosion. All the planets might be inhabited! Only very reluctantly was popular opinion shifted from this point of view, just as, in the last few years, we have reluctantly had to admit that the last hopes as far as refuges of life are concerned – Mars and Venus – are bleak prospects indeed. No humans. No lions and tigers. Not a bird. No plants even. A few lichens? Maybe a few lichens. This is the wretched pass we have been brought to by the progress of science!

While we hang on the hope that Venus, for all its impossible atmospheric pressures and temperatures, may support a few lichens, the Victorians hung on the hope that it might support Christians (Protestants or Catholic, according to persuasion). Brewster quotes approvingly from Dr. Lardner's *Museum of Science and Art,* in a reference to the populations of Mars, Venus, and Mercury: "They are, like the Earth, appropriated by the Omnipotent Creator and Ruler of the Universe to races very closely resembling, if not actually identical with, those with which the Earth is peopled."

But were they Christians? Had Christ died for them? "May not the Divine Nature, which can neither suffer nor die, and which in our planet, *once* only, clothed itself in humanity, resume elsewhere a physical form, and expiate the guilt of unnumbered worlds?"

Beliefs, as much as organic creatures, sicken and die. It is curious to read Brewster's words. For one of the most frightening ideas in recent science fiction has been almost a parody of Brewster's. I mean the idea that the guilty inhabitants of another world, maybe Venus*, might have infinitely variable physical forms which they could change so that they "clothed themselves in humanity" and appeared on Earth to betray mankind in some terrible way. Should this be regarded as a diseased salvation myth?

Brewster's book, *More Worlds Than One: The Creed of the Philosopher and the Hope of the Christian*, was a rebuttal of another book published in the 1850s – to our eyes, a sharper and better reasoned book, the anonymous *Of the Plurality of Worlds*, actually by William Whewell. Whewell derided the notion of life elsewhere. Yet, for the purpose of his argument, he puts the opposing viewpoint very well – for instance in this passage: "Jupiter and Saturn are much larger than the Earth. Mars and Venus are nearly as large. If these be inhabited, as the Earth is, which the analogy of their form, movements, and conditions seem to suggest, the population of the Earth is a very small portion of the population of the solar system." How things have changed! Now we live on a tiny globe, the population of which will have doubled in the next thirty or so years, in a system where the other globes – even fair-sounding Venus – are barren. No wonder an official of the British Conservation Society recently gave a talk in London called "Homo Sapiens: The Virus of the Solar System."

Whewell had no nonsense with the notion of Venus being inhabited. He says: "To believe that she has a surface

* As in Alan Nourse's 'Counterfeit' or Lester del Rey's 'Stability', or Eric Frank Russell's novel, *Three to Conquer*.

like the Earth, and tribes of animals, like terrestrial animals, and like man, is an exercise of imagination which not only is quite gratuitous, but contrary to all the information which the telescope gives us; and with this remark we may dismiss the hypothesis."

He was right. But there's little fun in being right before the right time, and many people preferred the gratuitous exercise of their imagination right up until yesterday. Among them – eminent among them – are the writers here assembled.

It appears that the first real journey to Venus ever made in fiction is the one described by Achille Eyraud, a French writer and contemporary of the great Jules Verne. Eyraud's *Voyage à Vénus* was published in Paris in 1865. It was never translated, and seems to have won none of the popularity of Verne's romances.

Some of the first English fictitious voyages to the Cytherean world are fun and full of charm. They are noticeably more cheerful than voyages undertaken in the opposite direction – to Mars, which, ever since Mr. H. G. Wells set metaphorical foot there, has tended to be peopled by alien horrors. In astronomical terms, the planets whose orbits lie inside Earth's are termed *inferior*, while those whose orbits lie outside are termed *superior*, but in fiction's terms, Mars is clearly the inferior planet, and Venus the superior.

Indeed, the religious aspects of the goddess have been of lasting benefit, and are felt in almost all the stories presented here.

It is notable, also, how dependent the writers have been, in the main, on the leads offered by the astronomers to feed their imaginations. Equally, the astronomers have been plentifully helped by *their* imaginations. The great French astronomer, Flammarion, must have been influenced by the pre-eminent beauty of Venus in the young night sky when he wrote of the planet in the sixties of the last century: "Clouds rise from the stormy ocean, and transport into the sky snowy, silvery, golden and purple tints. At morning and evening when the dazzling orb of day, twice as large as it appears from the Earth, lifts its enormous disc at the east or inclines towards the west, the twilight unfolds its splendours and charms."

The redoubtable Brewster, who was as fond as any man

of a purple prose patch, has his cake and eats it in front of his readers: "In Venus and Mercury their surface is variegated with mountain chains of great elevation, and but for the brilliancy of their discs, and the clouds which envelop them, the telescope would have discovered to us more minute details upon their surface."

The clouds, the oceans, the mountain chains – the majority of Earthmen who visit Venus in imagination confirm that they exist.

And yet, how few have been the visitors to Venus compared with the voyagers to Mars! How rarely sinister menaces have come from Venus, compared with the visitants from the Red Planet! The explanation for this, of course, takes us back to the elusive character of Venus. Under her silver camouflage of cloud, it was difficult to know just what the devil was going on. Above all, the astronomers did not know the length of its rotation period of "day". Such markings as could be detected telescopically on Venus were neither definite nor permanent enough to establish axial rotation. Writing in 1962, the astronomer and broadcaster Patrick Moore said that he had made a list of all published rotation periods covering the years 1666 to 1961; he found eighty-five of them. They ranged from 22 hours 17 minutes to 224.7 days.

This latter figure is also the length of Venus's year. It was suggested by Schiaparelli, who claimed that Venus took "as long to turn about her own axis as she does to go round the Sun, and that as a consequence she always presents the same side to the luminary." This Cytherean model is used by John Munro in his Venus novel; he must have sat with Schiaparelli's book in translation open by his side, since he incorporates Schiaparelli's exact phrase, as quoted here, into his text. In the event, Venus fooled everyone – she has a retrograde spin on her axis!

Such lack of certainty must largely account for the lack of stories centering on Venus.

Fortunately, the material that is available is very good. One reason for this immediately suggests itself. Mars has been the great planet of horrors. Mercury is the planet for spectacular effects. Moon is the setting for rugged-men-running-short-of-oxygen stories. Anyone wanting to write other kinds of story moves out of the solar system and thence mainly beyond the boundary of speculation governed by facts. But Venus is a convenient blank and, trailing clouds of its early divine glory, it forms the setting for mainly a sort of diluted utopian theme. Although the stories presented here show considerable variety, they all fall into such a category, I believe. Venus has attracted a meditative kind of writer – his brow clouded by thought like the aspect of the planet.

SHE has flowers in her hair. Her long gown reaches down to the floor of the cave. She offers a silvery cup to her lover. She might well be Venus herself: a late Victorian Venus.

And what of her lover? He stands there gloomily in impeccable bow tie, Norfolk jacket, and what look like stockings and satin breeches. He holds one of the fair apparition's hands in a manner that betrays his nervousness – and well he might be nervous, for he is undergoing an amorous adventure on Earth's sister planet.

So the unnamed narrator and his girl friend are depicted as the frontispiece to the third edition of John Munro's delightful novel, which was first published in 1897.

JOHN MUNRO: A Trip to Venus

What were the men like who made the first fictitious trip to Venus? The inventor of the flying "car" that made the hazardous journey was Naysmith Carmichael. Carmichael's career was an unusual one even before he left the Earth. In his own words, "I was born in the south of Scotland, and educated for the medical profession; but I emigrated to America and was engaged in one of Colonel Fremont's exploring expeditions to the Rocky Mountains. After that I was appointed to the chair of Physical Science in a college of Louisville, Kentucky, where my daughter was born."

Later, Carmichael resigned this post. He began the research which resulted in his invention. He gave his reasons for returning to Britain tersely. "I had become a citizen of the United States, but my wife was a Welshwoman, and had relations in England. So we came to London."

His wife died before the celestial car was invented, and his lovely daughter looked after him. She was destined to go with him on that momentous flight through space, and thus become the first voluntary woman astronaut in the pages of fiction. How appropriate that her destination should be Venus, dedicated to the beautiful Goddess of Love!

And what of the two men who accompanied Carmichael and his lovely daughter? They were the nameless narrator and his friend, the astronomer, Gazen. Would their friendship withstand the attraction that both felt for the alluring Miss Carmichael?

Our narrator, by his own account, was a feckless young chap. He had his serious side, being particularly interested in the question of whether there was life on Mars; but he was also given to lounging at his London club and playing reckless games of chess, particularly with a certain Viscount —.

Neither Gazen nor the narrator lacked courage. Though it was entirely untested, they did not hesitate to enter Carmichael's machine and venture where no man had ventured before.

The car – or so says author John Munro, who also wrote *Heroes of the Telegraph* and *The Romance of Electricity* – was propelled by electricity. It made good speed to Venus, and in no time was plunging gaily through the clouds of that mysterious world.

Gazen opened a hatch and took a careless sniff of the air. "It seems all right as regards quality, but there's too little body in it." The first wine connoisseur had arrived on Venus.

Below them they saw a range of snowy Alps, their dusky valleys filled with glaciers. Then the Alps fell away, and

21

they were crossing a wide ocean. It seemed to occupy half the globe. Great was their relief when they at last discerned a huge volcanic peak protruding from the sea, and surrounded by a barrier reef. This, they were to find, was the beautiful land of Womla.

Inside the huge extinct volcano, they found "a tremendous blooming wilderness ... Paradise run wild." Then came the architecture and gardens of a great city. They circled and landed outside the city.

The natives were friendly. The crowds that gathered were neither hostile nor over-curious.

"A man of dignified and venerable mien stepped from the crowd, and followed by a train of youths and maidens, each bearing a vase or a tray of fruit and flowers, came towards the car."

Evidently our explorers have chanced to arrive on a singularly cloudless day; for when Gazen and the Elder exchange signs, "the astronomer, indicating the Earth, which was now shining in the east as a beautiful green star, endeavoured to let him know by signs that we had come from there."

"They are treating us like superior beings," says Miss Carmichael. And she knows what she is talking about; the narrator and Gazen treated her that way all the voyage.

The vases that have been brought attract attention. They "seemed to be carved out of living opals, yet each was large enough to contain several pints of liquor ... Although we found the fruits and beverages delicious to the taste, we prudently partook very sparingly of them." Yet, when the evening came, the fireflies flashed like diamonds ...

Next day, the Elder and his son, whose names later emerge as Dinus and Otaré, bring along "some pictorial dictionaries and drawings which would enable us to learn their language. As the structure of it was simple, and the vocabulary not very copious, and as we also enjoyed the tuition of the young man, who was devoted to our service, and conducted us in most of our walks abroad, at the end of a fortnight we could maintain a conversation with tolerable fluency."

Everything in this Eden seemed lovely. The days were mild, the nights remained very light. The only slight problem was an astronomical one.

"The mysterious behaviour of the sun was a great puzzle to our astronomer. I have said that he rose very little above the horizon, or in other words the lip of the crater, as might be expected from our high southern latitude; but we soon found that he always rose and sank at the same place. In the morning he peeped above the cliffs, and in the evening he dipped again behind them, leaving a twilight or gloaming (I can scarcely call it dusk), which continued throughout the night.

"From his fixity in azimuth, Gazen concluded that Schiaparelli, the famous Italian observer, was right in supposing that Venus takes as long to turn about her own axis as she does to go round the sun, and that as a consequence she always presents the same side to her luminary.

"All that we heard from the natives tended to confirm this view. They told us that far away to the east and west of Womla there was a desert land, covered with snow and ice, on which the sun never shone. We also gathered that the sun rises to a greater and lesser height above the cliffs alternately, thus producing a succession of warmer and cooler seasons; a fact which agrees with Schiaparelli's observation that the axis of the planet sways to and from the sun.

"But why did the sun rise and set ever fifteen hours or thereabout, and so make what I have called a 'day' and 'night'? Why did he not continue in the same spot, except for the slow change caused by the nutation or nodding of Venus?"

This knotty problem is only resolved much later, when the party makes a side-trip to Mercury. There, Gazen realises that the "night" and "day" of Venus happen because the planet is a "wobbler".

"The Earth may be compared to a top that is whirling fast, and Venus to one that has slowed down. She is less able than the Earth to resist the disturbing attraction of the sun on the inequalities of her figure, and therefore she wobbles." Something like a libration effect, in fact, although the term seems not to have occurred to Gazen, whose mind is a little bemused by the charms of Miss Carmichael, to the narrator's annoyance.

Womla is a real paradise. Its natural wealth is very great.

23

"We saw metals which were quite new to us. Some of these had a purple, blue, or green colour, and emitted a most agreeable fragrance. Many of the flowers change their hues from hour to hour. We heard of 'singing flowers', including a water-lily which bursts open with a musical note. Fish burned in the water like broken rainbows." Reptiles are not very common in Womla, although there is one lizard which "could sit like a dog or fly in the air like a swallow." There are few large quadrupeds in the country, "and so far as we could learn none of these are predacious."

As for the people! "Their complexions vary from a dazzling blonde to an olive-green brunette. They are nearly all very handsome, both in face and figure, and I should say that many of them more than realise our ideals of beauty. As a rule, the countenances of the men are open, frank, and noble; those of the women are sweet, smiling and serene. Thanks to the purity of their blood, and the gentleness of their dispositions, together with their favourable circumstances, they live almost exempt from disease, or pain, or crime, and finally die in peace at the good old age of a hundred or a hundred and fifty years."

This remarkable longevity may be partly ascribed to the fact that there seem to be no cigars, cigarettes, or drugs in Womla. As for intoxicating beverages: "their drink is water."

So how do they get their kicks? "The sense of existence, apart from what they do or gain, is their chief happiness. Their 'ealo', or the height of felicity, is a passive rather than an active state. It is (if I am not mistaken) a kind of serene rapture or tranquil ecstasy of the soul, which is born doubtless from a perfect harmony between the person and his environment. In it, they say, the illusion of the world is complete, and life is another name for music and love.

"As far as I could learn, this condition, though independent of sexual love, is enhanced by it. On the one hand, it is spoiled by too much thought, and on the other by too much passion."

This is the only direct reference in the book to sex. It transpires that "They hold that the proper place for the woman is between the man and the child" is a reference merely to degrees of familial authority.

"The inhabitants of the whole island live as one happy

family. Their ideals of childish innocence, and the reign of love, seem to be essentially Christian," and certainly predate psycho-analytical theory.

Many pages are occupied with such general descriptions; but – at last – sex does rear its head in Womla, even if somewhat semitumescently.

The visitors from Earth witness Womla's great religious festival. The principal ceremony is called "Plucking the Flower". It is scarcely the defloration ceremony a modern reader might expect, but appears instead to symbolise the passage of the soul into a higher life. The ceremony is performed by a young priestess, the lovely Alumion, a divine seventeen-year-old. It happens that she is Dinus's daughter. Our narrator, forgetting the charms of Miss Carmichael (who has apparently refused to reveal even her Christian name), falls madly in love with Alumion.

"I would abandon the expedition if necessary and remain in Venus. If on the other hand, she refused me as my judgement feared, I would return to the Earth as a new man, ennobled by a glorious love . . ."

Thus inspired, he creeps up to her in the sacred grotto. This state of tension lasts only two pages, for, as soon as he reveals himself to Alumion, she admits that she also loves him. "I should have spoken sooner, but my heart was full of happiness."

He is going to try to kiss her but she is taboo as yet: "until tomorrow at sunset I am consecrated to The Giver."

Our narrator punctiliously turns up next day at sunset. And there is Alumion, hanging about in the woods and still looking sort of consecrated. "She was dressed in a filmy vesture of opalescent or pearly white, partly diaphanous, and having a deep fringe of gold"; as sexy, in fact, as a Hollywood nun.

Alumion gives him her little plump soft warm tender hand, and tells him that her idea is to get to Earth and "minister to the unfortunate". Well, the unfortunate aren't going to be that lucky, for chicanery is afoot. Unsuspectingly, the lovers walk into the sacred grotto. There lies a great white serpent with jewelled scales which has been screaming a lot; its attitude towards our narrator seems somewhat ambivalent; or perhaps it feels insecure as a phallic symbol, because later it is described contemptuously as simply "a rattlesnake." Despite the opposition from this snake, the narrator grabs Alumion round her little plump soft warm tender waist. They are married by a simple water-drinking ceremony.

He falls asleep, and wakes to find himself on Mercury, where a dragon flies off with Miss Carmichael.

Such things will happen – and it seems Carmichael drugged our narrator for his own good. He does not believe in intermarriage among the planets. There is no time for argument. They rescue Miss Carmichael, who is none the worse, or better, for her misadventure, and leave the planet.

More excitement is in store. The unusual heat jams the engines, poor Naysmith Carmichael faints, and they discover that the car is rushing towards the sun.

Just in time, Carmichael revives. "Although still unable to speak, he had contrived by means of his eyes to make his daughter understand that he wished another dose of oxygen."

The oxygen does the trick. They find that the engines cooled while they were jammed and so are now working again. They head back to earth. "We landed safely on some undiscovered islands in the Arctic Circle."

Back in Great Britain and civilisation, our narrator cooly leaves the others and drives to his London club, where he finishes off the game of chess he started with Viscount — two months earlier, thus winning a bet of one thousand sovereigns. "I played as I had never played before, and in three moves had won the wager." The cash, he claims, will cover his travelling expenses.

Gazen declares his intention of marrying Miss Carmichael. Our narrator promises to attend the wedding; but "as soon as the ceremony is over I shall return to Venus and Alumion."

*

These are the last words of this enchanting if dull novel. Its debt to Verne, who is mentioned in the text, is clear. But it also owes much to the tradition of utopian fiction, and that not only in its lack of anything which might bear the name of action. Utopias occur regularly on islands, those female symbols – Sir Thomas More's eponymous Utopia is merely the most striking example; and one might think that the interior of a volcanic cone was somewhat more deeply a female symbol than most.

It is easy to create a utopia if it is peopled by relatively sinless people – and bloodless, too, one might say. John Munro's picture of the people of Womla is charming and sympathetic, the whole thing is incredibly peaceful, the more especially when one recalls that even as *Trip to Venus* was published, H. G. Well's ferocious *War of the Worlds* was being serialised in *The Strand Magazine*.

Gentle though they may be, the people of Womla are no angels. Yet, toward the end of his story, Munro makes a singular suggestion, when he has his unnamed narrator remember that Alumion resembles a sweetheart of his who died in childhood "at the age of seventeen" (if the Victorians had shorter lives, they enjoyed longer childhoods); and he wonders if human beings may not go to Venus when they die.

One of the next space travellers to call on our sister planet, who is quoted after a brief excursion into scientific fact at the end of this section, seems to have nourished a parallel idea. George Griffith's *Honeymoon in Space* is not without its sentimental similarities to Munro's novel, but Griffith, who wrote several adventures during the Edwardian age, is much more entertaining than Munro, if only because he is more high-spirited, and his lapses are funnier. But one can detect also a more worldly approach to political and scientific and even romantic problems which perhaps marks a difference between the minor Victorian storytellers and the minor Edwardian ones.

AT the period in which Griffith and Munro were writing, astronomers dipped almost as freely into speculation as the novelists. Venus is a difficult planet to observe telescopically. When it comes closest to us, at inferior conjunction, it turns its night side to us; and at all times it clings close to the glare of the sun. We never view it when it is in the "full" phase – it is then hidden behind the sun.

Transits of Venus across the sun are rare: none has occurred or will occur this century. Consequently, astronomers have always eagerly studied these events. Transits occurred in 1761 and 1769. The French astronomer, Legantil, setting out for India to watch the first, got entangled in the Seven Years War, and missed both. He was shipwrecked on the way home, too.

The transit of 1882 was well-observed, though it yielded little but mellow prose. This is the delightful description of the transit seen by Robert Ball, an Astronomer Royal whose expositions played the same sort of role in popularising astronomy as Sir James Jeans's did later.

SIR ROBERT BALL: The Story of the Heavens

I venture to record our personal experience of the last transit of Venus, which we had the good fortune to view from Dunsink Observatory on the afternoon of the 6th of December, 1882.

The morning of the eventful day appeared to be about as unfavourable for a grand astronomical spectacle as could well be imagined. Snow, a couple of inches thick, covered the ground, and more was falling, with but little intermission, all the forenoon. It seemed almost hopeless that a view of the phenomenon could be obtained from that observatory; but it is well in such cases to bear in mind the injunction given to the observers on a celebrated eclipse expedition. They were instructed, no matter what the day should be like, that they were to make all their preparations precisely as they would have done were the sun shining with undimmed splendour. By this advice no doubt many observers have profited; and we acted upon it with very considerable success.

There were at that time at the observatory two equatorials, one of them an old, but tolerably good, instrument, of about six inches aperture; the other the great South equatorial, of twelve inches aperture, already referred to.

At eleven o'clock the day looked worse than ever; but we at once proceeded to make all ready. I stationed Mr. Rambaut at the small equatorial, while I myself took charge of the South instrument. The snow was still falling when the domes were opened; but, according to our prearranged scheme, the telescopes were directed, not indeed upon the sun, but to the place where we knew the sun was, and the clockwork was set in motion which carried round the telescopes, still constantly pointing towards the invisible sun. The predicted time of the transit had not yet arrived.

The eye-piece employed on the South equatorial must also receive a brief notice. It will, of course, be obvious that the full glare of the sun has to be greatly mitigated before the eye can view it with impunity. The light from the sun falls upon a piece of transparent glass inclined at a certain angle, and the chief portion of the sun's heat, as well as a certain amount of its light, pass through the glass and are lost. A certain fraction of the light is, however, reflected from the glass, and enters the eye-piece. This light is already much reduced in intensity, but it undergoes as much further reduction as we please by an ingenious contrivance. The glass which reflects the light does so at what is called the polarising angle, and between the eye-piece and the eye is a plate of tourmaline. This plate of tourmaline can be turned round by the observer. In one position it hardly interferes with the polarised light at all, while in the position at right angles thereto the tourmaline intercepts nearly all the light. By adjusting the position of the tourmaline, the observer has it in his power to render the image of any brightness that may be convenient, and thus the observations of the sun can be conducted with the appropriate degree of illumination.

But such appliances seemed on this occasion to be a mere mockery. The tourmaline was all ready, but up to one o'clock not a trace of the sun could be seen. Shortly after one o'clock, however, we noticed that the day was getting lighter; and, on looking to the north, whence the wind and the snow were coming, to our inexpressible delight, that the clouds were clearing. At length, the sky towards the south began to improve, and at last, as the critical moment approached, we could detect the spot where the sun was becoming visible. But the predicted moment arrived and passed, and still the sun had not broken through the clouds, though every moment the certainty that it would do so became more apparent. The external contact was therefore missed. We tried to console ourselves by the reflection that this was not, after all, a very important phase, and hoped that the internal contact would be more successful.

At length the struggling beams pierced the obstruction, and I saw the round, sharp disc of the sun in the finder, and eagerly glanced at the point on which attention was concentrated. Some minutes had now elapsed since the predicted moment of first contact, and, to my delight, I saw the small notch in the margin of the sun showing that the transit had commenced, and that the planet was then one-third on the sun. But the critical moment had not yet arrived. By the expression "first internal contact" we are to understand the moment when the planet has completely entered *on* the sun. This first contact was timed to occur twenty-one minutes later than the external contact already referred to. But the clouds again disappointed our hope of seeing the internal contact. While steadily looking at the exquisitely beautiful sight of the gradual advance of the planet, I became aware that there were other objects besides Venus between me and the sun. They were the snowflakes, which again began to fall rapidly. I must admit the phenomenon was singularly beautiful. The telescopic effect of a snowstorm with the sun as a background I had never before seen. It reminded me of the golden rain which is sometimes seen falling from a flight of sky-rockets during pyrotechnic displays; I would gladly have dispensed with the spectacle, for it necessarily followed that the sun and Venus again disappeared from view. The clouds gathered, the snowstorm descended as heavily as ever, and we hardly dared to hope that we should see anything more; 1 hr. 57 min. came and passed, the first internal contact was over, and Venus had fully entered on the sun. We had only obtained a brief view, and we had not yet been able to make any measurements or other observations that could be of service. Still, to have seen even a part of a transit of Venus is an event to remember for a lifetime, and we felt more delight than can be easily expressed at even this slight gleam of success.

But better things were in store. My assistant came over

with the report that he had also been successful in seeing Venus in the same phase as I had. We both resumed our posts, and at half-past two the clouds began to disperse, and the prospect of seeing the sun began to improve. It was now no question of the observations of contact. Venus by this time was well on the sun, and we therefore prepared to make observations with the micrometer attached to the eye-piece. The clouds at length dispersed, and at this time Venus had so completely entered on the sun that the distance from the edge of the planet to the edge of the sun was about twice the diameter of the planet. We measured the distance of the inner edge of Venus from the nearest limb of the sun. These observations were repeated as frequently as possible, but it should be added that they were only made with very considerable difficulty. The sun was now very low, and the edges of the sun and of Venus were by no means of that steady character which is suitable for micrometrical measurement. The margin of the luminary was quivering, and Venus, though no doubt it was sometimes circular, was very often distorted to such a degree as to make the measures very uncertain.

We succeeded in obtaining sixteen measures altogether; but the sun was now getting low, the clouds began again to interfere, and we saw that the pursuit of the transit must be left to the thousands of astronomers in happier climes who had been eagerly awaiting it. But before the phenomena had ceased I spared a few minutes from the somewhat mechanical work at the micrometer to take a view of the transit in the more picturesque form which the large field of the finder presented. The sun was already beginning to put on the ruddy hues of sunset, and there, far in on its face, was the sharp, round, black disc of Venus. It was then easy to sympathise with the supreme joy of Horrocks, when, in 1639, he for the first time witnessed this spectacle. The intrinsic interest of the phenomenon, its rarity, the fulfilment of the prediction, the noble problem which the transit of Venus helps us to solve, are all present to our thoughts when we look at this pleasing picture, a repetition of which will not occur again until the flowers are blooming in the June of A.D. 2004.

GEORGE GRIFFITH's *Honeymoon in Space* was published in 1901. While it is the fate of the hero of *A Trip to Venus* to remain nameless, the hero of Griffith's novel suffers from almost the opposite fate; he is introduced to the reader as Rollo Lenox Smeaton Aubrey, Earl of Redgrave, Baron Smeaton in the Peerage of England, and Viscount Aubrey in the Peerage of Ireland.

Redgrave has a "tall athletic figure and the regular-featured, bronzed, honest English face." Ah, they don't make them like that any more – and the same may be said for Redgrave's bride, the lovely American girl, Lilla Zaidie Rennick.

Zaidie's face wreaks havoc with Redgrave's heart. "It was a face which possessed at once the fair Anglo-Saxon skin, the firm and yet delicate Anglo-Saxon features, and the wavy wealth of the old Saxon gold-brown hair; but a pair of big, soft, pansy eyes, fringed with long, curling, black lashes, looked out from under dark and perhaps just a trifle heavy eyebrows. Moreover, there was that indescribable expression in the curve of her lips and the pose of her head; to say nothing of a lissome, vivacious grace in her whole carriage which proclaimed her a daughter of the younger branch of the Race that Rules."

They marry, and fly off in style to honeymoon in space, to the plaudits of the Anglo-Saxon world, both branches.

Their spaceship, the *Astronef*, is powered by "the R. Force". It, like the marriage, is a fine piece of Anglo-American teamwork; for the ship was built with English money and English skill but is the creature of American genius. It would be the other way round today, if at all. Zaidie's father discovered that gravitation could be broken down into two separate forces, attraction and repulsion. The latter is the R. Force. The whole ship is simplicity itself; the crew consists only of Murgatroyd.

Nowadays, Murgatroyd, I suppose, would be a cyborg. Griffith wrote at the turn of the century; his Murgatroyd is "the most wholesouled Wesleyan that Yorkshire ever produced," as well as being Redgrave's old retainer, whose family has been in service to the House of Redgrave for the last seven hundred years. Just the man to bring the newly-weds safely to the romantic new world of Venus ...

GEORGE GRIFFITH: Honeymoon in Space

The *Astronef*, still falling, but now easily under the command of the helmsman, shot forwards and downwards towards a vast dome of snow which, rising some two thousand feet above the cloud-sea, shone with dazzling brilliance in the light of the rising Sun. She landed just above the edge of the clouds. Meanwhile they had put on their breathing-suits, and Redgrave had seen that the air chamber through which they had to pass from their own little world into the new ones that they visited was in working order. When the outer door was opened and the ladder lowered he stood aside, as he had done on the Moon, and Zaidie's was the first human foot which made an imprint on the virgin snows of Venus.

The first thing Redgrave did was to raise the visor of his helmet and taste the air of the new world. It was cool, and fresh, and sweet, and the first draught of it sent the blood tingling and dancing through his veins. Perfect as the arrangements of the *Astronef* were in this respect, the air of Venus tasted like clear running spring water would have done to a man who had been drinking filtered water for several days. He threw the visor right up and motioned to Zaidie to do the same. She obeyed, and, after drawing a long breath, she said:

"That's glorious! It's like wine after water, and rather stagnant water too. But what a world, snowpeaks and cloud-seas, islands of ice and snow in an ocean of mist! Just look at them! Did you ever see anything so lovely and unearthly in your life? I wonder how high this mountain is, and what there is on the other side of the clouds. Isn't the air delicious! Not a bit too cold after all – but, still, I think we may as well go back and put on something more be-

33

coming. I shouldn't quite like the ladies of Venus to see me dressed like a diver."

"Come along, then," laughed Lenox, as he turned back towards the vessel. "That's just like a woman. You're about a hundred and fifty million miles away from Broadway or Regent Street. You are standing on the top of a snow mountain above the clouds of Venus, and the moment that you find the air is fit to breathe you begin thinking about dress. How do you know that the inhabitants of Venus, if there are any, dress at all?"

"What nonsense! Of course they do – at least, if they are anything like us."

As soon as they got back on board the *Astronef* and had taken their breathing-dresses off, Redgrave and the old engineer, who appeared to take no visible interest in their new surroundings, threw open all the sliding doors on the upper and lower decks so that the vessel might be thoroughly ventilated by the fresh sweet air. Then a gentle repulsion was applied to the huge snow mass on which the *Astronef* rested. She rose a couple of hundred feet, her propellers began to whirl round, and Redgrave steered her out towards the centre of the vast, cloud-sea which was almost surrounded by a thousand glittering peaks of ice and domes of snow.

"I think we may as well put off dinner, or breakfast as it will be now, until we see what the world below is like," he said to Zaidie, who was standing beside him on the conning-tower.

"Oh, never mind about eating just now, this is altogether too wonderful to be missed for the sake of ordinary meat and drink. Let's go down and see what there is on the other side."

He sent a message down the speaking tube to Murgatroyd, who was below among his beloved engines and, the next moment sun and clouds and ice-peaks had disappeared and nothing was visible save the all-enveloping silver-grey mist.

For several minutes they remained silent, watching and wondering what they would find beneath the veil which hid the surface of Venus from their view. Then the mist thinned out and broke up into patches which drifted past them as they descended on their downward slanting course.

Below them they saw vast, ghostly shapes of mountains

and valleys, lakes and rivers, continents, islands, and seas. Every moment these became more and more distinct, and soon they were in full view of the most marvellous landscape that human eyes had ever beheld. The distances were tremendous. Mountains, compared with which the Alps or even the Andes would have seemed mere hillocks, towered up out of the vast depths beneath them.

Up to the lower edge of the all-covering cloud-sea they were clad with a golden-yellow vegetation, fields and forests, open, smiling valleys, and deep, dark ravines through which a thousand torrents thundered down from the eternal snows beyond, to spread themselves out in rivers and lakes in the valleys and plains which lay many thousands of feet below.

"What a lovely world!" said Zaidie, as she at last found her voice after what was almost a stupor of speechless wonder and admiration. "And the light! Did you ever see anything like it? It's neither moonlight nor sunlight. See, there are no shadows down there, it's just all lovely silvery twilight. Lenox, if Venus is as nice as she looks from here I don't think I shall want to go back. It reminds me of Tennyson's Lotus Eaters, 'the Land where it is always afternoon.'"

"I think you are right after all. We are thirty million miles nearer to the Sun than we were on Earth, and the light and heat have to filter through these clouds. They are not at all like Earth clouds from this side. It's the other way about. The silver lining is on this side. Look, there isn't a black or a brown one, or even a grey one, within sight. They are just like a thin mist, lighted by a million of electric lamps. It's a delicious world, and if it isn't inhabited by angels it ought to be."

While Zaidie was talking the *Astronef* was sweeping swiftly down towards the surface of Venus, through scenery of whose almost inconceivable magnificence no human words could convey any adequate idea. Underneath the cloud-veil the air was absolutely clear and transparent, clearer, indeed, than terrestrial air at the highest elevations reached by mountain-climbers, and, moreover, it seemed to be endowed with a strange, luminous quality, which made objects, no matter how distant, stand out with almost startling distinctness.

The rivers and lakes and seas which spread out beneath them, seemed never to have been ruffled by blast of storm or breath of wind, and their surfaces shone with a soft, silvery light, which seemed to come from below rather than from above.

"If this isn't heaven it must be the half-way house," said Redgrave, with what was, perhaps, under the circumstances, a pardonable irreverence. "Still, after all, we don't know what the inhabitants may be like, so I think we'd better close the doors, and drop on the top of that mountain-spur running out between the two rivers into the bay. Do you notice how curious the water looks after the Earth seas; bright silver, instead of blue and green?"

"Oh, it's just lovely," said Zaidie. "Let's go down and have a walk. There's nothing to be afraid of. You'll never make me believe that a world like this can be inhabited by anything dangerous."

"Perhaps, but we mustn't forget what happened on Mars, *Madonna mia*. Still, there's one thing, we haven't been tackled by any aerial fleets yet."

"I don't think the people here want air-ships. They can fly themselves. Look! there are a lot of them coming to meet us. That was a rather wicked remark of yours, Lenox, about the half-way house to heaven; but those certainly do look something like angels."

As Zaidie said this, after a somewhat lengthy pause, during which the *Astronef* had descended to within a few hundred feet of the mountain-spur, she handed her field-glasses to her husband, and pointed downwards towards an island which lay a couple of miles or so off the end of the spur.

He put the glasses to his eyes, and took a long look through them. Moving them slowly up and down, and from side to side, he saw hundreds of winged figures rising from the island and floating towards them.

"You were right, dear," he said, without taking the glass from his eyes, "and so was I. If those aren't angels, they're certainly something like men, and, I suppose, women too who can fly. We may as well stop here and wait for them. I wonder what sort of an animal they take the *Astronef* for."

He sent a message down the tube to Murgatroyd and

gave a turn and a half to the steering-wheel. The propellers slowed down and the *Astronef* dropped with a hardly-perceptible shock in the midst of a little plateau covered with a thick, soft moss of a pale yellowish green, and fringed by a belt of trees which seemed to be over three hundred feet high, and whose foliage was a deep golden bronze.

They had scarcely landed before the flying figures reappeared over the tree tops and swept downwards in long spiral curves towards the *Astronef*.

"If they're not angels, they're very like them," said Zaidie, putting down her glasses.

"There's one thing, they fly a lot better than the old masters' angels or Doré's could have done, because they have tails – or at least something that seems to serve the same purpose, and yet they haven't got feathers."

"Yes, they have, at least round the edges of their wings or whatever they are, and they've got clothes, too, silk tunics or something of that sort – and there are men and women."

"You're quite right, those fringes down their legs are feathers, and that's how they can fly. They seem to have four arms."

The flying figures which came hovering near to the *Astronef*, without evincing any apparent sign of fear, were the strangest that human eyes had looked upon. In some respects they had a sufficient resemblance for them to be taken for winged men and women, while in other they bore a decided resemblance to birds. Their bodies and limbs were human in shape, but of slenderer and lighter build; and from the shoulder-blades and muscles of the back there sprang a second pair of arms arching up above their heads. Between these and the lower arms, and continued from them down the side to the ankles, there appeared to be a flexible membrane covered with a light feathery down, pure white on the inside, but on the back a brilliant golden yellow, deepening to bronze towards the edges, round which ran a deep feathery fringe.

The body was covered in front and down the back between the wings with a sort of divided tunic of a light, silken-looking material, which must have been clothing, since there were many different colours all more or less of different hue among them. Below this and attached to the

37

inner sides of the leg from the knee downward, was another membrane which reached down to the heels, and it was this which Redgrave somewhat flippantly alluded to as a tail. Its obvious purpose was to maintain the longitudinal balance when flying.

In stature the inhabitants of the Love-Star varied from about five feet six to five feet, but both the taller and the shorter of them were all of nearly the same size, from which it was easy to conclude that this difference in stature was on Venus as well as on the Earth, one of the broad distinctions between the sexes.

They flew round the *Astronef* with an exquisite ease and grace which made Zaidie exclaim:

"Now, why weren't we made like that on Earth?"

To which Redgrave, after a look at the barometer, replied:

"Partly, I suppose, because we weren't built that way, and partly because we don't live in an atmosphere about two and a half times as dense as ours."

Then several of the winged figures alighted on the mossy covering of the plain and walked towards the vessel.

"Why, they walk just like us, only much more prettily!" said Zaidie. "And look what funny little faces they've got! Half bird, half human, and soft, downy feathers instead of hair. I wonder whether they talk or sing. I wish you'd open the doors again, Lenox. I'm sure they can't possibly mean us any harm; they are far too pretty for that. What lovely soft eyes they have, and what a thousand pities it is we shan't be able to understand them."

They had left the conning-tower, and both his lordship and Murgatroyd were throwing open the sliding-doors and, to Zaidie's considerable displeasure, getting the deck Maxims ready for action in case they should be required. As soon as the doors were open Zaidie's judgment of the inhabitants of Venus was entirely justified.

Without the slightest sign of fear, but with very evident astonishment in their round golden-yellow eyes, they came walking close up to the sides of the *Astronef*. Some of them stroked her smooth, shining sides with their little hands, which Zadie now found had only three fingers and a thumb. Many ages before they might have been birds' claws, but now they were soft and pink and plump, utterly strange to manual work as it is understood upon Earth.

"Just fancy getting Maxim guns ready to shoot those delightful things," said Zaidie, almost indignantly, as she went towards the doorway from which the gangway ladder ran down to the soft, mossy turf. "Why, not one of them has got a weapon of any sort; and just listen," she went on, stopping in the opening of the doorway, "have you ever heard music like that on Earth? I haven't. I suppose it's the way they talk. I'd give a good deal to be able to understand them. But still, it's very lovely, isn't it?"

"Ay, like the voices of syrens," said Murgatroyd, speaking for the first time since the *Astronef* had landed; for this big, grizzled taciturn Yorkshireman, who looked upon the whole cruise through Space as a mad and almost impious adventure, which nothing but his hereditary loyalty to his master's name and family could have persuaded him to share in, had grown more and more silent as the millions of miles between the *Astronef* and his native Yorkshire village had multiplied day by day.

"Syrens – and why not, Andrew?" laughed Redgrave. "At any rate, I don't think they look likely to lure us and the *Astronef* to destruction." Then he went on: "Yes, Zaidie, I never heard anything like that before. Unearthly, of course it is, but then we're not on Earth. Now, Zaidie, they seem to talk in song-language. You did pretty well on Mars with your American, suppose we go out and show them that you can speak the song-language, too."

"What do you mean?" she said; "sing them something?"

"Yes," he replied; "they'll try to talk to you in song, and you won't be able to understand them; at least, not as far as words and sentences go. But music is the universal language on Earth, and there's no reason why it shouldn't be the same through the Solar System. Come along, tune up, little woman!"

They went together down the gangway stairs, he dressed in an ordinary suit of grey, English tweed, with a golf cap on the back of his head, and she in the last and daintiest of the costumes which the art of Paris and London and New York had produced before the *Astronef* soared up from far-off Washington.

The moment that she set foot on the golden-yellow

sward she was surrounded by a swarm of the winged, and yet strangely human creatures. Those nearest to her came and touched her hands and face, and stroked the folds of her dress. Others looked into her violet-blue eyes, and others put out their queer little hands and stroked her hair.

This and her clothing seemed to be the most wonderful experience for them, saving always the fact that she had only two arms and no wings. Redgrave kept close beside her until he was satisfied that these exquisite inhabitants of the new-found fairy-land were innocent of any intention of harm, and when he saw two of the winged daughters of the Love-Star put up their hands and touch the thick coils of her hair, he said:

"Take those pins and things out and let it down. They seem to think that you hair's part of your head. It's the first chance you've had to work a miracle, so you may as well do it. Show them the most beautiful thing they've ever seen."

"What babies you men can be when you get sentimental!" laughed Zaidie, as she put her hands up to her head. "How do you know that this may not be ugly in their eyes?"

"Quite impossible!" he replied. "They're a great deal too pretty themselves to think *you* ugly. Let it down!"

While he was speaking Zaidie had taken off a Spanish mantilla which she had thrown over her head as she came out, and which the ladies of Venus seemed to think was part of her hair. Then she took out the comb and one or two hair-pins which kept the coils in position, deftly caught the ends, and then, after a few rapid movements of her fingers, she shook her head, and the wondering crowd about her saw, what seemed to them a shimmering veil, half gold, half silver, in the soft reflected light from the cloud-veil, fall down from her head over her shoulders.

They crowded still more closely round her, but so quietly and so gently that she felt nothing more than the touch of wondering hands on her arms, and dress, and hair. As Redgrave said afterwards, he was "absolutely out of it." They seemed to imagine him to be a kind of uncouth monster, possibly the slave of this radiant being which had come so strangely from somewhere beyond the cloud-veil. They looked at him with their golden-yellow eyes wide open,

40

and some of them came up rather timidly and touched his clothes, which they seemed to think were his skin.

Then one or two, more daring, put their little hands up to his face and touched his moustache, and all of them, while both examinations were going on, kept up a running conversation of cooing and singing which evidently conveyed their ideas from one to the other on the subject of this most marvellous visit of these two strange beings with neither wings nor feathers, but who, most undoubtedly, had other means of flying, since it was quite certain that they had come from another world.

Their ordinary speech was a low crooning note, like the language in which doves converse, mingled with a twittering current of undertone. But every moment it rose into higher notes, evidently expressing wonder or admiration, or both.

"You were right about the universal language," said Redgrave, when he had submitted to the stroking process for a few moments. "These people talk in music, and, as far as I can see or hear, their opinion of us, or, at least, of you, is distinctly flattering. I don't know what they take *me* for, and I don't care, but as we'd better make friends with them suppose you sing them 'Home, Sweet Home', or 'The Swanee River'. I shouldn't wonder if they consider our talking voices most horrible discords, so you might as well give them something different."

While he was speaking the sounds about them suddenly hushed, and, as Redgrave said afterwards, it was something like the silence that follows a cannon shot. Then, in the midst of the hush, Zaidie put her hands behind her, looked up towards the luminous silver surface which formed the only visible sky of Venus, and began to sing "The Swanee River".

The clear, sweet notes rang up through the midst of a sudden silence. The sons and daughters of the Love-Star instantly ceased their own soft musical conversation, and Zaidie sang the old plantation song through for the first time that a human voice had sung it to ears other than human.

As the last note thrilled sweetly from her lips she looked round at the crowd of queer half-human shapes about her, and something in their unlikeness to her own kind brought

41

back to her mind the familiar scenes which lay so far away, so many millions of miles across the dark and silent Ocean of Space.

Other winged figures, attracted by the sound of her singing, had crossed the trees, and these, during the silence which came after the singing of the song, were swiftly followed by others, until there were nearly a thousand of them gathered about the side of the *Astronef*.

There was no crowding or jostling among them. Each one treated every other with the most perfect gentleness and courtesy. No such thing as enmity or ill-feeling seemed to exist among them, and, in perfect silence, they waited for Zaidie to continue what they thought was her long speech of greeting. The temper of the throng somehow coincided exactly with the mood which her own memories had brought to her, and the next moment she sent the first line of "Home, Sweet Home" soaring up to the cloud-veiled sky.

As the notes rang up into the still soft air, a deeper hush fell on the listening throng. Heads were bowed with a gesture almost of adoration, and many of those standing nearest to her bent their bodies forward, and expanded their wings, bringing them together over their breasts with a motion which, as they afterwards learnt, was intended to convey the idea of wonder and admiration, mingled with something like a sentiment of worship.

Zaidie sang the sweet old song through from end to end, forgetting for the time being everything but the home she had left behind her on the banks of the Hudson. As the last notes left her lips, she turned round to Redgrave and looked at him with eyes dim with the first tears that had filled them since her father's death, and said, as he caught hold of her outstretched hand:

"I believe they've understood every word of it."

"Or, at any rate, every note. You may be quite certain of that," he replied. "If you had done that on Mars it might have been ever more effective than the Maxims."

"For goodness sake don't talk about things like that in a heaven like this! Oh, listen! They've got the tune already!"

It was true! The dwellers of the Love-Star, whose speech was song, had instantly recognised the sweetness of the sweetest of all earthly songs. They had, of course, no idea of the meaning of the words; but the music spoke to them and told them that this fair visitant from another world could speak the same speech as theirs. Every note and cadence was repeated with absolute fidelity, and so the speech, common to the two far-distant worlds, became a link connecting this wandering son and daughter of the Earth with the sons and daughters of the Love-Star.

The throng fell back a little and two figures, apparently male and female, came to Zaidie and held out their right hands and began addressing her in perfectly harmonised song, which, though utterly unintelligible to her in the sense of speech, expressed sentiments which could not possibly be mistaken, as there was a faint suggestion of the old English song running through the little song-speech that they made, and both Zadie and her husband rightly concluded that it was intended to convey a welcome to the strangers from beyond the cloud-veil.

And then the strangest of all possible conversations began. Redgrave, who had no more notion of music than a walrus, perforce kept silence. In fact, he noticed with a certain displeasure which vanished speedily with a musical, and half-malicious little laugh from Zaidie, that when he spoke the Bird-Folk drew back a little and looked in something like astonishment at him; but Zaidie was already in touch with them, and half by song and half by signs she very soon gave them an idea of what they were and where they had come from. Her husband afterwards told her that it was the best piece of operatic acting he had ever seen, and, considering all the circumstances, this was very possibly true.

In the end the two who had come to give her what seemed to be the formal greeting, were invited into the *Astronef*. They went on board without the slightest sign of mistrust and with only an expression of mild wonder on their beautiful and strangely childlike faces.

Then, while the other doors were being closed, Zaidie stood at the open one above the gangway and made signs showing that they were going up beyond the clouds and then down into the valley, and as she made the signs she sang through the scale, her voice rising and falling in harmony with her gestures. The Bird-Folk understood her instantly, and as the door closed and the *Astronef* rose from the ground, a thousand wings were outspread and presently hundreds of beautiful soaring forms were circling about the Navigator of the Stars.

"Don't they look lovely!" said Zaidie. "I wonder what they would think if they could see us flying above New York or London or Paris with an escort like this. I suppose they're going to show us the way. Perhaps they have a city down there. Suppose you were to go and get a bottle of champagne and see if Master Cupid and Miss Venus would like a drink. We'll see then if our nectar is anything like theirs."

Redgrave went below. Meanwhile, for lack of other possible conversation, Zaidie began to sing the last verse of "Never Again". The melody almost exactly described the upward motion of the *Astronef*, and she could see that it was instantly understood, for when she had finished their two voices joined in an almost exact imitation of it.

When Redgrace brought up the wine and the glasses they looked at them without any sign of surprise. The pop of the cork did not even make them look round.

"Evidently a semi-angelic people, living on nectar and ambrosia, with nectar very like our own," he said, as he filled the glasses. "Perhaps you'd better give it to them. They seem to understand you better than they do me – you being, of course, a good bit nearer to the angels than I am."

"Thanks!" she said, as she took a couple of glasses up, wondering a little what their visitors would do with them. Somewhat to her surprise, they took them with a little bow and a smile and sipped at the wine, first with a swift glint of wonder in their eyes, and then with smiles which are unmistakable evidence of perfect appreciation.

"I thought so," said Redgrave, as he raised his own glass, and bowed gravely towards them. "This is our nearest approach to nectar, and they seem to recognise it."

"And don't they just look like the sort of people who live on it, and, of course, other things?" added Zaidie, as she too lifted her glass, and looked with laughing eyes across the brim at her two guests.

But meanwhile Murgatroyd had been applying the repulsive force, a little too strongly. The *Astronef* shot up with a rapidity which soon left her winged escort far below.

She entered the cloud-veil and passed beyond it. The instant that the unclouded sun-rays struck the glass-roofing of the deck-chamber their two guests, who had been moving about examining everything with a childlike curiosity, closed their eyes and clasped their hands over them, uttering little cries, tuneful and musical, but still with a note of strange discord in them.

"Lenox, we must go down again," exclaimed Zaidie. "Don't you see they can't stand the light; it hurts them. Perhaps, poor dears, it's the first time they've ever been hurt in their lives. I don't believe they have any of our ideas of pain or sorrow or anything of that sort. Take us back under the clouds – quick, or we may blind them."

Before she had ceased speaking, Redgrave had sent a signal down to Murgatroyd, and the *Astronef* began to drop back again towards the surface of the cloud-sea. Zaidie had, meanwhile, gone to her lady guest and dropped the black lace mantilla over her head, and, as she did so, she caught herself saying:

"There, dear, we shall soon be back in your light. I hope it hasn't hurt you. It was very stupid of us to do a thing like that."

The answer came in a little cooing murmur, which said, "Thank you!" quite as effectively as any earthly words could have done, and then the *Astronef* passed through the cloud-sea. The soaring forms of her lost escort came into view again and clustered about her; and, surrounded by them, she dropped, in obedience to their signs, down between the tremendous mountains and towards the island, thick with golden foliage, which lay two or three Earth-miles out in a bay, where four converging rivers spread out through a vast estuary into the sea.

As Lady Redgrave said afterwards to Mrs. Van Stuyler, she could have filled a whole volume with a description of the exquisitely arcadian delights with which the hours of the next ten days and nights were filled. Possibly if she had been able to do justice to them, even her account might have been received with qualified credence; but still some idea of them may be gathered from this extract of a conversation which took place in the saloon of the *Astronef* on the eleventh evening.

"But look here, Zaidie," said Redgrave, "as we've found
45

a world which is certainly much more delightful than our own, why shouldn't we stop here a bit? The air suits us and the people are simply enchanting. I think they like us, and I'm sure you're in love with every one of them, male and female. Of course, it's rather a pity that we can't fly unless we do it in the *Astronef*. But that's only a detail. You're enjoying yourself thoroughly, and I never saw you looking better or, if possible, more beautiful; and why on Earth – or Venus – do you want to go?"

She looked at him steadily for a few moments, and with an expression which he had never seen on her face or in her eyes before, and then she said slowly and very sweetly, although there was something like a note of solemnity running through her tone:

"I altogether agree with you, dear; but there is something which you don't seem to have noticed. As you say, we have had a perfectly delightful time. It's a delicious world, and just everything that one would think it to be; but if we were to stop here we should be committing one of the greatest of crimes, perhaps the greatest, that ever was committed within the limits of the Solar System."

"My dear Zaidie, what, in the name of what we used to call morals on the Earth, *do* you mean?"

"Just this," she replied, leaning a little towards him in her deck-chair. "These people, half angels, and half men and women, welcomed us after we dropped through their cloud-veil, as friends; we were a little strange to them, certainly, but still they welcomed us as friends. They had no suspicions of us; they didn't try to poison us or blow us up as those wretches on Mars did. They're just like a lot of grown-up children with wings on. In fact they're about as nearly angels as anything we can think of. They've taken us into their palaces, they've given us, one might say, the whole planet. Everything was ours that we liked to take. You know we have two or three hundredweights of precious stones on board now, which they would make me take just because they saw my rings.

"We've been living with them ten days now, and neither you nor I, nor even Murgatroyd, who, like the old Puritan that he is, seems to see sin or wrong in everything that looks nice, has seen a single sign among them that they know anything about what we call sin or wrong on Earth.

46

There's no jealousy, no selfishness. In short, no envy, hatred, malice, and all uncharitableness; no vice, or meanness, or cheating, or any of the abominations of the planet Terra, and *we come from that planet*. Do you see what I mean now?"

"I think I understand what you're driving at," said Redgrave; "you mean, I suppose, that this world is something like Eden before the fall, and that you and I – oh – but that's all rubbish you know. I've got my own share of original sin, of course, but here it doesn't seem to come in; and as for you, the very idea of *you* imagining yourself a feminine edition of the Serpent in Eden. Nonsense!"

She got up out of her chair and, leaning over his, put her arm round his shoulder. Then she said very softly:

"I see you understand what I mean, Lenox. That's just it – original sin. It doesn't matter how good you think me or I think you, but we have it. You're an Earth-born man and I'm an Earth-born woman, and, as I'm your wife, I can say it plainly. We may think a good bit of each other, but that's no reason why we might not be a couple of plague-spots in a sinless world like this. Surely you see what I mean, I needn't put it plainer, need I?"

Their eyes met, and he read her meaning in hers. He put his arm up over her shoulder and drew her down towards him. Their lips met, and then he got up and went down to the engine-room.

A couple of minutes later the *Astronef* sprang upwards from the midst of the delightful valley in which she was resting. No lights were shown. In five minutes she had passed through the cloud-veil, and the next morning when their new friends came to visit them and found that they had vanished back into Space, there was sorrow for the first time among the sons and daughters of the Love-Star.

Never-fading Flowers

BUTTERFLIES, flowers, fish, angels ... In every writer, however dedicated he may be to progress, the primitive lurks. The ancient idea of Venus as a goddess of fertility was clung to as long as possible, often with great ingenuity, even when the hope for any highly organized life had shrunk almost to vanishing point; the story *Before Eden* in Section V is an admirable example of such tendencies.

Tennyson expresses the general idea:

> Venus, near her, smiling downwards at this earthier earth of ours,
> Closer on the sun, perhaps a world of never-fading flowers.

As this notion came to appear less likely, so the fauna and flora distort into somewhat stranger forms, as we see in this section, which embraces the Golden Age of Cytherean Prose. Underwater civilizations develop, enormous trees spring up, vast mats of seaweed spread everywhere. And the hope is always lying there, explicitly, if not expressed: Let there be Life!

The idea of life elsewhere is certainly as old as Lucretius, who declares in his *De Rerum Natura* that "Somewhere in the universe are other meetings of the atom stuff resembling this of ours ..." His belief is "Things must be made". The attraction for life must always be towards such a philosophy. Robert Burton, writing his *Anatomy of Melancholy* at a time when he is still somewhat torn between Ptolemy's and Copernicus's models of the universe, argues the matter another way: "Though they (the stars) seem close to us, they are infinitely distant, and so *per consequens*, they are infinite inhabitable worlds: what hinders? Why should not an infinite cause (as God is) produce infinite effects?"

Ripeness is all. Nobody could accept Whewell's chilly view that, because of her proximity to the sun, Venus "may have cooled more slowly and quietly, like glass which is annealed in the fire; and hence, may have a smooth surface instead of the furrowed and pimpled visage which the Moon presents to us." The Witch-Ball model was unacceptable even to astronomers. They, too, opted unwittingly for the never-fading flowers.

WE can best understand how our own ideas are moulded by studying the ideas of the past. The greatest genius inherits. The Swedish astronomer, Arrhenius, in the following wonderful meditation on Venus, published in 1917, leans more heavily than he can have realised on such theories as Laplace's Nebular Hypothesis, a model for the creation of the solar system which presupposes that the outer planets are the oldest, and the inner, such as Venus and Mercury, the youngest. Even when serious weaknesses in the theory were revealed, even after it was abandoned, the idea that Mars was older and Venus younger than Earth persisted – and persists.

Arrhenius also leans on the fin de siècle notion, so temptingly full of bitter-sweet regrets and anticipations, of the burning out of the sun. For a generation that spent its childhood in gas-lit homes, and wonderingly saw, when the gas was extinguished, the glowing mantle fade and die – and vanish with a delicate pop – such a simple if large-scale extinction of the sun must have seemed not only immediately convincing but immensely nostalgic.

49

Following the passage from Arrhenius come the three major writers on Venus. Their works, like the works of Arrhenius, are long as well as imaginative, and can be represented in anthologies only by selection. Happily, the selection from the first writer represents the entire Venus episode; while the other two are sufficient to establish the individual flavour of the writers of this Cytherean Golden Age of Prose.

SVANTE ARRHENIUS: The Destinies of the Stars

If we wish to picture to us the future fate of our Earth when it gradually enters the reign of darkness and cold in consequence of the enfeebling of the Sun, we must seek our illustration on Mars and not on the Moon. Slowly are the oceans going to freeze, finally down to their bottom, the abundance of the rainfalls will diminish, only light snow will now and then bring change to a surface evermore transformed into a sand desert as far as the continents reach. Rents in the rocky substrata of the latter will appear as dark lines, caused by the gases rising from the interior. When the temperature at the equator has fallen below the freezing point, the polar regions will remain the only parts where a light covering of frost will melt in the height of the summer season and where the last feeble organisms will eke out their hard existence, resorting to a prolonged winter's sleep of their seeds and spores. Finally the last remnant of life will also disappear and sandstorms alone, save for the gasps of gas emanation from fissures in the rocky ground, will bring relief to the monotonous desolation. Falling meteoric dust, which now exists in original state only on the bottom of the oceans, will gradually cover the entire surface of the Earth with a mantle coloured brick-red through the influence of atmospheric oxygen. When the oxygen itself is used up, the meteoric dust will retain its original greyish-green hue and lend it to the funeral pall of the Earth.

Very different conditions obtain on our neighbour planet, which is closer both to the Sun and to ourselves, the radiant Venus, an object of interested human attention already in ancient times. The average temperature there is calculated at about 47°C. (116.6°F.) assuming the sun constant to two calories per cubic centimeter (.061 cu. in.) per minute. The humidity is probably about six times the average of that on the Earth, or three times that in Congo where the average temperature is 26°C. (78.8°F.). The atmosphere of Venus holds about as much water vapour 5 km. (3.1 miles) *above* the surface as does the atmosphere of the Earth *at* the surface. We must therefore conclude that everything on Venus is dripping wet. The rainstorms on the other hand do not necessarily bring greater precipitation than with us. The cloud-formation is enormous and dense rain-clouds travel as high up as 10 km. (6.2 miles). The heat from the Sun does not attack the ground but the dense clouds, causing a powerful external circulation of air which carries the vapour to higher strata where it condenses into new clouds. Thus, an effective barrier is formed against horizontal air currents in the great expanses below. At the surface of Venus, therefore, there exists a complete absence of wind both vertically, as the Sun's radiation is absorbed by the ever present clouds above, and horizontally due to friction. Disintegration takes place with enormous rapidity, probably about eight times as fast as on Earth, and the violent rains carry the products speedily downhill where they fill the valleys and the oceans in front of all river mouths.

A very great part of the surface of Venus is no doubt covered with swamps, corresponding to those on the Earth in which the coal deposits were formed, except that they are about 30°C. (54°F.) warmer. No dust is lifted high into the air to lend it a distinct colour; only the dazzling white reflex from the clouds reaches the outside space and gives the planet its remarkable, brilliantly white, lustre. The powerful air currents in the highest strata of the atmosphere equalize the temperature difference between poles and equator almost completely so that a uniform climate exists all over the planet analogous to conditions on the Earth during its hottest periods.

The temperature on Venus is not so high as to prevent a luxuriant vegetation. The constantly uniform climatic conditions which exist everywhere result in an entire absence of adaptation to changing exterior conditions. Only low forms of life are therefore represented, mostly no doubt

51

belonging to the vegetable kingdom; and the organisms are nearly of the same kind all over the planet. The vegetative processes are greatly accelerated by the high temperature. Therefore, the lifetime of the organisms is probably short. Their dead bodies, decaying rapidly, if lying in the open air, fill it with stifling gases; if embedded in the slime carried down by the rivers, they speedily turn into small lumps of coal, which, later, under the pressure of new layers combined with high temperature, become particles of graphite. Fossils proper are not formed as was also the case in the early periods of the Earth.

The temperature at the poles of Venus is probably somewhat lower, perhaps about 10°C. (18°F.), than the average temperature on the planet. The organisms there should have developed into higher forms than elsewhere, and progress and culture, if we may so express it, will gradually spread from the poles toward the equator. Later, the temperature will sink, the dense clouds and the gloom disperse, and some time, perhaps not before life on the Earth has reverted to its simpler forms or has even become extinct, a flora and a fauna will appear, similar in kind to those that now delight our human eye, and Venus will then indeed be the "Heavenly Queen" of Babylonian fame, not because of her radiant lustre alone, but as the dwelling place of the highest beings in our solar system.

WHEN H. G. Wells wrote, at the beginning of *The War of the Worlds* of the intellects "vast and cool and unsympathetic" who were watching Earth and laying their plans against us, he was referring to the Martians. Vast and cool and unsympathetic — so the Cytherean inhabitants would have found the intellect of Olaf Stapledon.

His long history of man's transformation of Venus which

follows is only a small part of the enormous chronicle, *Last and First Men*, published in 1930

OLAF STAPLEDON: Last and First Men

But though the mere navigation of space was thus easily accomplished, the major task was still untouched. It was necessary either to remake man's nature to suit another planet, or to modify conditions upon another planet to suit man's nature. The former alternative was repugnant to the Fifth Men. Obviously it would entail an almost complete refashioning of the human organism. No existing individual could possibly be so altered as to live in the present conditions of Mars or Venus. And it would probably prove impossible to create a new being, adapted to these conditions, without sacrificing the brilliant and harmonious constitution of the extant species.

On the other hand, Mars could not be made habitable without first being stocked with air and water; and such an undertaking seemed impossible. There was nothing for it, then, but to attack Venus. The polar surfaces of that planet, shielded by impenetrable depths of cloud, proved after all not unendurably hot. Subsequent generations might perhaps be modified so as to withstand even the sub-arctic and "temperate" climates. Oxygen was plentiful, but it was all tied up in chemical combination. Inevitably so, since oxygen combines very readily, and on Venus there was no vegetable life to exhale the free gas and replenish the ever-vanishing supply. It was necessary, then, to equip Venus with an appropriate vegetation, which in the course of ages should render the planet's atmosphere hospitable to man. The chemical and physical conditions on Venus had therefore to be studied in great detail, so that it might be possible to design a kind of life which would have a chance of flourishing. This research had to be carried out from within the ether-ships, or with gas helmets, since no human being could live in the natural atmosphere of the planet.

We must not dwell upon the age of heroic research and adventure which now began. Observations of the lunar orbit were showing that ten million years was too long an estimate of the future habitability of the earth; and it was soon realized that Venus could not be made ready soon enough unless some more rapid change was set on foot. It was therefore decided to split up some of the ocean of the planet into hydrogen and oxygen by a vast process of electrolysis. This would have been a more difficult task, had not the ocean been relatively free from salt, owing to the fact that there was so little dry land to be denuded of salts by rain and river. The oxygen thus formed by electrolysis would be allowed to mix with the atmosphere. The hydrogen had to be got rid of somehow, and an ingenious method was devised by which it should be ejected beyond the limits of the atmosphere at so great a speed that it would never return. Once sufficient free oxygen had been produced, the new vegetation would replenish the loss due to oxidation. This work was duly set on foot. Great automatic electrolysing stations were founded on several of the islands; and biological research produced at length a whole flora of specialized vegetable types to cover the land surface of the planet. It was hoped that in less than a million years Venus would be fit to receive the human race, and the race fit to live on Venus.

Meanwhile a careful survey of the planet had been undertaken. Its land surface, scarcely more than a thousandth that of the earth, consisted of an unevenly distributed archipelago of mountainous islands. The planet had evidently not long ago been through a mountain-forming era, for soundings proved its whole surface to be extravagantly corrugated. The ocean was subject to terrific storms and currents; for since the planet took several weeks to rotate, there was a great difference of temperature and atmospheric pressure between the almost Arctic hemisphere of night and the sweltering hemisphere of day. So great was the evaporation, that open sky was almost never visible from any part of the planet's surface; and indeed the average day-time weather was a succession of thick fogs and fantastic thunder-storms. Rain in the evening was a continuous torrent. Yet before night was over the waves clattered with fragments of ice.

Man looked upon his future home with loathing, and on his birthplace with an affection which became passionate. With its blue sky, its incomparable starry nights, its temperate and varied continents, its ample spaces of agriculture, wilderness, and park, its well-known beasts and plants, and all the material fabric of the most enduring of terrestrial civilizations, it seems to the men and women who were planning flight almost a living thing imploring them not to desert it. They looked often with hate at the quiet moon, now visibly larger than the moon of history. They revised again and again their astronomical and physical theories, hoping for some flaw which should render the moon's observed behaviour less mysterious, less terrifying. But they found nothing. It was as though a fiend out of some ancient myth had come to life in the modern world, to interfere with the laws of nature for man's undoing.

Preparing for a New World

Another trouble now occurred. Several electrolysis stations on Venus were wrecked, apparently by submarine eruption. Also, a number of ether-ships, engaged in surveying the ocean, mysteriously exploded. The explanation was found when one of these vessels, though damaged, was able to return to the earth. The commander reported that, when the sounding line was drawn up, a large spherical object was seen to be attached to it. Closer inspection showed that this object was fastened to the sounding apparatus by a hook, and was indeed unmistakeably artificial, a structure of small metal plates riveted together. While preparations were being made to bring the object within the ship, it happened to bump against the hull, and then it exploded.

Evidently there must be intelligent life somewhere in the ocean of Venus. Evidently the marine Venerians resented the steady depletion of their aqueous world, and were determined to stop it. The terrestrials had assumed that water in which no free oxygen was dissolved could not support life. But observation soon revealed that in this world-wide ocean there were many living species, some sessile, others free-swimming, some microscopic, others as large as whales. The basis of life in these creatures lay not in photosynthesis and chemical combination, but in the controlled disintegration of radio-active atoms. Venus was particularly rich in these atoms, and still contained certain elements which had long ago ceased to exist on the earth. The oceanic fauna subsisted in the destruction of minute quantities of radio-active atoms throughout its tissues.

Several of the Venerian species had attained considerable mastery over their physical environment, and were able to destroy one another very competently with various mechanical contrivances. Many types were indeed definitely intelligent and versatile within certain limits. And of these intelligent types, one had come to dominate all the others by virtue of its superior intelligence, and had constructed a genuine civilization on the basis of radioactive power. These most developed of all the Venerian creatures were beings of about the size and shape of a swordfish. They had three manipulative organs, normally sheathed within the long "sword", but capable of extension beyond its point, as three branched muscular tentacles. They swam with a curious screw-like motion of their bodies and triple tails. Three fins enabled them to steer. They had also organs of phosphorescence, vision, touch, and something analogous to hearing. They appeared to reproduce asexually, laying eggs in the ooze of the ocean bed. They had no need of nutrition in the ordinary sense; but in infancy they seemed to gather enough radio-active matter to keep them alive for many years. Each individual, when his stock was running out and he began to be feeble, was either destroyed by his juniors or buried in a radio-active mine, to rise from this living death in a few months completely rejuvenated.

At the bottom of the Venerian ocean these creatures thronged in cities of proliferated coral-like buildings, equipped with many complex articles, which must have constituted the necessities and luxuries of their civilization. So much was ascertained by the Terrestrials in the course of their submarine exploration. But the mental life of the Venerians remained hidden. It was clear, indeed, that like all living things, they were concerned with self-maintenance and the exercise of their capacities; but of the nature of these capacities little was discoverable. Clearly they used some kind of symbolic language, based on mechanical vibrations set up in the water by the snapping claws of their tentacles. But their more complex activities were quite unintelligible. All that could be recorded with certainty was that they were much addicted to warfare,

56

even to warfare between groups of one species; and that even in the stress of military disaster they maintained a feverish production of material articles of all sorts, which they proceeded to destroy and neglect.

One activity was observed which was peculiarly mysterious. At certain seasons three individuals, suddenly developing unusual luminosity, would approach one another with rhythmic swayings and tremors, and would then rise on their tails and press their bodies together. Sometimes at this stage an excited crowd would collect, whirling around the three like driven snow. The chief performers would now furiously tear one another to pieces with their crablike pincers, till nothing was left but tangled shreds of flesh, the great swords, and the still twitching claws. The Terrestrials, observing these matters with difficulty, at first suspected some kind of sexual intercourse; but no reproduction was ever traced to this source. Possibly the behaviour had once served a biological end, and had now become a useless ritual. Possibly it was a kind of voluntary religious sacrifice. More probably it was of a quite different nature, unintelligible to the human mind.

As man's activities on Venus became more extensive, the Venerians became more energetic in seeking to destroy him. They could not come out of the ocean to grapple with him, for they were deep-sea organisms. Deprived of oceanic pressure, they would have burst. But they contrived to hurl explosives into the centres of the islands, or to undermine them from tunnels. The work of electrolysis was thus very seriously hampered. And as all efforts to parley with the Venerians failed completely, it was impossible to effect a compromise. The Fifth Men were thus faced with a grave moral problem. What right had man to interfere in a world already possessed by beings who were obviously intelligent, even though their mental life was incomprehensible to man? Long ago man himself had suffered at the hands of Martian invaders, who doubtless regarded themselves as more noble than the human race. And now man was committing a similar crime. On the other hand, either the migration to Venus must go forward, or humanity must be destroyed; for it seemed quite certain by now that the moon would fall, and at no very distant date. And though man's understanding of the Venerians

57

was so incomplete, what he did know of them strongly suggested that they were definitely inferior to himself in mental range. This judgment might, of course, be mistaken; the Venerians might after all be so superior to man that man could not get an inkling of their superiority. But this argument would apply equally to jelly-fish and microorganisms. Judgment had to be passed according to the evidence available. So far as man could judge at all in the matter, he was definitely the higher type.

There was another fact to be taken into account. The life of the Venerian organism depended on the existence of radio-active atoms. Since those atoms are subject to disintegration, they must become rarer. Venus was far better supplied than the earth in this respect, but there must inevitably come a time when there would be no more radio-active matter in Venus. Now submarine research showed that the Venerian fauna had once been more extensive, and that the increasing difficulty of procuring radio-active matter was already the great limiting factor of civilization. Thus the Venerians were doomed, and man would merely hasten their destruction.

It was hoped, of course, that in colonizing Venus mankind would be able to accommodate itself without seriously intefering with the native population. But this proved impossible for two reasons. In the first place, the natives seemed determined to destroy the invader even if they should destroy themselves in the process. Titanic explosions were engineered, which caused the invaders serious damage, but also strewed the ocean surface with thousands of dead Venerians. Secondly, it was found that, as electrolysis poured more and more free oxygen into the atmosphere, the ocean absorbed some of the potent element back into itself by solution; and this dissolved oxygen had a disastrous effect upon the oceanic organisms. Their tissues began to oxidize. They were burnt up, internally and externally, by a slow fire. Man dared not stop the process of electrolysis until the atmosphere had become as rich in oxygen as his native air. Long before this state was reached, it was already clear that the Venerians were beginning to feel the effects of the poison, and that in a few thousand years, at most, they would be exterminated. It was therefore determined to put them out of their misery as quickly as possible. Men could by now walk abroad on the islands of Venus, and indeed the first settlements were already being founded. They were thus able to build a fleet of powerful submarine vessels to scour the ocean and destroy the whole native fauna.

This vast slaughter influenced the mind of the fifth human species in two opposite directions, now flinging it into despair, now rousing it to grave elation. For on the one hand the horror of the slaughter produced a haunting guiltiness in all men's minds, an unreasoning disgust with humanity for having been driven to murder in order to save itself. And this guiltiness combined with the purely intellectual loss of self-confidence which had produced by the failure of science to account for the moon's approach. It reawakened, also, that other quite irrational sense of guilt which had been bred of sympathy with the everlasting distress of the past. Together, these three influences tended toward racial neurosis.

On the other hand a very different mood sometimes sprang from the same three sources. After all, the failure of science was a challenge to be gladly accepted; it opened up a wealth of possibilities hitherto unimagined. Even the unalterable distress of the past constituted a challenge; for in some strange manner the present and future, it was said, must transfigure the past. As for the murder of Venerian life, it was, indeed, terrible, but right. It had been committed without hate; indeed, rather in love. For as the navy proceeded with its relentless work, it had gathered much insight into the life of the natives, and had learned to admire, even in a sense to love, while it killed. This mood, of inexorable yet not ruthless will, intensified the spiritual sensibility of the species, refined, so to speak, its spiritual hearing, and revealed to it tones and themes in the universal music which were hitherto obscure.

Which of these two moods, despair or courage, would triumph? All depended on the skill of the species to maintain a high degree of vitality in untoward circumstances.

Man now busied himself in preparing his new home. Many kinds of plant life, derived from the terrestrial stock, but bred for the Venerian environment, now began to swarm on the islands and in the sea. For so restricted was the land surface, that great areas of ocean had to be given

59

over to specially designed marine plants, which now formed immense floating continents of vegetable matter. On the least torrid islands appeared habitual pylons, forming an architectural forest, with vegetation on every acre of free ground. Even so, it would be impossible for Venus ever to support the huge population of the earth. Steps had therefore been taken to ensure that the birth-rate should fall far short of the death-rate; so that, when the time should come, the race might emigrate without leaving any living members behind. No more than a hundred million, it was reckoned, could live tolerably on Venus. The population had therefore to be reduced to a hundredth of its former size. And since, in the terrestrial community, with its vast social and cultural activity, every individual had fulfilled some definite function in society, it was obvious that the new community must be not merely small but mentally impoverished. Hitherto, each individual had been enriched by intercourse with a far more intricate and diverse social environment than would be possible on Venus.

Such was the prospect when at length it was judged advisable to leave the earth to its fate. The moon was now so huge that it periodically turned day into night, and night into a ghastly day. Prodigious tides and distressful weather conditions had already spoilt the amenities of the earth, and done great damage to the fabric of civilization. And so at length humanity reluctantly took flight. Some centuries passed before the migration was completed, before Venus had received, not only the whole remaining human population, but also representatives of many other species of organisms, and all the most precious treasure of man's culture.

Taking Root Again

Man's sojourn on Venus lasted somewhat longer than his whole career on the Earth. From the days of Pithecanthropus to the final evacuation of his native planet he passed, as we have seen, through a bewildering diversity of form and circumstance. On Venus, though the human type was somewhat more constant biologically, it was scarcely less variegated in culture.

To give an account of this period, even on the minute

scale that has been adopted hitherto, would entail another volume. I can only sketch its bare outline. The sapling, humanity, transplanted into foreign soil, withers at first almost to the root, slowly readjusts itself, grows into strength and a certain permanence of form, burgeons, season by season, with leaf and flower of many successive civilizations and cultures, sleeps winter by winter, through many ages of reduced vitality, but at length (to force the metaphor), avoids this recurrent defeat by attaining an evergreen constitution and a continuous effloresence. Then once more, through the whim of Fate, it is plucked up by the roots and cast upon another world.

The first human settlers on Venus knew well that life would be a sorry business. They had done their best to alter the planet to suit human nature, but they could not make Venus into another Earth. The land surface was minute. The climate was almost unendurable. The extreme difference of temperature between the protracted day and night produced incredible storms, rain like a thousand contiguous waterfalls, terrifying electrical disturbances, and fogs in which a man could not see his own feet. To make matters worse, the oxygen supply was as yet barely enough to render the air breathable. Worse still, the liberated hydrogen was not always successfully ejected from the atmosphere. It would sometimes mingle with the air to form an explosive mixture, and sooner or later there would occur a vast atmospheric flash. Recurrent disasters of this sort destroyed the architecture and the human inhabitants of many islands, and further reduced the oxygen supply. In time, however, the increasing vegetation made it possible to put an end to the dangerous process of electrolysis.

Meanwhile, these atmospheric explosions crippled the race so seriously that it was unable to cope with a more mysterious trouble which beset it some time after the migration. A new and inexplicable decay of the digestive organs, which first occurred as a rare disease, threatened within a few centuries to destroy mankind. The physical effects of this plague were scarcely more disastrous than the psychological effects of the complete failure to master it; for, what with the mystery of the moon's vagaries and the deep-seated, unreasoning sense of guilt produced by the extermination of the Venerians, man's self-confidence was already seriously shaken, and his highly organized mentality began to show symptoms of derangement. The new plague was, indeed, finally traced to something in the Venerian water, and was supposed to be due to certain molecular groupings, formerly rare, but subsequently fostered by the presence of terrestrial organic matter in the ocean. No cure was discovered.

And now another plague seized upon the enfeebled race. Human tissues had never perfectly assimilated the Martian units which were the means of "telepathic" communications. The universal ill-health now favoured a kind of "cancer" of the nervous system, which was due to the ungoverned proliferation of these units. The harrowing results of this disease may be left unmentioned. Century by century it increased; and even those who did not actually contract the sickness lived in constant terror of madness.

These troubles were aggravated by the devastating heat. The hope that, as the generations passed, human nature would adapt itself even to the more sultry regions, seemed to be unfounded. Far otherwise, within a thousand years the once-populous arctic and antarctic islands were almost deserted. Out of each hundred of the great pylons, scarcely more than two were inhabited, and these only by a few plague-stricken and broken-spirited human relics. These alone were left to turn their telescopes upon the earth and watch the unexpectedly delayed bombardment of their native world by the fragments of the moon.

Population decreased still further. Each brief generation was slightly less well developed than its parents. Intelligence declined. Education became superficial and restricted. Contact with the past was no longer possible. Art lost its significance, and philosophy its dominion over the minds of men. Even applied science began to be too difficult. Unskilled control of the subatomic sources of power led to a number of disasters, which finally gave rise to a superstition that all "tampering with nature" was wicked, and all the ancient wisdom a snare of Man's Enemy. Books, instruments, all the treasures of human culture, were therefore burnt. Only the perdurable buildings resisted destruction. Of the incomparable world-order of the Fifth Men nothing was left but a few island tribes cut off from one another by the ocean, and from the rest of space-time by the depths of their own ignorance.

After many thousands of years human nature did begin to adapt itself to the climate and to the poisoned water without which life was impossible. At the same time a new variety of the fifth species now began to appear, in which the Martian units were not included. Thus at last the race regained a certain mental stability, at the expense of its faculty of "telepathy", which man was not to regain until almost the last phase of his career. Meanwhile, though he had recovered somewhat from the effects of an alien world, the glory that had been was no more. Let us therefore hurry through the ages that passed before noteworthy events again occurred.

In early days on Venus men had gathered their foodstuff from the great floating islands of vegetable matter which had been artificially produced before the migration. But as the oceans became populous with modifications of the terrestrial fauna, the human tribes turned more and more to fishing. Under the influence of its marine environment, one branch of the species assumed such an aquatic habit that in time it actually began to develop biological adaptations for marine life. It is perhaps surprising that man was still capable of spontaneous variation; but the fifth human species was artificial, and had always been prone to epidemics of mutation. After some millions of years of variation and selection there appeared a very successful species of seal-like submen. The whole body was moulded to stream-lines. The lung capacity was greatly developed. The spine had elongated, and increased in flexibility. The legs were shrunken, grown together, and flattened into a horizontal rudder. The arms also were diminitive and fin-like, though they still retained the manipulative fore-finger and thumb. The head had sunk into the body and looked forward in the direction of swimming. Strong carnivorous teeth, emphatic gregariousness, and a new, almost human, cunning in the chase, combined to make these seal-men lords of the ocean. And so they remained for many million years, until a more human race, annoyed at their piscatorial successes, harpooned them out of existence.

For another branch of the degenerated fifth species had retained a more terrestrial habit and the ancient human form. Sadly reduced in stature and in brain, these abject beings were so unlike the original invaders that they are rightly considered a new species, and may therefore be called the Sixth Men. Age after age they gained a precarious livelihood by grubbing roots upon the forest-clad islands, trapping the innumerable birds, and catching fish in the tidal inlets with ground bait. Not infrequently they devoured, or were devoured by, their seal-like relatives. So restricted and constant was the environment of these human remnants, that they remained biologically and culturally stagnant for some millions of years.

At length, however, geological events afforded man's nature once more the opportunity of change. A mighty warping of the planet's crust produced an island almost as large as Australia. In time this was peopled, and from the clash of tribes a new and versatile race emerged. Once more there was methodical tillage, craftsmanship, complex social organization, and adventure in the realm of thought.

During the next two hundred million years all the main phases of man's life on earth were many times repeated on Venus with characteristic differences. Theocratic empires; free and intellectualistic island cities; insecure overlordships of feudal archipelagos; rivalries of high priest and emperor; religious feuds over the interpretation of sacred scriptures; recurrent fluctuations of though from naive animism, through polytheism, conflicting monotheisms, and all the desperate "isms" by which mind seeks to blur the severe outline of truth; recurrent fashions of comfort-seeking fantasy and cold intelligence; social disorders through the misuse of volcanic or wind power in industry; business empires and pseudo-communistic empires – all these forms flitted over the changing substance of mankind again and again, as in an enduring hearth-fire there appear and vanish the infinitely diverse forms of flame and smoke. But all the while the brief spirits, in whose massed configurations these forms inhered, were intent chiefly on the primitive needs of food, shelter, companionship, crowd-lust, love-making, the two-edged relationship of parent and child, the exercise of muscle and intelligence in facile sport. Very seldom, only in rare moments of clarity, only after ages of misapprehension, did a few of them, here and there, now and again, begin to have the deeper insight into the world's nature and man's. And no sooner had this precious insight begun to propagate itself, than it would be blotted out by some small or great disaster, by epidemic disease, by the spontaneous disruption of society, by an access of racial imbecility, by a prolonged bombardment of meteorites, or by the mere cowardice and vertigo that dared not look down the precipice of the fact.

The Flying Men

We need not dwell upon these multitudinous reiterations of culture, but must glance for a moment at the last phase of this sixth human species, so that we may pass on to the artificial species which it produced.

Throughout their career the Sixth Men had often been fascinated by the idea of flight. The bird was again and again their most sacred symbol. Their monotheism was apt to be worship not of a god-man, but of a god-bird, conceived now as the divine sea eagle, winged with power, now as the giant swift, winged with mercy, now as disembodied spirit of air, and once as the bird-god that became man to endow the human race with flight, physical and spiritual.

It was inevitable that flight should obsess man on Venus, for the planet afforded but a cramping home for groundlings; and the riotous efflorescence of avian species shamed man's pedestrian habit. When in due course the Sixth Men attained knowledge and power comparable to that of the First Men at their height, they invented flying machines of various types. Many times, indeed, mechanical flight was rediscovered and lost again with the downfall of civilization. But at its best it was regarded only as a makeshift. And when at length, with the advance of the biological sciences, the Sixth Men were in a position to influence the human organism itself, they determined to produce a true flying man. Many civilizations strove vainly for this result, sometimes half-heartedly, sometimes with religious earnestness. Finally the most enduring and brilliant of all the civilizations of the Sixth Men actually attained the goal.

The Seventh Men were pigmies, scarcely heavier than the largest of terrestrial flying birds. Through and through they were organized for flight. A leathery membrane spread from the foot to the tip of the immensely elongated and strengthened "middle finger". The three "outer" fingers, equally elongated, served as ribs to the membrane; while the index and thumb remained free for manipulation. The body assumed the streamlines of a bird, and was covered with a deep quilt of feathery wool. This, and the silken down of the flight-membranes, varied greatly from individual to individual in colouring and texture. On the ground the Seventh Men walked much as other human beings, for the flight-membranes were folded close to the legs and body, and hung from the arms like exaggerated sleeves. In flight the legs were held extended as a flattened tail, with the feet locked together by the big toes. The breastbone was greatly developed as a keel, and as a base for the muscles of flight. The other bones were hollow, for lightness, and their internal surfaces were utilized as supplementary lungs. For, like the birds, these flying men had to maintain a high rate of oxidation. A state which others would regard as fever was normal to them.

Their brains were given ample tracts for the organization of prowess in flight. In fact, it was found possible to equip the species with a system of reflexes for aerial balance, and a true, though artificial, instinctive aptitude for flight, and interest in flight. Compared with their makers their brain volume was of necessity small, but their whole neural system was very carefully organized. Also it matured rapidly, and was extremely facile in the acquirement of new modes of activity. This was very desirable; for the individual's natural life period was but fifty years, and in most cases it was deliberately cut short by some impossible feat at about forty, or whenever the symptoms of old age began to be felt.

Of all human species these bat-like Flying Men, the Seventh Men, were probably the most carefree. Gifted with harmonious physique and gay temperament, they came into a social heritage well adapted to their nature. There was no occasion for them, as there had often been for some others, to regard the world as fundamentally hostile to life, or themselves as essentially deformed. Of quick intelligence in respect of daily personal affairs and social organization, they were untroubled by the insatiable lust of understanding. Not that they were an unintellectual race, for they soon formulated a beautifully systematic account of experience. They clearly perceived, however, that the perfect sphere of their thought was but a bubble adrift in chaos. Yet it was an elegant bubble. And the system was true, in its own gay and frankly insincere manner, true as significant metaphor, not literally true. What more, it was asked, could be expected of human intellect? Adolescents were encouraged to study the ancient problems of philosophy, for no reason but to convince themselves of the futility of probing beyond the limits of the orthodox system. "Prick the bubble of thought at any point", it was said, "and you shatter the whole of it. And since thought is one of the necessities of human life, it must be preserved."

Natural science was taken over from the earlier species with half-contemptuous gratitude, as a necessary means of sane adjustment to the environment. Its practical applications were valued as the ground of the social order; but as the millenia advanced, and society approached that remarkable perfection and stability which was to endure for many million years, scientific inventiveness became less and less needful, and science itself was relegated to the infant schools. Htstory also was given in outline during childhood, and subsequently ignored.

This curiously sincere intellectual insincerity was due to the fact that the Seventh Men were chiefly concerned with matters other than abstract thought. It is difficult to give to members of the first human species an inkling of the great preoccupation of these Flying Men. To say that it was flight would be true, yet far less than the truth. To say that they sought to live dangerously and vividly, to crowd as much experience as possible into each moment, would again be a caricature of the truth. On the physical plane, indeed, "the universe of flight", with all the variety of peril and skill afforded by a tempestuous atmosphere, was every individual's chief medium of self-expression. Yet it was not flight itself, but the spiritual aspect of flight which obsessed the species.

In the air and on the ground the Seventh Men were different beings. Whenever they exercised themselves in flight they suffered a remarkable change of spirit. Much of their time had to be spent on the ground, since most of the work upon which civilization rested was impossible in the air. Moreover, life in the air was life at high pressure, and necessitated spells of recuperation on the ground. In their pedestrian phase the Seventh Men were sober folk, mildly bored, yet in the main cheerful, humorously impatient of the drabness and irk of pedestrian affairs, but ever supported by memory and anticipation of the vivid life of the air. Often they were tired, after the strain of that other life, but seldom were they despondent or lazy. Indeed, in the routine of agriculture and industry they were industrious as the wingless ants. Yet they worked in a strange mood of attentive absentmindedness; for their hearts were ever in the air. So long as they could have frequent periods of aviation, they remained bland even on the ground. But if for any reason such as illness they were confined to the ground for a long period, they pined, developed acute melancholia, and died. Their makers had so contrived them that with the onset of any very great pain or misery their hearts should stop. Thus they were to avoid all serious distress. But, in fact, this merciful device worked only on the ground. In the air they assumed a very different and more heroic nature, which their makers had not forseen, though indeed it was a natural consequence of their design.

In the air the flying man's heart beat more powerfully. His temperature rose. His sensation became more vivid and more discriminate, his intelligence more agile and penetrating. He experienced a more intense pleasure or pain in all that happened to him. It would not be true to say that he became more emotional; rather the reverse, if by emotionality is meant enslavement to the emotions. For the most remarkable feature of the aerial phase was that this enhanced power of appreciation was dispassionate. So long as the individual was in the air, whether in lonely struggle with the storm, or in the ceremonial ballet with sky-darkening hosts of his fellows; whether in the ecstatic love dance with a sexual partner, or in solitary and meditative circlings far above the world; whether his enterprise was fortunate, or he found himself dismembered by the hurricane, and crashing to death; always the gay and the tragic fortunes of his own person were regarded equally with detached aesthetic delight. Even when his dearest companion was mutilated or destroyed by some aerial disaster, he exulted; though also he would give his own life in the hope of effecting a rescue. But very soon after he had returned to the ground he would be overwhelmed with grief, would strive vainly to recapture the lost vision, and would perhaps die of heart failure.

Even when, as happened occasionally in the wild climate of Venus, a whole aerial population was destroyed by some worldwide atmospheric tumult, the few broken survivors, so long as they could remain in the air, exulted. And actually while at length they sank exhausted towards the ground, towards certain disillusionment and death, they laughed inwardly. Yet an hour after they had alighted, their constitution would be changed, their vision lost. They would remember only the horror of the disaster, and the memory would kill them.

No wonder the Seventh Men grudged every moment that was passed on the ground. While they were in the air, of course, the prospect of a pedestrian interlude, or indeed of endless pedestrianism, though in a manner repugnant, would be accepted with unswerving gaiety; but while they were on the ground, they grudged bitterly to be there. Early in the career of the species the proportion of aerial to terrestrial hours was increased by a biological invention. A minute food-plant was produced which spent the winter rooted in the ground, and the summer adrift in the sunlit upper air, engaged solely in photosynthesis. Henceforth the populations of the Flying Men were able to browse upon the bright pastures of the sky, like swallows. As the ages passed, material civilization became more and more simplified. Needs which could not be satisfied without terrestrial labour tended to be outgrown. Manufactured articles became increasingly rare. Books were no longer written or read. In the main, indeed, they were no longer necessary; but to some extent their place was taken by verbal tradition and discussion, in the upper air. Of the arts, music, spoken lyric and epic verse, and the supreme art of winged dance, were constantly practised. The rest vanished. Many of the sciences inevitably faded into tradition; yet the true scientific spirit was preserved in a very exact meteorology, a sufficient biology, and a human psychology surpassed only by the second and fifth species at their height. None of these sciences, however, was taken very seriously, save in its practical applications. For instance, psychology explained the ecstasy of flight very neatly as a

69

febrile and "irrational" beatitude. But no one was disconcerted by this theory; for every one, while on the wing, felt it to be merely an amusing half-truth.

The social order of the Seventh Men was in essence neither utilitarian, nor humanistic, nor religious, but aesthetic. Every act and every institution were to be justified as contributing to the perfect form of the community. Even social prosperity was conceived as merely the medium in which beauty should be embodied, the beauty, namely, of vivid individual lives harmoniously related. Yet not only for the individual, but even for the race itself (so the wise insisted), death on the wing was more excellent than prolonged life on the ground. Better, far better, would be racial suicide than a future of pedestrianism. Yet though both the individual and the race were conceived as instrumental to objective beauty, there was nothing religious, in any ordinary sense, in this conviction. The Seventh Men were completely without interest in the universal and the unseen. The beauty which they sought to create was ephemeral and very largely sensuous. And they were well content that it should be so. Personal immortality, said a dying sage, would be as tedious as an endless song. Equally so with the race. The lovely flame, of which we all are members, must die, he said, must die; for without death she would fall short of beauty.

For close on a hundred million terrestrial years this aerial society endured with little change. On many of the islands throughout this period stood even yet a number of the ancient pylons, though repaired almost beyond recognition. In these nests the men and women of the seventh species slept through the long Venerian nights, crowded like roosting swallows. By day the same great towers were sparsely peopled with those who were serving their turn in industry, while in the fields and on the sea others laboured. But most were in the air. Many would be skimming the ocean, to plunge, gannet-like, for fish. Many, circling over land or sea, would now and again swoop like hawks upon the wildfowl which formed the chief meat of the species. Others, forty or fifty thousand feet above the waves, where even the plentiful atmosphere of Venus was scarcely capable of supporting them, would be soaring, circling, sweeping, for pure joy of flight. Others, in the

70

calm and sunshine of high altitudes, would be hanging effortless upon some steady up-current of air for meditation and the rapture of mere percipience. Not a few love-intoxicated pairs would be entwining their courses in aerial patterns, in spires, cascades, and true-love knots of flight, presently to embrace and drop ten thousand feet in bodily union. Some would be driving hither and thither through the green mists of vegetable particles, gathering the manna in their open mouths. Companies, circling together, would be discussing matters social or aesthetic; others would be singing together, or listening to recitative epic verse. Thousands, gathering in the sky like migratory birds, would perform massed convolutions, reminiscent of the vast mechanical aerial choreography of the First World State, but more vital and expressive, as a bird's flight is more vital than the flight of any machine. And all the while there would be some, solitary or in companies, who, in the pursuit of fish and wild-fowl, or out of pure devilment, pitted their strength and skill against the hurricane, often tragically, but never without zest, and laughter of the spirit.

It may seem to some incredible that the culture of the Seventh Men should have lasted so long. Surely it must either have decayed through mere monotony and stagnation or have advanced into richer experience. But no. Generation succeeded generation, and each was too short-lived to outlast its young delight and discover boredom. Moreover, so perfect was the adjustment of these beings to their world, that even if they had lived for centuries they would have felt no need of change. Flight provided them with intense physical exhilaration, and with the physical basis of a genuine and ecstatic, though limited, spiritual experience. In this their supreme attainment they rejoiced not only in the diversity of flight itself, but also in the perceived beauties of their variegated world, and most of all, perhaps, in the thousand lyric and epic ventures of human intercourse in an aerial community.

The end of this seemingly everlasting elysium was nevertheless involved in the very nature of the species. In the first place, as the ages lengthened into aeons, the generations preserved less and less of the ancient scientific lore. For it became insignificant to them. The aerial community had no need of it. This loss of mere information did not matter so long as their condition remained unaltered; but in due course biological changes began to undermine them. The species had always been prone to a certain biological instability. A proportion of infants, varying with circumstances, had always been misshapen, and the deformity had generally been such as to make flight impossible. The normal infant was able to fly early in its second year. If some accident prevented it from doing so, it invariably fell into a decline and died before its third year was passed. But many of the deformed types, being the result of a partial reversion to the pedestrian nature, were able to live on indefinitely without flight. According to a merciful custom these cripples had always to be destroyed. But at length, owing to the gradual exhaustion of a certain marine salt essential to the high-strung nature of the Seventh Men, infants were more often deformed than true to type. The world population declined so seriously that the organized aerial life of the comumnity could not longer be carried on according to the time-honoured aesthetic principles. No one knew how to check his racial decay, but many felt that with greater biological knowledge it might be avoided. A disastrous policy was now adopted. It was decided to spare a carefully selected proportion of the deformed infants, those namely which, though doomed to pedestrianism, were likely to develop high intelligence. Thus it was hoped to raise a specialized group of persons whose work should be biological research untrammelled by the intoxication of flight.

The brilliant cripples that resulted from this policy looked at existence from a new angle. Deprived of the supreme experience for which their fellows lived, envious of a bliss which they knew only by report, yet contemptuous of the naïve mentality which cared for nothing (it seemed) but physical exercise, love-making, the beauty of nature, and the elegances of society, these flightless intelligences sought satisfaction almost wholly in the life of research and scientific control. At the best, however, they were a tortured and resentful race. For their natures were fashioned for the aerial life which they could not lead. Although they received from the winged folk just treatment and a certain compassionate respect, they writhed under this kindness, locked their hearts against all the orthodox values, and sought out new ideals. Within a few centuries they had rehabilitated the life of intellect, and, with the power that knowledge gives, they had made themselves masters of the world. The amiable fliers were surprised, perplexed, even pained; and yet withal amused. Even when it became evident that the pedestrians were determined to create a new world-order in which there would be no place for the beauties of natural flight, the fliers were only distressed while they were on the ground.

The islands were becoming crowded with machinery and flightless industrialists. In the air itself the winged folk found themselves outstripped by the base but effective instruments of mechanical flight. Wings became a laughing stock, and the life of natural flight was condemned as a barren luxury. It was ordained that in future every flier must serve the pedestrian world-order, or starve. And as the cultivation of wind-borne plants had been abandoned, and fishing and fowling rights were strictly controlled, this law was no empty form. At first it was impossible for the fliers to work on the ground for long hours, day after day, without incurring serious ill-health and an early death. But the pedestrian physiologists invented a drug which preserved the poor wage-slaves in something like physical health, and actually prolonged their life. No drug, however, could restore their spirit, for their normal aerial habit was reduced to a few tired hours of recreation once a week. Meanwhile, breeding experiments were undertaken to produce a wholly wingless large-brained type. And finally a law was enacted by which all winged infants must be either mutilated or destroyed. At this point the fliers made an heroic but ineffectual bid for power. They attacked the pedestrian population from the air. In reply the enemy rode them down in his great aeroplanes and blew them to pieces with high explosive.

The fighting squadrons of the natural fliers were finally driven to the ground in a remote and barren island. Thither the whole flying population, a mere remnant of its former strength, fled out of every civilized archipelago in search of freedom: the whole population – save the sick, who committed suicide, and all infants that could not yet fly. These were stifled by their mothers or next-of-kin, in obedience to a decree of the leaders. About a million men, women and children, some of whom were scarcely old enough for the prolonged flight, now gathered on the rocks, regardless that there was not food in the neighbourhood for a great company.

Their leaders, conferring together, saw clearly that the day of Flying Man was done, and that it would be more fitting for a high-souled race to die at once than to drag on in subjection to contemptuous masters. They therefore ordered the population to take part in an act of racial suicide that should at least make death a noble gesture of freedom. The people received the message while they were resting on the stony moorland. A wail of sorrow broke from them. It was checked by the speaker, who bade them strive to see, even on the ground, the beauty of the thing that was to be done. They could not see it; but they knew that if they had the strength to take wing again they would see it clearly, almost as soon as their tired muscles bore them aloft. There was no time to waste, for many were already faint with hunger, and anxious lest they should fail to rise. At the appointed signal the whole population rose into the air with a deep roar of wings. Sorrow was left behind. Even the children, when their mothers explained what was to be done, accepted their fate with zest; though, had they learned of it on the ground, they would have been terror-stricken. The company now flew steadily West, forming themselves into a double file many miles long. The cone of a volcano appeared over the horizon, and rose as they approached. The leaders pressed on towards its ruddy smoke plume; and unflinchingly, couple by couple, the whole multitude darted into its fiery breath and vanished. So ended the career of Flying Man.

A Minor Astronomical Event

The flightless yet still half avian race that now possessed the planet settled down to construct a society based on industry and science. After many vicissitudes of fortune and of aim, they produced a new human species, the Eighth Men. These longheaded and substantial folk were designed to be strictly pedestrian, physically and mentally. Apt for manipulation, calculation, and invention, they very soon turned Venus into an engineer's paradise. With power drawn from the planet's central heat, their huge electric

74

ships bored steadily through the perennial monsoons and hurricanes, which also their aircraft treated with contempt. Islands were joined by tunnels and by millipede bridges. Every inch of land served some industrial or agricultural end. So successfully did the generations amass wealth that their rival races and rival castes were able to indulge, every few centuries, in vast revelries of mutual slaughter and material destruction without, as a rule, impoverishing their descendants. And so insensitive had man become that these orgies shamed him not at all. Indeed, only by the ardours of physical violence could this most philistine species wrench itself for a while out of its complacency. Strife, which to nobler beings would have been a grave spiritual disaster, was for these a tonic, almost a religious exercise. These cathartic paroxysms, it should be observed, were but the rare and brief crises which automatically punctuated ages of stolid peace. At no time did they threaten the existence of the species; seldom did they even destroy its civilization.

It was after a lengthy period of peace and scientific advancement that the Eighth Men made a startling astronomical discovery. Ever since the First men had learned that in the life of every star there comes a critical moment when the great orb collapses, shrinking to a minute, dense grain with feeble radiation, men had periodically suspected that the sun was about to undergo this change, and become a typical "White Dwarf". The Eighth Men detected sure signs of the catastrophe, and predicted its date. Twenty thousand years they gave themselves before the change should begin. In another fifty thousand years, they guessed Venus would probably be frozen and uninhabitable. The only hope was to migrate to Mercury during the great change, when that planet was already ceasing to be intolerably hot. It was necessary then to give Mercury an atmosphere, and to breed a new species which should be capable of adapting itself finally to a world of extreme cold.

This desperate operation was already on foot when a new astronomical discovery rendered it futile. Astronomers detected, some distance from the solar system, a volume of non-luminous gas. Calculation showed that this object and the sun were approaching one another at a tangent, and that they would collide. Further calculation revealed the probable results of this event. The sun would flare up and expand prodigiously. Life would be quite impossible on any of the planets save, just possibly, Uranus, and more probably Neptune. The three planets beyond Neptune would escape roasting, but were unsuitable for other reasons. The two outermost would remain glacial, and, moreover, lay beyond the range of the imperfect ether-ships of the Eighth Men.

The innermost was practically a bald globe of iron, devoid not merely of atmosphere and water, but also of the normal covering of rock. Neptune alone might be able to support life; but how could even Neptune be populated? Not only was its atmosphere very unsuitable, and its gravitational pull such as to make man's body an intolerable burden, but also up to the time of the collision it would remain excessively cold. Not till after the collision could it support any kind of life known to man.

How these difficulties were overcome I have no time to tell, though the story of man's attack upon his final home is well worthy of recording. Nor can I tell in detail of the conflict of policy which now occurred. Some, realizing that the Eighth Men themselves could never live on Neptune, advocated an orgy of pleasure-living till the end. But at length the race excelled itself in an almost unanimous resolve to devote its remaining centuries to the production of a human being capable of carrying the torch of mentality into a new world.

Ether-vessels were able to reach that remote world and set up chemical changes for the improvement of the atmosphere. It was also possible, by means of the lately rediscovered process of automatic annihilation of matter, to produce a constant supply of energy for the warming of an area where life might hope to survive until the sun should be rejuvenated.

When at last the time for migration was approaching, a specially designed vegetation was shipped to Neptune and esatblished in the warm area to fit it for man's use. Animals, it was decided, would be unnecessary. Subsequently a specially designed human species, the Ninth Men, was transported to man's new home. The giant Eighth Men could not themselves inhabit Neptune. The trouble was not merely that they could scarcely support their own weight, let alone walk, but that the atmospheric pressure on Neptune was unendurable. For the great planet bore a gaseous envelope thousands of miles deep. The solid globe was scarcely more than the yolk of a huge egg. The mass of the air itself combined with the mass of the solid to produce a gravitational pressure greater than that upon the Venerian ocean floor. The Eighth Men, therefore, dared not emerge from their ethers-hips to tread the surface of the planet save for brief spells in steel diving suits. For them there was nothing else to do but to return to the archipelagos of Venus, and make the best of life until the end. They were not spared for long. A few centuries after the settlement of Neptune had been completed by transfering thither all the most precious material relics of humanity, the great planet itself narrowly missed collision with the dark stranger from space. Uranus and Jupiter were at the time well out of its track. Not so Saturn, which a few years after Neptune's escape, was engulfed with all its rings and satellites. The sudden incandescene which resulted from this minor collision was but a prelude. The huge foreigner rushed on. Like a finger poked into a spider's web, it tangled up the planetary orbits. Having devoured its way through the asteroids, it missed Mars, caught Earth and Venus in its blazing hair, and leapt at the sun. Henceforth the centre of the solar system was a star nearly as wide as the old orbit of Mercury and the system was transformed.

"EVERYTHING on Venus is dripping wet" says Arrhenius. The words sunk in, as well they might.

Heat and wet – they suggested luxuriant growth. Coupled with the idea that Venus was a younger world than Earth, they suggested that Venus might be undergoing a Jurassic or Carboniferous Age of its own.

Carboniferous Ages suggest trees. With lighter gravity, Cytherean trees could be gigantic.

Such reasoning may have been behind Edgar Rice Burroughs' Venus novels of which *Pirates of Venus* is the first and, in many judgments, the best. It was published in 1932. The following extract begins when the hero, Carson Napier, has plunged through the Cytherean clouds and landed in treetops.

Poor Napier had aimed his rocket at Mars! But Venus was to provide him with adventures enough.

EDGAR RICE BURROUGHS: Pirates of Venus.

I dropped into a mass of foliage and grasped wildly for support. A moment later I began to fall more rapidly and guessed what had happened; the parachute had been uptilted by contact with the foliage. I clutched at leaves and branches, fruitlessly, and then I was brought to a sudden stop; evidently the 'chute had fouled something. I hoped that it would hold until I found a secure resting-place.

As I groped about in the dark, my hand finally located a sturdy branch, and a moment later I was astride it, my back to the bole of a large tree – another theory gone the ignoble path of countless predecessors; it was evident that there was vegetation on Venus. At least, there was one tree; I could vouch for that, as I was sitting in it, and doubtless the black shadows I had passed were other, taller trees.

Having found secure lodgment, I divested myself of my parachute after salvaging some of its ropes and the straps from the harness, which I thought I might find helpful in descending the tree. Starting at the top of a tree, in darkness and among clouds, one may not be positive what the tree is like nearer the ground. I also removed my goggles. Then I commenced to descend. The girth of the tree was enormous but the branches grew sufficiently close together to permit me to find safe footing.

I did not know how far I had fallen through the second cloud stratum before I lodged in the tree nor how far I had descended the tree, but all together it must have been close to two thousand feet; yet I was still in the clouds.

Could the entire atmosphere of Venus be for ever fog laden? I hoped not, for it was a dreary prospect.

The light from below had increased a little as I descended, but not much; it was still dark about me. I continued to descend. It was tiresome work and not without danger, this climbing down an unfamiliar tree in a fog, at night, toward an unknown world. But I could not remain where I was, and there was nothing above to entice me upward; so I continued to descend.

What a strange trick fate had played me. I had wanted to visit Venus, but had discarded the idea when assured by my astronomer friends that the planet could not support either animals or vegetable life. I had started for Mars, and now, fully ten days before I had hoped to reach the red planet, I was on Venus, breathing perfectly good air among the branches of a tree that evidently dwarfed the giant Sequoias.

The illumination was increasing rapidly now, the clouds were thinning; through breaks I caught glimpses far below, glimpses of what appeared to be an endless vista of foliage, softly moonlit – but Venus had no moon. In that, in so far as the seeming moonlight was concerned, I could fully concur with the astronomers. This illumination came from no moon, unless Venus's satellite lay beneath her inner envelope of clouds, which was preposterous.

A moment later I emerged entirely from the cloud bank, but though I searched in all directions, I saw nothing but foliage above, around, below me, yet I could see far down into that abyss of leaves. In the soft light I could not determined the colours of the foliage, but I was sure that it was not green; it was some light, delicate shade of another colour.

I had descended another thousand feet since I had emerged from the clouds, and I was pretty well exhausted (the month of inactivity and overeating had softened me), when I saw just below me what appeared to be a causeway leading from the tree I was descending to another adjacent. I also discovered that from just below where I clung the limbs had been cut away from the tree to a point below the causeway. Here were two startling and unequivocal evidences of the presence of intelligent beings. Venus was inhabited! But by what? What strange, arboreal creatures built causeways high among these giant trees? Were they a species of monkcy-man? Were they of a high or low order of intelligence? How would they receive me?

At this juncture in my vain speculations I was startled by a noise above me. Something was moving in the branches overhead. The sound was coming nearer, and it seemed to me that it was being made by something of considerable size and weight, but perhaps, I realized, that conjecture was the child of my imagination. However, I felt most uncomfortable. I was unarmed. I have never carried weapons. My friends had urged a perfect arsenal upon me before I embarked upon my adventure, but I had argued that if I arrived on Mars unarmed it would be *prima facie* evidence of my friendly intentions, and even if my reception were war-like, I should be no worse off, since I could not hope, singlehanded, to conquer a world, no matter how well armed I were.

Suddenly, above me, to the crashing of some heavy body through the foliage were added hideous screams and snarls; and in the terrifying dissonance I recognized the presence of more than a single creature. Was I being pursued by all the fearsome denizens of this Venusian forest?

Perhaps my nerves were slightly unstrung; and who may blame them if they were, after what I had passed through so recently and during the long, preceding month? They were not entirely shattered, however, and I could still appreciate the fact that night noises often multiply themselves in a most disconcerting way. I have heard coyotes yapping and screaming around my camp on Arizona nights when, but for the actual knowledge that there were but one or two of them, I could have sworn that there were a hundred, had I trusted only to my sense of hearing.

But in this instance I was quite positive that the voices of more than a single beast were mingling to produce the horrid din that, together with the sound of their passage, was definitely and unquestionably drawing rapidly nearer me. Of course I did not know that the owners of those awesome voices were pursuing me, though a still, small voice within seemed to be assuring me that such was the fact.

I wished that I might reach the causeway below me (I

should feel better standing squarely on two feet), but it was too far to drop and there were no more friendly branches to give me support; then I thought of the ropes I had salvaged from the abandoned parachute. Quickly uncoiling them from about my waist, I looped one of them over the branch upon which I sat, grasped both strands firmly in my hands, and prepared to swing from my perch. Suddenly the screams and snarling growls ceased; and then, close above me now, I heard the noise of something descending towards me and saw the branches shaking to its weight.

Lowering my body from the branch, I swung downward and slid the fifteen or more feet to the causeway, and as I alighted the silence of the great forest was again shattered by a hideous scream just above my head. Looking up quickly, I saw a creature launching itself toward me and just beyond it a snarling face of utter hideousness. I caught but the briefest glimpse of it – just enough to see that it was a face, with eyes and a mouth – then it was withdrawn amidst the foliage.

Perhaps I only sensed that hideous vision subconsciously at the time, for the whole scene was but a flash upon the retina of my eye, and the other beast was in mid-air above me at the instant; but it remained indelibly impressed upon my memory, and I was to recall it upon a later day under circumstances so harrowing that the mind of mortal earth man may scarce conceive them.

As I leaped back to avoid the creature springing upon me, I still clung to one strand of the rope down which I had lowered myself to the causeway. My grasp upon the rope was unconscious and purely mechanical; it was in my hand, and my fist was clenched; and as I leaped away, I dragged the rope with me. A fortuitous circumstance, no doubt, but a most fortunate one.

The creature missed me, alighting on all-fours a few feet from me, and there it crouched, apparently slightly bewildered, and fortunately for me, it did not immediately charge, giving me the opportunity to collect my wits and back slowly away, at the same time mechanically coiling the rope in my right hand. The little, simple things one does in moments of stress or excitement often seem entirely beyond reason and incapable of explanation; but I have thought that they may be dictated by a subconscious mind reacting to the urge of self-preservation. Possibly they are not always well directed and may as often fail to be of service as not, but then it may be possible that subconscious minds are no less fallible than the objective mind, which is wrong far more often than it is right. I cannot but seek for some explanation of the urge that caused me to retain that rope, since, all unknown to me, it was to be the slender thread upon which my life was to hang.

Silence had again descended upon the weird scene. Since the final scream of the hideous creature that had retreated into the foliage after this thing had leaped for me, there had been no sound. The creature that crouched facing me seemed slightly bewildered. I am positive now that it had not been pursuing me, but that it itself had been the object of pursuit by the other beast that had retreated.

In the dim half-light of the Venusian night I saw confronting me a creature that might be conjured only in the half-delirium of some horrid nightmare. It was about as large as a full-grown puma, and stood upon four hand-like feet that suggested that it might be almost wholly arboreal. The front legs were much longer than the hind, suggesting, in this respect, the hyena; but here the similarity ceased, for the creature's furry pelt was striped longitudinally with alternate bands of red and yellow, and its hideous head bore no resemblance to any earthly animal. No external ears were visible, and in the low forehead was a single large, round eye at the end of a thick antenna about four inches long. The jaws were powerful and armed with long, sharp fangs, while from either side of the neck projected a powerful chela. Never have I seen a creature so fearsomely armed for offence as was this nameless beast of another world. With those powerful crab-like pincers it could easily have held an opponent far stronger than a man and dragged it to those terrible jaws.

For a time it eyed me with that single, terrifying eye that moved to and fro at the end of its antenna, and all the time its chelae were waving slowly, opening and closing. In that brief moment of delay I looked about me, and the first thing that I discovered was that I stood directly in front of an opening cut in the bole of the tree; an opening about three feet wide and over six feet high. But the most remarkable thing about it was that it was closed by a door; not a solid door, but one suggesting a massive wooden grill.

As I stood contemplating it and wondering what to do, I thought that I saw something moving behind it. Then a voice spoke to me out of the darkness beyond the door. It sounded like a human voice, though it spoke in a language that I could not understand. The tones were peremptory. I could almost imagine that it said, "Who are you, and what do you want here in the middle of the night?"

"I am a stranger," I said. "I come in peace and friendship."

Of course I knew that whatever it was behind the door, it could not understand me; but I hoped that my tone would assure it of my peaceful designs. There was a moment's silence and then I heard other voices. Evidently the situation was being discussed; then I saw that the creature facing me upon the causeway was creeping toward me and I turned my attention from the doorway to the beast.

I had no weapons, nothing but a length of futile rope; but I knew that I must do something. I could not stand there supinely and let the creature seize and devour me without striking a blow in my own defence. I uncoiled a portion of the rope and, more in despair than with any hope that I could accomplish anything of a defensive nature, flicked the end of it in the face of the advancing beast. You have seen a boy snap a wet towel at a companion; perhaps you have been flicked in that way, and if you have, you know that it hurts.

Of course I did not expect to overcome my adversary by any such means as this; to be truthful, I did not know what I did expect to accomplish. Perhaps I just felt that I must do something, and this was the only thing that occurred to me. The result merely demonstrated the efficiency of that single eye and the quickness of the chelae. I snapped that rope as a ringmaster snaps a whip; but though the rope-end travelled with great speed and the act must have been unexpected, the creature caught the rope in one of its chelae before it reached its face. Then it hung on and sought to drag me toward those frightful jaws.

I learned many a trick of roping from a cowboy friend of my motion-picture days and one of these I now put into use in an endeavour to entangle the crab-like chelae.

Suddenly giving the rope sufficient slack, I threw a half-hitch around the chelac that gripped it, immediately following it with a second, whereupon the creature commenced to pull desperately away. I think it was motivated solely by an instinctive urge to pull toward its jaws anything that was held in its chelae; but for how long it would continue to pull away before it decided to change its tactics and charge me, I could not even guess; and so I acted upon a sudden inspiration and hurriedly made fast the end of the rope that I held to one of the stout posts that supported the hand-rail of the causeway; then, of a sudden the thing charged me, roaring furiously.

I turned and ran, hoping that I could get out of the reach of those terrible chelae before the creature was stopped by the rope; and this I but barely managed to do. I breathed a sigh of relief as I saw the great body flipped completely over on its back as the rope tautened but the hideous scream of rage that followed left me cold. Nor was my relief of any great duration, for as soon as the creature had scrambled to its feet, it seized the rope in its other chela and severed it as neatly as one might with a pair of monstrous tinner's snips; and then it was after me again, but this time it did not creep.

It seemed evident that my stay upon Venus was to be brief, when suddenly the door in the tree swung open and three men leaped to the causeway just behind the charging terror that was swiftly driving down upon me. The leading man hurled a short, heavy spear that sank deep into the back of my infuriated pursuer. Instantly the creature stopped in its tracks and wheeled about to face these new and more dangerous tormentors; and as he did so two more spears, hurled by the companions of the first man, drove into the chest, and, with a last frightful scream, the thing dropped in its tracks, dead.

Then the leading man came toward me. In the subdued light of the forest he appeared no different from an earth man. He held the point of a straight, sharp sword pointed at my vitals. Close behind him were the other two men, each with a drawn sword.

The first man spoke to me in a stern, commanding voice, but I shook my head to indicate that I could not understand; then he pressed the point of his weapon against my coveralls, opposite the pit of my stomach, and jabbed. I backed away. He advanced and jabbed at me again, and again I backed along the causeway. Now the other two men advanced and the three of them fell to examining me, meanwhile talking among themselves.

I could see them better now. They were about my own height and in every detail of their visible anatomy they appeared identical with terrestrial human beings, nor was a great deal left to my imagination – the men were almost naked. They wore loincloths and little else other than the belts that supported the scabbards of their swords. Their skins appeared to be much darker than mine, but not so dark as a negro's, and their faces were smooth and handsome.

Several times one or another of them addressed me and I always replied, but neither understood what the others said. Finally, after a lengthy discussion, one of them re-entered the opening in the tree and a moment later I saw the interior of a chamber, just within the doorway, illuminated; then one of the two remaining men motioned me forward and pointed toward the doorway.

Understanding that he wished me to enter, I stepped forward, and, as I passed them, they kept their sword-points against my body – they were taking no chances with me. The other man awaited me in the centre of a large room hewn from the interior of the great tree. Beyond him were other doorways leading from this room, doubtless into other apartments. There were chairs and a table in the room; the walls were carved and painted; there was a large rug upon the floor; from a small vessel depending from the centre of the ceiling a soft light illuminated the interior as brightly as might sunlight flooding through an open window, but there was no glare.

The other men had entered and closed the door, which they fastened by a device that was not apparent to me at the time; then one of them pointed to a chair and motioned me to be seated. Under the bright light they examined me intently; and I them. My clothing appeared to puzzle them most; they examined and discussed its material, texture, and weave, if I could judge correctly by their gestures and inflections.

Finding the heat unendurable in my fleece-lined coveralls, I removed them and my leather coat and polo shirt. Each newly revealed article aroused their curiosity and comment. My light skin and blond hair also received their speculative attention.

Presently one of them left the chamber and while he was absent another removed the various articles that had lain upon the table. These consisted of what I took to be books bound in wooden and in leather covers, several ornaments, and a dagger in a beautifully wrought sheath.

When the man who had left the room returned, he brought food and drink which he placed upon the table; and by signs the three indicated that I might eat. There were fruits and nuts in highly polished, carved wooden bowls; there was something I took to be bread, on a golden platter; and there was honey in a silver jug. A tall, slender goblet contained a whitish liquid that resembled milk. This last receptacle was a delicate, translucent ceramic of an exquisite blue shade. These things and the appointments of the room bespoke culture, refinement, and good taste, making the savage apparel of their owners appear incongruous.

The fruits and nuts were unlike any with which I was familiar, both in appearance and flavour; the bread was coarse but delicious; and the honey, if such it were, suggested candied violets to the taste. The milk (I can find no other earthly word to describe it) was strong and almost pungent, yet far from unpleasant. I imagined at the time that one might grow to be quite fond of it.

The table utensils were similar to those with which we are familiar in civilized portions of the earth; there were hollowed instruments with which to dip or scoop, sharp ones with which to cut, and others with tines with which to impale. There was also a handled pusher, which I recommend to earthly hostesses. All these were of metal.

While I ate, the three men conversed earnestly, one or another of them occasionally offering me more food. They seemed hospitable and courteous, and I felt that if they were typical of the inhabitants of Venus I should find my life here a pleasant one. That it would not be a bed of roses, however, was attested by the weapons that the men constantly wore; one does not carry a sword and a dagger about with him unless he expects to have occasion to use them, except on dress parade.

86

C. S. LEWIS was a man of many parts, a scholar and dia-
lectician, and friend of two other notable British fantasists,
Charles Williams and J. R. R. Tolkien. Lewis was also a
connoisseur of science fiction; besides reading widely in it,
he produced a trilogy consisting of *Out of the Silent Planet,
Perelandra*, and *That Hideous Strength.*

The following extract from *Perelandra,* describing the
ocean world of Venus, is arguably the loveliest portrait of
an imaginary planet ever written. The prose Lewis employs
is rich in vigorous female imaginary, made the lusher, perhaps, because Lewis was writing in the context of an aus-
tere wartime England: for the novel first appeared in 1943.
Revolutionary though the story then seemed, and still
seems, in its conjoining of well-buttressed theological argument with the interplanetary adventure, Lewis's Venus
comes trailing clouds of glory which are tinted by the
same hues used by Munro and Griffith. Nevertheless, the
central character, Ransom, is recognizably Lewis's man;
and the enchantment of this world, Perelandra, is recognis-
ably Lewis's magic . . .

C. S. LEWIS: Perelandra

There was no casket now. He was turned out – deposited –
solitary. He was in Perelandra.

His first impression was of nothing more definite than of
something slanted – as though he were looking at a photograph which had been taken when the camera was not
held level. And even this lasted only for an instant. The
slant was replaced by a different slant; then two slants
rushed together and made a peak, and the peak flattened
suddenly into a horizontal line, and the horizontal line
tilted and became the edge of a vast gleaming slope which

rushed furiously towards him. At the same moment he felt that he was being lifted. Up and up he soared till it seemed as if he must reach the burning dome of gold that hung above him instead of a sky. Then he was at a summit; but almost before his glance had taken in a huge valley that yawned beneath him – shining green like glass and marbled with streaks of scummy white – he was rushing down into that valley at perhaps thirty miles an hour. And now he realised that there was a delicious coolness over every part of him except his head, that his feet rested on nothing, and that he had for some time been performing unconsciously the actions of a swimmer. He was riding the foamless swell of an ocean, fresh and cool after the fierce temperatures of Heaven, but warm by earthly standards – as warm as a shallow bay with sandy bottom in a sub-tropical climate. As he rushed smoothly up the great convex hillside of the next wave he got a mouthful of the water. It was hardly at all flavoured with salt; it was drinkable – like fresh water and only, by an infinitesimal degree, less insipid. Though he had not been aware of thirst till now, his drink gave him a quite astonishing pleasure. It was almost like meeting Pleasure itself for the first time. He buried his flushed face in the green translucence, and when he withdrew it, found himself once more on the top of a wave.

There was no land in sight. The sky was pure, flat gold like the background of a mediaeval picture. It looked very distant – as far off as a cirrus cloud looks from earth. The ocean was gold too, in the offing, flecked with innumerable shadows. The nearer waves, though golden where their summits caught the light, were green on their slopes: first emerald, and lower down a lustrous bottle green, deepening to blue where they passed beneath the shadow of other waves.

All this he saw in a flash; then he was speeding down once more into the trough. He had somehow turned on his back. He saw the golden roof of that world quivering with a rapid variation of paler lights as a ceiling quivers at the reflected sunlight from the bath-water when you step into your bath on a summer morning. He guessed that this was the reflection of the waves wherein he swam. It is a phenomenon observable three days out of five in the planet of love. The queen of those seas views herself continually in a celestial mirror.

Up again to the crest, and still no sight of land. Something that looked like clouds – or could it be ships? – far away on his left. Then down, down, down – he thought he would never reach the end of it ... this time he noticed how dim the light was. Such tepid revelry in water – such glorious bathing, as one would have called it on earth, suggested as its natural accompaniment a blazing sun. But here there was no such thing. The water gleamed, the sky burned with gold, but all was rich and dim, and his eyes fed upon it undazzled and unaching. The very names of green and gold, which he used perforce in describing the scene, are too harsh for the tenderness, the muted irridescence, of that warm, maternal, delicately gorgeous world. It was mild to look upon as evening, warm like summer noon, gentle and winning like early dawn. It was altogether pleasurable. He sighed.

There was a wave ahead of him now so high that it was dreadful. We speak idly in our own world of seas mountain high when they are not much more than mast high. But this was the real thing. If the huge shape had been a hill of land and not of water he might have spent a whole afternoon or longer walking the slope before he reached the summit. It gathered him into itself and hurled him up to that elevation in a matter of seconds. But before he reached the top, he almost cried out in terror. For this wave had not a smooth top like the others. A horrible crest appeared; jagged and billowy and fantastic shapes, unnatural, even unliquid, in appearance, sprouted from the ridge. Rocks? Foam? Beasts? The question hardly had time to flash through his mind before the thing was upon him. Involuntarily he shut his eyes. Then he found himself once more rushing downhill. Whatever it was, it had gone past him. But it had been something. He had been struck in the face. Dabbing with his hands he found no blood. He had been struck by something soft which did him no harm but merely stung like a lash because of the speed at which he met it. He turned round on his back again – already, as he did so, soaring thousands of feet aloft to the high water of the next ridge. Far down below him in a vast, momentary valley he saw the thing that had missed him. It was an irregularly shaped object with many curves and re-entrants. It was variegated in colour like a patchwork quilt – flame-colour, ultramarine, crimson, orange, gamboge, and violet. He could not say more about it for the whole glimpse lasted so short a time. Whatever the thing was, it was floating, for it rushed up the slope of the opposite wave and over the summit and out of sight. It sat to the water like a skin, curving as the water curved. It took the wave's shape at the top, so that for a moment half of it was already out of sight beyond the ridge and the other half still lying on the hither slope. It behaved rather like a mat of weeds on a river – a mat of weeds that takes on every contour of the little ripples you make by rowing past it – but on a very different scale. This thing might have been thirty acres or more in area.

Words are slow. You must not lose sight of the fact that his whole life on Venus up till now had lasted less than five minutes. He was not in the least tired, and not yet seriously alarmed as to his power of surviving in such a world. He had confidence in those who had sent him there, and for the meantime the coolness of the water and the freedom of his limbs were still a novelty and a delight; but more than all these was something else at which I have already hinted and which can hardly be put into words – the strange sense of excessive pleasure which seemed somehow to be communicated to him through all his senses at once. I use the word "excessive" because Ransom himself could only describe it by saying that for his first few days on Perelandra he was haunted, not by a feeling of guilt, but by surprise that he had no such feeling. There was an exuberance of prodigality of sweetness about the mere act of living which our race finds it difficult not to associate with forbidden and extravagant actions. Yet it is a violent world too. Hardly had he lost sight of the floating object when his eyes were stabbed by an unendurable light. A grading, blue-to-violet illumination made the golden sky seem dark by comparison and in a moment of time revealed more of the new planet than he had yet seen. He saw the waste of waves spread illimitably before him, and far, far away, at the very end of the world, against the sky, a single smooth column of ghastly green standing up, the one thing fixed and vertical in this universe of shifting slopes. Then the rich twilight rushed back (now seeming almost darkness) and he heard thunder. But it was a different *timbre* from terrestrial thunder, more resonance, and even, when distant, a kind of tinkling. It is the laugh, rather than the roar, of heaven. Another flash followed, and another, and then the storm was all about him. Enormous purple clouds came driving between him and the golden sky, and with no preliminary drops a rain such as he had never experienced began to fall. There were no lines on it; the water above him seemed only less continuous than the sea, and he found it difficult to breathe. The flashes were incessant. In between them, when he looked in any direction except that of the clouds, he saw a completely changed world. It was like being at the centre of a rainbow, or in a cloud of multi-coloured steam. The water which now filled the air was turning sea and sky into a bedlam of flaming and writhing transparencies. He was dazzled and now for the first time a little frightened. In the flashes he saw, as before, only the endless sea and the still green column at the end of the world. No land anywhere – not the suggestion of a shore from one horizon to the other.

The thunder was ear-splitting and it was difficult to get enough air. All sorts of things seemed to be coming down in the rain – living things apparently. They looked like preternaturally airy and graceful frogs – sublimated frogs – and had the colour of dragon-flies, but he was in no plight to make careful observations. He was beginning to feel the first symptoms of exhaustion and was completely confused by the riot of colours in the atmosphere. How long this state of affairs lasted he could not say, but the next thing that he remembers noticing with any accuracy was that the swell was decreasing. He got the impression of being near the end of a range of water-mountains and looking down into lower country. For a long time he never reached this lower country; what had seemed, by comparison with the seas which he had met on his first arrival, to be calm water, always turned out to be only slightly smaller waves when he rushed down into them. There seemed to be a good many of the big floating objects about. And these, again, from some distance looked like an archipelago, but always, as he drew nearer and found the roughness of the water they were riding, they became more like a fleet. But in the end there was no doubt that the swell was subsiding. The rain stopped. The waves were merely of Atlantic height. The rainbow colours grew fainter and more transparent and the golden sky first showed timidly through them and then established itself again from horizon to horizon. The waves grew smaller still. He began to breathe freely. But he was now really tired, and beginning to find leisure to be afraid.

One of the great patches of floating stuff was sidling down a wave not more than a few hundred yards away. He eyed it eagerly, wondering whether he could climb on to one of these things for rest. He strongly suspected that they would prove mere mats of weed, or the topmost branches of submarine forests, incapable of supporting him. But while he thought this, the particular one on which his eyes were fixed crept up a wave and came between him and the sky. It was not flat. From its tawny surface a whole series of feathery and billowy shapes arose, very unequal in height; they looked darkish against the dim glow of the golden roof. Then they all tilted one way as the thing which carried them curled over the crown of the water and dipped out of sight. But here was another, not thirty yards away and bearing down on him. He struck out towards it, noticing as he did so how sore and feeble his arms were and feeling his first thrill of true fear. As he approached it he saw that it ended in a fringe of undoubtedly vegetable matter; it trailed, in fact, a dark red skirt of tubes and strings and bladders. He grabbed at them and found he was not yet near enough. He began swimming desperately, for the thing was gliding past him at some ten miles an hour. He grabbed again and got a handful of whip-like red strings, but they pulled out of his hand and almost cut him. Then he thrust himself right in among them, snatching wildly straight before him. For one second he was in a kind of vegetable broth of gurgling tubes and exploding bladders; next moment his hands caught something firmer ahead, something almost like very soft wood. Then, with the breath nearly knocked out of him and a bruised knee, he found himself lying face downward on a resistant surface. He pulled himself an inch or so further. Yes – there was no doubt now; one did not go through; it was something one could lie on.

It seems that he must have remained lying on his face, doing nothing and thinking nothing for a very long time. When he next began to take any notice of his surroundings he was, at all events, well rested. His first discovery was that he lay on a dry surface, which on examination turned out to consist of something very like heather, except for the colour which was coppery. Burrowing idly with his fingers he found something friable like dry soil, but very little of it, for almost at once he came upon a base of tough inter-locked fibres. Then he rolled round on his back, and in doing so discovered the extreme resilience of the surface on which he lay. It was something much more than the pliancy of the heather-like vegetation, and felt more as if the whole floating island beneath that vegetation were a kind of mattress. He turned and looked inland – if that is the right word – and for one instant what he saw looked very like a country. He was looking up a long lonely valley with a copper-coloured floor bordered on each side by gentle slopes clothed in a kind of many-coloured forest. But even as he took this in, it became a long copper-coloured ridge with the forest sloping *down* on each side of it. Of course he ought to have been prepared for this, but he says that it gave him an almost sickening shock. The thing had looked, in that first glance, so like a real country that he had forgotten it was floating – an island if you like, with hills and valleys, but hills and valleys which changed places every minute so that only a cinematograph could make a contour map of it. And that is the nature of the floating islands of Perelandra. A photograph, omitting the colours and the perpetual variation of shape, would make them look deceptively like landscapes in our own world, but the reality is very different; for they are dry and fruitful like land but their only shape is the inconstant shape of the water beneath them. Yet the land-like appearance proved hard to resist. Although he had now grasped with his brain what was happening, Ransom had not yet grasped it with his muscles and nerves. He rose to take a few paces inland – and downhill, as it was at the moment of his rising – and immediately found himself flung down on his face, unhurt because of the softness of the weed. He scrambled to his feet – saw that he now had a steep slope to ascend – and fell a second time. A blessed relaxation of the strain in which he had been living since his arrival dissolved him into weak laughter. He rolled to and fro on the soft fragrant surface in a real schoolboy fit of the giggles.

This passed. And then for the next hour or two he was teaching himself to walk. It was much harder than getting your sea-legs on a ship, for whatever the sea is doing the deck of the ship remains a plane. But this was like learning to walk on water itself. It took him several hours to get a hundred yards away from the edge, or coast, of the floating island; and he was proud when he could go five paces without a fall, arms outstretched, knees bent in readiness for sudden change of balance, his whole body swaying and tense like that of one who is learning to walk the tight-rope. Perhaps he would have learned more quickly if his falls had not been so soft, if it had not been so pleasant, having fallen, to lie still and gaze at the golden roof and hear the endless soothing noise of the water and breathe in the curiously delightful smell of the herbage. And then, too, it was so strange, after rolling head over heels down into some little dell, to open his eyes and find himself seated on the central mountain peak of the whole island looking down like Robinson Crusoe on field and forest to the shores in every direction, that a man could hardly help sitting there a few minutes longer – and then being detained again because, even as he made to rise, mountain and valley alike had been obliterated and the whole island had become a level plain.

At long last he reached the wooded part. There was an undergrowth of feathery vegetation, about the height of gooseberry bushes, coloured like sea anemones. Above this were the taller growths – strange trees with tube-like trunks of grey and purple spreading rich canopies above his head, in which orange, silver, and blue were the predominant colours. Here, with the aid of the tree trunks, he could keep his feet more easily. The smells in the forest were beyond all that he had ever conceived. To say that they made him feel hungry and thirsty would be misleading; almost, they created a new kind of hunger and thirst, a longing that seemed to flow over from the body into the soul and which was a heaven to feel. Again and again he stood still, clinging to some branch to steady himself, and

94

breathed it all in, as if breathing had become a kind of ritual. And at the same time the forest landscape furnished what would have been a dozen landscapes on earth – now level wood with trees as vertical as towers, now a deep bottom where it was surprising not to find a stream, now a wood growing on a hillside, and now again, a hilltop whence one looked down through slanted boles at the distant sea. Save for the inorganic sound of waves there was utter silence about him. The sense of his solitude became intense without becoming at all painful – only adding, as it were, a last touch of wildness to the unearthly pleasures that surrounded him. If he had any fear now, it was a faint apprehension that his reason might be in danger. There was something in Perelandra that might overload a human brain.

Now he had come to a part of the wood where great globes of yellow fruit hung from the trees – clustered as toy-balloons are clustered on the back of the balloon-man and about the same size. He picked one of them and turned it over and over. The rind was smooth and firm and seemed impossible to tear open. Then by accident one of his fingers punctured it and went through into coldness. After a moment's hesitation he put the little aperture to his lips. He had meant to extract the smallest, experimental sip, but the first taste put his caution all to flight. It was, of course, a taste, just as his thirst and hunger had been thirst and hunger. But then it was so different from every other taste that it seemed mere pedantry to call it a taste at all. It was like the discovery of a totally new *genus* of pleasures, something unheard of among men, out of all reckoning, beyond all covenant. For one draught of this on earth wars would be fought and nations betrayed. It could not be classified. He could never tell us, when he came back to the world of men, whether it was sharp or sweet, savoury or voluptuous, creamy or piercing. "Not like that" was all he could ever say to such inquiries. As he let the empty gourd fall from his hand and was about to pluck a second one, it came into his head that he was now neither hungry nor thirsty. And yet to repeat a pleasure so intense and almost so spiritual seemed an obvious thing to do. His reason, or what we commonly take to be reason in our own world, was all in favour of tasting this miracle again; the child-like

innocence of fruit, the labours he had undergone, the un-
certainty of the future, all seemed to commend the action.
Yet something seemed opposed to this "reason". It is difficult to suppose that this opposition came from desire, for
what desire would turn from so much deliciousness? But
for whatever cause, it appeared to him better not to taste
again. Perhaps the experience had been so complete that
repetition would be a vulgarity – like asking to hear the
same symphony twice a day.

As he stood pondering over this and wondering how
often in his life on earth he had reiterated pleasures not
through desire, but in the teeth of desire and in obedience
to a spurious rationalism, he noticed that the light was
changing. It was darker behind him than it had been;
ahead, the sky and sea shone through the wood with a
changed intensity. To step out of the forest would have
been a minute's work on earth; on this undulating island
it took him longer, and when he finally emerged into the
open an extraordinary spectacle met his eyes. All day there
had been no variation at any point in the golden roof to
mark the sun's position, but now the whole of one half-
heaven revealed it. The orb itself remained invisible, but
on the rim of the sea rested an arc of green so luminous
that he could not look at it, and beyond that, spreading
almost to the zenith, a great fan of colour like a peacock's
tail. Looking over his shoulder he saw the whole island
ablaze with blue, and across it and beyond it, even to the
ends of the world, his own enormous shadow. The sea, far
calmer now than he had yet seen it, smoked towards heaven
in huge dolomites and elephants of blue and purple vapour,
and a light wind, full of sweetness, lifted the hair on his
forehead. The day was burning to death. Each moment
the waters grew more level; something not far removed
from silence began to be felt. He sat down cross-legged
on the edge of the island, the desolate lord, it seemed, of
this solemnity. For the first time it crossed his mind that
he might have been sent to an uninhabited world, and the
terror added, as it were, a razor-edge to all that profusion
of pleasure.

Once more, a phenomenon which reason might have
anticipated took him by surprise. To be naked yet warm,
to wander among summer fruits and lie in sweet heather

– all this had led him to count on a twilit night, a mild mid-summer greyness. But before the great apocalyptic colours had died out in the west, the eastern heaven was black. A few moments, and the blackness had reached the western horizon. A little reddish light lingered at the zenith for a time, during which he crawled back to the woods. It was already, in common parlance, "too dark to see your way." But before he had lain down among the trees the real night had come – seamless darkness, not like night but like being in a coal-cellar, darkness in which his own hand held before his face was totally invisible. Absolute blackness, the un-dimensioned, the impenetrable, pressed on his eyeballs. There is no moon in that land, no star pierces the golden roof. But the darkness was warm. Sweet new scents came stealing out of it. The world had no size now. Its boundaries were the length and breadth of his own body and the little patch of soft fragrance which made his hammock, swaying ever more and more gently. Night covered him like a blanket and kept all loneliness from him. The blackness might have been his own room. Sleep came like a fruit which falls into the hand almost before you have touched the stem.

At Ransom's waking something happened to him which perhaps never happens to a man until he is out of his own world: he saw reality, and thought it was a dream. He opened his eyes and saw a strange heraldically coloured tree loaded with yellow fruits and silver leaves. Round the base of the indigo stem was coiled a small dragon covered with scales of red gold. He recognised the garden of the Hesperides at once. "This is the most vivid dream I have ever had," he thought. By some means or other he then realised that he was awake; but extreme comfort and some trance-like quality, both in the sleep which had just left him and in the experience to which he had awaked, kept him lying motionless. He remembered how in the very different world called Malacandra – that cold, archaic world, as it now seemed to him – he had met the original of the Cyclops, a giant in a cave and a shepherd. Were all the things which appeared as mythology on earth scattered through other worlds as realities? Then the realisation came to him: "You are in an unknown planet, naked and alone, and that may be a dangerous animal." But he was not badly frightened. He knew that the ferocity of terrestrial animals was, by cosmic standards, an exception, and had found kindness in stranger creatures than this. But he lay quiet a little longer and looked at it. It was a creature of the lizard type, about the size of a St. Bernard dog, with a serrated back. Its eyes were open.

Presently he ventured to rise on one elbow. The creature went on looking at him. He noticed that the island was perfectly level. He sat up and saw, between the stems of the trees, that they were in calm water. The sea looked like gilded glass. He resumed his study of the dragon. Could this be a rational animal – a *hnau* as they said in Malacandra – and the very thing he had been sent there to meet? It did not look like one, but it was worth trying. Speaking in the Old Solar tongue he formed his first sentence – and his own voice sounded to him unfamiliar.

"Stranger," he said, "I have been sent to your world through the Heaven by the servants of Maleldil. Do you give me welcome?"

The thing looked at him very hard and perhaps very wisely. Then, for the first time, it shut its eyes. This seemed an unpromising start. Ransom decided to rise to his feet. The dragon reopened its eyes. He stood looking at it while you could count twenty, very uncertain how to proceed. Then he saw that it was beginning to uncoil itself. By a great effort of will he stood his ground; whether the thing were rational or irrational, flight could hardly help him for long. It detached itself from the tree, gave itself a shake, and opened two shining reptilian wings – bluish gold and bat-like. When it had shaken these and closed them again, it gave Ransom another long stare, and at last, half waddled and half crawling, made its way to the edge of the island and buried its long metallic-looking snout in the water. When it had drunk it raised its head and gave a kind of croaking bleat which was not entirely unmusical. Then it turned, looked yet again at Ransom, and finally approached him. "It's madness to *wait* for it," said the false reason, but Ransom set his teeth and stood. It came right up and began nudging him with its cold snout about his knees. He was in great perplexity. Was it rational and was this how it talked? Was it irrational but friendly – and if so, how should he respond? You could hardly stroke a creature with scales! Or was it merely scratching itself against him?

At that moment, with a suddenness which convinced him it was only a beast, it seemed to forget all about him, turned away, and began tearing up the herbage with great avidity. Feeling that honour was now satisfied, he also turned away back to the woods.

There were trees near him loaded with the fruit which he had already tasted, but his attention was diverted by a strange appearance a little farther off. Amid the darker foliage of a greenish-grey thicket something seemed to be sparkling. The impression, caught out of the corner of his eye, had been that of a greenhouse roof with the sun on it. Now that he looked at it squarely it still suggested glass, but glass in perpetual motion. Light seemed to be coming and going in a spasmodic fashion. Just as he was moving to investigate this phenomenon he was startled by a touch on his left leg. The beast had followed him. It was once more nosing and nudging. Ransom quickened his pace. So did the dragon. He stopped; so did it. When he went on again it accompanied him so closely that its side pressed against his thighs and sometimes its cold, hard, heavy foot descended on his. The arrangement was so little to his satisfaction that he was beginning to wonder seriously how he could put an end to it when suddenly his whole attention was attracted by something else. Over his head there hung from a hairy tube-like branch a great spherical object, almost transparent, and shining. It held an area of reflected light in it and at one place a suggestion of rainbow colouring. So this was the explanation of the glass-like appearance in the wood. And looking round he perceived innumerable shimmering globes of the same kind in every direction. He began to examine the nearest one attentively. At first he thought it was moving, then he thought it was not. Moved by a natural impulse he put out his hand to touch it. Immediately his head, face, and shoulders were drenched with what seemed (in that warm world) an ice-cold shower bath, and his nostrils filled with a sharp, shrill, exquisite scent that somehow brought to his mind the verse in Pope, "die of a rose in aromatic pain." Such was the refreshment that he seemed to himself to have been, till now, but half awake. When he opened his eyes – which had closed involuntarily at the shock of moisture – all the colours about him seemed richer and the dimness of that world seemed clarified. A re-enchantment fell upon him. The golden beast at his side seemed no longer either a danger or a nuisance. If a naked man and a wise dragon were indeed the sole inhabitants of this floating paradise, then this also was fitting, for at that moment he had a sensation not of following an adventure but of enacting a myth. To be the figure that he was in this unearthly pattern appeared sufficient.

He turned again to the tree. The thing that had drenched him was quite vanished. The tube or branch, deprived of its pendent globe, now ended in a little quivering orifice from which there hung a bead of crystal moisture. He looked round in some bewilderment. The grove was still full of its iridescent fruit but now he perceived that there was a slow continual movement. A second later he had mastered the phenomenon. Each of the bright spheres was very gradually increasing in size, and each, on reaching a certain dimension, vanished with a faint noise, and in its place there was a momentary dampness on the soil and a soon-fading, delicious fragrance and coldness in the air. In fact, the things were not fruit at all but bubbles. The trees (he christened them at that moment) were bubble-trees. Their life, apparently, consisted in drawing up water from the ocean and then expelling it in this form, but enriched by its short sojourn in their sappy inwards. He sat down to feed his eyes upon the spectacle. Now that he knew the secret he could explain to himself why this wood looked and felt so different from every other part of the island. Each bubble, looked at individually, could be seen to emerge from its parent-branch as a mere bead, the size of a pea, and swell and burst; but looking at the wood as a whole, one was conscious only of a continual faint disturbance of light, an elusive interference with the prevailing Perelandrian silence, an unusual coolness in the air, and a fresher quality in the perfume. To a man born in our world it felt a more out-door place than the open parts of the island, or even the sea. Looking at a fine cluster of the bubbles which hung above his head he thought how easy it would be to get up and plunge oneself through the whole lot of them and to feel, all at once, that magical refreshment multiplied tenfold. But he was restrained by the same sort of feeling which had restrained him over-night from tasting a second gourd. He had always disliked the people who encored a favourite air in an opera – "That just spoils it" had been his comment. But this now appeared to him as a principle of far wider application and deeper moment. This itch to have things over again, as if life were a film that could be unrolled twice or even made to work backwards ... was it possibly the root of all evil? No: of course the love of money was called that. But money itself – perhaps one valued it chiefly as a defence against chance, a security for being able to have things over again, a means of arresting the unrolling of the film.

He was escorted from his meditation by the physical discomfort of some weight on his knees. The dragon had lain down and deposited its long, heavy head across them. "Do you know," he said to it in English, "that you are a considerable nuisance?" It never moved. He decided that he had better try and make friends with it. He stroked the hard dry head, but the creature took no notice. Then his hand passed lower down and found softer surface, or even a chink in the mail. Ah ... that was where it liked being tickled. It grunted and shot out a long cylindrical slate-coloured tongue to lick him. It rolled round on its back revealing an almost white belly, which Ransom kneaded with his toes. His acquaintance with the dragon prospered exceedingly. In the end it went to sleep.

He rose and got a second shower from a bubble-tree. This made him feel so fresh and alert that he began to think of food. He had forgotten whereabouts on the island the yellow gourds were to be found, and as he set out to look for them he discovered that it was difficult to walk. For a moment he wondered whether the liquid in the bubbles had some intoxicating quality, but a glance around assured him of the real reason. The plain of copper-coloured heather before him, even as he watched, swelled into a low hill and the low hill moved in his direction. Spellbound anew at the sight of land rolling towards him, like water, in a wave, he forgot to adjust himself to the movement and lost his feet. Picking himself up, he proceeded more carefully This time there was no doubt about it. The sea was rising. Where two neighbouring woods made a vista to the edge of this living raft he could see troubled water, and the warm wind was now strong enough to ruffle his hair. He made his way gingerly towards the coast, but before he reached it he passed some bushes which carried a rich crop of oval berries, about three times the size of almonds. He picked one and broke it in two. The flesh was dryish and breadlike, something of the same kind as a banana. It turned out to be good to eat. It did not give the orgiastic and almost alarming pleasure of the gourds, but rather the specific pleasure of plain food – the delight of munching and being nourished, a "Sober certainty of waking bliss". A man, or at least a man like Ransom, felt he ought to say grace over it; and so he presently did. The gourds would have required rather an oratorio or a mythical meditation. But the meal had its unexpected high lights. Every now and then one struck a berry which had a bright red centre: and these were so savoury, so memorable among a thousand tastes, that he would have begun to look for them and to feed on them only, but that he was once more forbidden by that same inner adviser which had already spoken to him twice since he came to Perelandra. "Now on earth," thought Ransom, "they'd soon discover how to breed these redhearts, and they'd cost a great deal more than the others." Money, in fact, would provide the means of saying *encore* in a voice that could not be disobeyed.

When he had finished his meal he went down to the water's edge to drink, but before he arrived there it was already "up" to the water's edge. The island at that moment was a little valley of bright land nestling between hills of green water, and as he lay on his belly to drink he had the extraordinary experience of dipping his mouth in a sea that was higher than the shore. Then he sat upright for a bit with his legs dangling over the edge among the red weeds that fringed this little country. His solitude became a more persistent element in his consciousness. What had he been brought here to do? A wild fancy came into his head that this empty world had been waiting for him as for its first inhabitant, that he was singled out to be the founder, the beginner. It was strange that the utter loneliness through all these hours had not troubled him so much as one night of it on Malacandra. He thought the difference lay in this, that mere chance, or what he took for chance, had turned him adrift in Mars, but here he knew that he was part of a plan. He was no longer unattached, no longer on the outside.

As his country climbed the smooth mountains of dimly lustrous water he had frequent opportunity to see that many other islands were close at hand. They varied from his own island and from one another in their colouring more than he would have thought possible. It was a wonder to see these big mats or carpets of land tossing all around him like yachts in harbour on a rough day – their trees each moment at a different angle just as the masts of the yachts would be. It was a wonder to see some edge of vivid green or velvety crimson come creeping over the top of a wave far above him and then wait till the whole country unrolled itself down the wave's side for him to study. Sometimes his own land and a neighbouring land would be on opposite slopes of a trough, with only a narrow strait of water between them; and then, for the moment, you were cheated with the semblance of a terrestrial landscape. It looked exactly as though you were in a well-wooded valley with a river at the bottom of it. But while you watched, that seeming river did the impossible. It thrust itself up so that the land on either side sloped downwards from it; and then up farther still and shouldered half the landscape out of sight beyond its ridge; and became a huge greeny-gold hog's back of water hanging in the sky and threatening to engulf your own land, which now was concave and reeled backwards to the next roller, and rushing upwards, became convex again.

Section III

Swamp and Sand

IN the science fiction magazines, imagination, like joy, was never at home. The further from Earth, the better, at least as far as the dedicated in-group reader was concerned. Facts have always made uneasy bedfellows for fantasists, and facts are harder to check in a story set in distant galaxies than in one set right down here in New York or London.

For this reason, Venus should have presented an ideal location for science-fantasy. Yet, time and again, it was passed over in favour of Mars or Mercury, or the moons of Jupiter. Perhaps it was because nobody was really sure whether it was going to be all sand or all swamp out there. The speculation that our sister planet might be all bourbon had not yet arisen (see the last item in this book), although that might have given rise to some interesting speculative possibilities.

One of the most interesting swamp stories is Robert A. Heinlein's *Logic of Empire*. Heinlein populates his swamps with marsupials, which are oppressed by the human colonists. Wingate, the central character of the story, arrives on Venus as little more than a slave, and has to undergo a series of immunisations and innoculations before he can set foot on Venus. This must be one of the first – certainly the most detailed – discussions of extraterrestrial immunology.

Heinlein speaks of the "ceaseless fight of life against life which is the dominant characteristic anywhere". Yet the master of secret movements and revolutions produces a curiously abortive revolt in this story; his hero, when back on Earth, actually laughs off his early idealism. Well, Heinlein has always been expert at surprising his fans; but it seems as if this time the traditionally mild influences of the Cytherean world got him!

Logic of Empire was published in 1943. In 1947, another stalwart of the science fiction field, Henry Kuttner, published under a pen-name a novel entitled *Fury*. In his novel, and in an earlier novelette, *Clash by Night*, on the same theme, the setting is a Venus in a Jurassic stage of development. It has enormous oceans, beneath the surface of which the human survivors of a nuclear catastrophe on Earth live in "keeps".

Towards the end of the novel, the humans decide they must conquer the savage lands and live on them. Their battle with nature is a colourful one, and includes the classic statement "anything under a foot long was classified as a bug."

The jungles are given a five-spray treatment to tame them. In his vivid description of the operation, Kuttner might almost be looking ahead to similar operations carried out over Vietnam.

"The five-spray treatment helped considerably. They had learned much in colonising five islands. The first step now was to shower the island very thoroughly with solutions that didn't like bugs. One formula hit the lichens chiefly – a vital matter. Another damaged a good deal of the flora. The critters, at best, got slightly sick, but they charged at you with bared fangs and you could shoot them, if you were fast; they didn't have the unpleasant trick of infiltrating your lungs and sprouting quickly into a spongy mass that paralyzed your respiratory apparatus.

"Island Six didn't look like the colonized islands or the raw ones now. It looked sick. The jungle wasn't a blazing green riot. It seemed to hang, like Spanish moss draped across the great boles, and occasionally slow, lethargic movements stirred in it."

In 1956, an English author, S. Makepeace Lott, wrote *Escape to Venus,* which utilises a very hot and dusty Venus model. "The surfaces of the rocks were indeed smooth, washed to shining flatness by the battering of the gas storms which flung the suspended dust particles across the face of the planet at several hundred kilometres an hour . . ."

Escape to Venus also offers unique speculations on the

Cytherean calendar. An introductory lecture tells new recruits to Venus that "the date at this moment is Tuesday the tenth of Jupiter, thirty-seven. There are four weeks of eight days in each month, the eighth day being called Earthday and coming between Sunday and Monday. Each month starts on Monday the first and the months are called after the planets other than Venus and Earth in the order of their distance from the sun."

Mr. Lott's unfortunate colonists learn that they will live in windowless blocks and that "outdoor recreation is normally limited to the periods of twilight and dawn, each of which lasts for approximately twelve hours and occurs at sixteen Earth-day intervals." But what is really alarming is the briefing's statement, "There is at present no equivalent to the conception of private property on the planet and hence no question of capital ..." This is, among other things, a political novel, which bears a distant relationship to Orwell's *1984*; as such, it is a very untypical Cytherean tale! See page 208.

The story '*Alchemy*' was first published in 1950. It is based on one of the less popular models of Venus, the dry, sandy world. A nice tale in its own right, it reverts to the tradition of the pleasant which Heinlein, Kuttner, and Makepeace Lott so ably overthrew.

The two shorter items are interesting samples from the magazines, in which almost pure fancy is presented as speculative fact. Artist Frank R. Paul's piece on "The Man from Venus" appeared with a back cover illustration on *Fantastic* for July, 1939, and Henry Gade's "A City on Venus" with a back cover illustration, also by Paul, on the January 1941 *Amazing*.

By way of counterbalance to these imaginative flights, there is the greater part of Willy Ley's article on Venus from his regular "For Your Information" column in a 1955 *Galaxy*. We are coming up to date; Ley is already thinking of sending sampling missiles to discover exactly what gases that obscuring and obscurantist atmosphere contains.

JOHN and DOROTHY DE COURCY: Alchemy

IT is only an alien who can really enjoy the exotic, but the alien who has no connection with the scene, who has not even the vaguest idea what will come next, he truly experiences an unusual and wonderful thing for he smells strange smells, touches strange textures, hears strange sounds and the very air he breathes is somehow different. And so it was with me, lying on the ground, unfamiliar ground with an odd, soft feel, powdery to the touch yet not clinging as earth dust would. Suddenly remembering where I was, I sat up and looked about me.

When I had left the earth, I hadn't known where to go first as there were so many places to visit, so many exciting and unusual sights to see and an infinite variety to choose from; but I had finally selected Venus, partly because it would be a short hop but mostly because exploration had revealed so little about it. Those who had gone there had found only a waterless dust bowl with unending dust storms which made any extensive investigation next to impossible.

Yesterday, very tired and in need of sleep, I had landed and had climbed out of my ship to find not a dust storm but a curious crowd watching me. I stood there dumbly, wondering what to do, until one who seemed to have authority took me with him into their city. He seemed to know I was tired for he left me in a compartment barren of furniture yet seemingly possessed with all the comforts. Assuredly I had slept well for this soft, springy ground had been my bed.

As I gazed about me, I wondered if it had been wise to leave my ship, but so strange and foreign were my surroundings, I soon forgot about it. I walked through an archway which led outside and discovered that most of the dwellings about me were much the same. There were neither doors nor windows and there seemed to be no streets. The houses could have been made of earth for the walls were the same color as the ground and they were round, hexagonal and octagonal, generally.

Beyond the houses in what appeared to be approximately the city's center rose towers, high into the air. They seemed somewhat triangular to me and tended to come to a point although the distance made seeing difficult. Then I heard the bell as its sound rolled out across the city in a great, ringing crash. I jumped and looked in the direction of the towers. Again that strange, rumbling clang struck me like a physical blow. As yet I saw not a soul in the spaces between the domiciles and I thought it incredible that anyone could sleep through such a racket.

For the final time, the voice in that mighty bell rolled out, leaving a pregnant silence in its wake, a silence that must soon give birth to new sounds or it would surely burst asunder from its own electric tension. I stood there waiting, for what I did not know, avidly drinking in each detail of a new world. At that moment, my host appeared.

Perhaps it was the light of morning or perhaps it was because I had drunk of the refreshing cup of sleep but he seemed less formless and more concrete than when I had last seen him. Actually, he could have been a man, a rather large man and not the least bit freakish. His features were classic and his nose was long enough to be distinguished yet not so much as to be ridiculous. His hair was pale and golden tinted and his eyes were a bright blue. The mark that would set him apart from earth men was his skin, for it too was blue.

"Was he barbarian?" I wondered, "or was his a philosophy too deep for my mind to grasp?" His feet were bare, yet what need for shoes on such resilient soil? He wore a short skirt which for its color could have been woven silver, yet by its weight and flexibility must be cloth or perhaps some plastic which we did not have. There was no belt nor did he wear adornments. Indeed, his smooth skin with long powerful muscles flexing beneath it had no need of ornamentation.

He smiled then just as anyone would smile. He had teeth, seemingly like mine but more even and white, perhaps because of the contrast in his skin. He asked me a question in his deep voice, making motions with his flexible hands.

I did not understand.

He pointed to his mouth and made chewing motions.

This was clear and I nodded my head. "I eat," I said, then went through the motions of lifting a fork full of food to my mouth and masticating it.

He repeated the word. "Eat."

I moved my jaws and nodded my head.

"I," he repeated flatly.

I pointed a finger at myself and said, "I."

He pointed his forefinger at me and said, "I."

This time I shook my head violently and grasping his firm hand, turned it around so that he too pointed to himself.

He smiled again, pointing to himself and said, "bo – I."

I pointed to myself then and said questionably, "bo?"

Gravely he nodded.

We surmounted the "you" problem in a moment. "You" appeared to be "ti."

My host, believing that he had enough fundamentals said, "I eat, you eat," and then nodded his head.

It was a rather rudimentary thing but it gave me food for thought while my tall host led me toward food for the body. We went into the house again through a different archway and there I found what appeared to be a board or piece of plastic about three feet square on which rested little pyramids of assorted food stuffs. My friend seated himself, or more accurately, contorted himself, for he folded his legs into the manner of a statue of Buddha. This I tried and found I could still do since at one time I had practised yoga for my health.

The food was certainly unique but tasty. Not one familiar flavor was represented although there was salt in a small pyramid in the centre of the table. There was a pile of small, green things which resembled radishes but which tasted vaguely like cooked potatoes with a dash of parsnip added. There were many other curious things but I cannot describe them for there is nothing to compare them with. All of them seemed to be vegetables except the beverage. This was served in small opalescent cups slightly smaller than our own cups and about the shape of a flower pot. I should say, was already there, since no one appeared to add food or take any away.

The liquid was sweet but had body in the manner of

coffee. It was quite clear and had a distinct blue color. My friend named each item of food as he picked it up and I endeavoured to remember them.

Again I asked myself the question, "Are they barbarians or have they passed beyond civilization?" When all things needful are present, it could indicate either the idyllic existence of a tropical island or the culmination of millernia of progress.

When the meal was finished, we arose and I stretched my rather cramped legs. My host made a circular motion toward the outside, smiling broadly. I nodded and followed, my legs still aching a bit. When we were outside, I thought of my ship and how maybe I should go back but then I reasoned that I came here to see the planet and not the ship. Certainly there had been no sign of hostility so far and I felt somehow that my rather battered craft would be left alone.

The light on Venus is peculiar. There seems to be something in the air which screens off most of the sunlight, yet the day seemed as bright as on earth when it is slightly overcast. I saw no shadows, for light seemed to be everywhere and then I remembered that I had not seen any artificial lighting of any kind in the house. I looked back through the archway we had just come through and saw that it was just as light inside as it was outside, that some peculiar bluish light which seemed to be everywhere yet came from nowhere.

The air was warm. The temperature appeared to be unvarying as I remembered that the same warmth had persisted throughout the night. I wondered about these things and wished desperately there were some way I could ask questions.

My friend waited patiently for me whenever I stopped to look about. We walked between innumerable houses, all doorless. A number of people were outside and I discovered they were actually a beautiful people. They were all blue although the shade varied from a rather pale tint to a pronounced purple hue. The women were generally paler and were clad the same as the men. The colors of the short skirts varied through the spectrum including colors that we cannot as yet impress upon fabrics. Some noticed us, some called greeting to my friend and some gave us only a passing glance.

We walked for a long time, several hours, always in the general direction of the towers. As we approached them, I could see that there were four of them spaced about a hundred feet apart in a diamond shape. They rose approximately six hundred feet although I could be far wrong.

My host allowed me to wander around the base of the first tower and scrutinize it. I thought at first it was made of copper or a rose gold yet when I touched it, it was not cold like metal but rather neutral like a plastic. There was an open archway on the side facing the inward part of the diamond and I could make out another on the farthest tower.

Again I had that intense desire to ask questions, to make myself understood. But how could I? Even if this man could guess my questions, how could he answer me so that I would understand? Wondering, I looked at my friend and he smiled. I studied him for a moment, trying to decide what lay behind that smile. Was it one of understanding or just an automatic response to what he thought ridiculous? I couldn't tell.

The smile faded gradually from his face as he stared back at me. Then he smiled again and said, "I eat."

I hadn't noticed but I too was hungry. It had been a long walk. I nodded and he began walking toward the nearest of the houses. I walked along beside him, trying to keep in step but it was almost impossible to match those long, effortless strides. We went through an archway and found a woman within. Before her was a triangular board, a little larger than the one we had dined from in the morning. She smiled at me reassuringly and behaved in every way as though she had fully expected both of us.

I wondered how this could be, for my friend had spoken to no one in this vicinity and again the thought occurred. "Primitive or beyond understanding?"

The food was totally different from what I had eaten earlier except for the beverage. My friend chatted with our hostess, smiling occasionally and using gestures which could have meant most anything. When the meal was over, I smiled at the woman, trying to convey the impression that I had enjoyed the meal. Perhaps it was wishful thinking on my part but she seemed to understand.

111

My friend rose gracefully and walked to the archway. I attempted to do the same but my legs were so stiff and sore from the long walk and the cramped sitting position that when I tried to straighten up, I fell. So surprised was I at the incredible softness and rubber-like quality of the ground that I just lay there for a moment. Then realizing that I wasn't the least bit hurt, I pulled myself into a sitting position and when I thought of my clumsiness, I laughed. Once started, I couldn't stop and the tears rolled down my face.

My friend helped me to my feet and it was then I noticed that he too was laughing, only it was more like a heavy rumble which came from his throat. He bid our hostess good-bye and we went outside.

I looked at my friend questioningly. He smiled and pointed to the towers. I nodded and followed but this time we walked straight through the archway. Almost immediately I saw why we were here, for leading upward around the central well was a spiral ramp. It was of a material as soft and resilient as the ground.

On an impulse, I sat down and removed my shoes, heavy, cumbersome things. I tucked my woollen socks inside the shoes and stood up; and for the first time I realized that the ground was warm. My tall friend smiled, a seeming knowing smile. Yes, it was obvious and had been, that I needed no shoes here. We started up the ramp and I found walking much easier indeed.

On the wall beside the ramp lay the purpose of our visit, for painted or impressed with a starting clarity were figures, acting out a wordless drama. I saw the way these people were in the early beginning, learning fire, learning to work stone though I had not seen a stone since my arrival.

Up the familiar climb toward civilization, we walked. The higher we ascended, the higher the civilization. I stopped at each picture, studying it carefully until there appeared technology, a strange technology which certainly no longer existed. "Why had they slipped back?" I wondered. "Why the decline?" And then I saw an all too familiar thing: war.

For some reason, I was saddened. They seemed such a peaceful people. It was a shame that they had had to taste war, death and destruction. Perhaps they were better off as they were.

We walked further and further upward and I began to feel strange things, vague stirrings in my mind. At first, I thought it was the effect of the alien pictures, pictures that were too clear. But as we ascended, I found it growing stronger. On and on we went, passing by the panorama of life and death, of man rising to new peaks and falling to new depths but this time it was man whose skin was blue.

And then we came upon another series depicting war and I started as I stood before a mushroom-shaped cloud. So they had even had atomic energy. It seemed incredible. Something surged inside of me, a strange something and I thought perhaps it was the horror I somehow knew would be depicted soon, the ghastly spectacle of suicidal atomic war. Yet when it came, the feeling inside of me grew, the surging became intense, that something which eluded me seemed almost within my grasp. Here, pictured with unworldly vividness, was the end of a world.

Yet I found it was not the end, for many had survived and they began rebuilding. Gradually, the shape of the thing they were building became plain. It was the towers or a group like them, rising up into the heavens. Here again was advancement. So the end had not come in the hell of atomic war. But where then? Where had all of this knowledge gone?

Onward and upward we walked and now I saw space craft. They had traversed the depths of space, even to our earth. They had built cities everywhere, had become a great and mighty people. I marvelled that so much had been gained and was so obviously lost. But was it lost? It seemed to be. I had seen nothing that would indicate otherwise.

Then came a series of pictures which puzzled me for they showed the blue-skinned people leaving their great cities, re-entering their space ships and returning to their home planet. There seemed to be no reason for this exodus and I pondered each picture for some time. The more I thought, the more sure I became that somewhere locked in my mind was the answer to the puzzle. It was though I were trying to remember something, something logic told me I could not possibly know and yet it was there, just on the rim of consciousness.

And then we came to the last picture. I felt as though I had been shocked electrically. I know the blood drained

113

from my face as I stared, unbelievingly. How could it be? Yet there it was, the final picture, showing my friend standing just as he was standing and myself just as I was, even barefoot. How could they have known? It was a perfect mirror image in miniature. I moved a little but the picture of me did not. It was not a reflection. I continued to stare, fascinated, and slowly I realized that the picture was a familiar one to me. I had seen it before but where? I groped, sought frantically within my mind for the explanation but it continually escaped me, remaining just beyond my reach.

Dazed, I turned to my friend but he only smiled. It was a smile with the quality of all knowing wiseness and suddenly, he too seemed familiar to me, someone I had known for a long time. He motioned me to go onward through an archway but I couldn't move. I felt as though I were half in and half out of my body.

Gently but firmly, my friend took my arm and guided me to the archway. I paused on the threshold, fear beginning to clutch at me, but my friend urged me on. We entered to face an ageing man whose skin was quite light though still blue. He motioned me to sit as he was, crosslegged, and I did, hardly knowing what I was doing and only vaguely conscious that my friend had done likewise. Then the old man reached out, touched my forehead just above my nose. I fainted.

When I opened my eyes, I felt that time had passed, but there was no way of knowing. My friend held me upright, my head resting against his massive shoulders. Within myself I felt peace, a quietness I had never known and then all at once I realized I knew. I lifted my head and looked at the aged one who sat unmoving. Yes, I knew! I understood these people!

"Are you feeling better now?" the aged man asked.

It was an alien language yet somehow I understood. I knew many other things, I felt many other things, but all I could express was, "Yes – yes – I'm much better now."

Now I knew that here was perfection, that theirs was not a civilization of the body but one of the soul, and that somehow I was part of them and they were a part of me.

"Yes," the old man said aloud. "You are one of us. You always have been. If you were not –" He broke off but I understood. I was a descendant of those early pioneers who had come to earth. This I knew. If it were not so, I would have found nothing when I landed; for where I was now was in, and yet not in, the world – a place apart and not visible to ordinary eyes.

I looked into the face of the man beside me and knew I would never leave, would never want to leave. This was my home, my real home, and these were my people, my people because of a bond more powerful and everlasting than one of flesh and blood for I was with myself, a truly integrated being, and therefore one with all men who were as I.

Unbidden, I stepped through another archway and found what I knew would be there, a short skirt such as all the people wore. I removed my clothes quickly and drew on the little garment; then, turning, I looked into the polished oval of metal, finer than the finest mirror. Already my skin was bluish. Smiling, I ran my fingers through my hair, fluffing it.

I prepared to leave then hesitated a moment. I knew that waiting for me was the man with whom I would be forever, forever his as he would be forever mine, and yet I had one tiny regret, a regret which quickly changed into humor. When I finally emerged from the little room, I was laughing. I hadn't brought my lipstick.

FRANK R. PAUL: The Man from Venus

OF all the planets in the solar system, it is Venus to whom science attributes the greatest possibility of life forms at the present time. Its size and gravity are nearly equal to that of earth, and its atmosphere is much denser, which would tend to make it a planet of almost tropic richness over its total expanse. Its nearness to the sun is also a factor which aids this hypothesis. However, we don't know a great deal about the surface, because the continual blanket of thick cloud surrounding the planet prevents any observation of the surface.

More than likely, the watery areas are in greater abundance than on earth, and any life existing must have adapted itself to a quasi-aquatic existence. Its life must be lived a great deal of its time in the water.

Thus, our man of Venus is more than likely greatly fishlike in structure. He would possess a fish-like skin, and possibly protective scales of great strength. He would be both an air-breathing creature, and possessed of gills in addition to lungs. It would be possible for him to exist in water for a great length of time, even though submerged, and equally possible for him to emerge and live on the swampy, treacherous land areas.

The Venus men would be numerous, for this is a young world, full of danger, and possible monster forms of life. Death would be commonplace, and nature would make the Venusian a prolific breeder. Children would be numerous, and more than likely, viviparous birth would be nature's answer to the problem. An egg-laying creature would be most efficient. Because the warm climate would hatch the egg, unattended by the female.

In form, the Venusian would be large, with webbed feet and hands, and powerful swimming appendages. His head would be stubby and round, and not exceptionally intelligent. Eyes would be recessed and covered by horny protective lids which could be closed to retain moisture on land, and to protect from injury under water. Most likely the Venusian would be entirely carnivorous, or fish-eating, and plenty of food would make life easy, and savagery a pastime.

*

HENRY GADE: A City on Venus

How would you like to see a city on Venus, the watery world? You would? Then step right up and take a seat in the spaceship *Imagination*, which is ready to take off on a sight-seeing tour to the world of the goddess of romance.

Our ship is powered with a fuel called scientific fact, however, and remember that whatever you see, won't be entirely a dream. It could, logically, be as we shall try to show it to you.

Nearing Venus, we find that the planet's surface isn't visible. Venus is surrounded by a perpetual cloud blanket, many miles thick. The sun never shines on its true surface.

Into the clouds we plunge, rockets roaring in the heavy atmosphere. Then, abruptly, after we had begun to fear the clouds extended all the way to the ground, we burst into open air.

And what a weird world meets our eyes! It is just like on Earth, after an afternoon shower, when all is bathed in that weirdly beautiful yellow light of the sun struggling to penetrate the heavy rain clouds. But where can there be cities, for far below us, rolling in glassy swells, is an endless sea.

But swooping down near the surface, we skim along, ever searching the horizon. Finally, after hours, we see something looming up out of the haze. It is land!

But what land. It is a raw, rocky mountain range, rising out of the sea, sheer and brutal, and somehow *new*. There is no air of the ages about this expanse of rock. But clustering around its base is something that reminds us of our south seas, somehow. It is formations of coral reefs, exposed now to the air by the upheaval of the young planet which raised the first raw mountain range not so many thousands of years ago. And on the coral reefs is the first vegetation we have seen.

Now we see that the smooth sea is dotted by floating islands composed of plant life and marine animals. Some of them are quite large. Here we may find a city.

Further down the coast of this lone continent we find larger islands, some of them now permanently anchored to the shore. And as we near them through the mist, we find our city.

But what a city. It is a simple little thing of scattered dwellings roofed by huge fungus caps. All about the islands, and even perched up on the rugged mountainside, are the prosaic, homey-looking little dwellings with their rounded roofs.

They are brilliantly colored, in spite of the lack of sun-

117

light. The clouds do not shield the important rays of the sun, much nearer to this world than to ours. All the brilliant reds and yellows and whites of Earth fungus are here.

We circle slowly over the city. It seems to be an idyllic world, at first, but then we see the first citizens of this strange city. They sweep towards us perched on the backs of great pterodactyls. They are quasi-amphibian creatures and apparently are more at home in water than on land, or in their city.

Going lower, after we get over our amazement at this unusual form of aerial transportation, we see yet another form of travel, about the waterways of this floating city. Groups of citizens ride the lagoons atop the backs of great amphibian reptiles of gargantuan proportions. This indeed is the oddest ferry we have ever seen. And no fare is required.

Not only do these reptiles carry passengers, but also freight. They obey their masters, who somehow impress us with their common and not too distant origin, which may explain how it is all done.

We see other animals performing duties. For instance, trained pterodactyls bring captured animals from the mountain heights to their masters for food. But most of the food is harvested right in the water, or on the smaller islands that float past. Vegetable foods, loaded copiously on the amphibian ferries and stored in the fungus-roofed houses.

The islands themselves, and the island-cities, are a riot of beautiful vegetation almost tropical in nature. It is very warm, and no Venusian wears clothes. All in all, this City on Venus seems to be a placid place. Its inhabitants seem to work hard for food, wage no wars, and cheerfully construct their growing empire which may one day produce the giant cities of earth, when more land has appeared. The city of Venus is youthful!

WILLY LEY: Unveiling the Mystery Planet

NAME the planet which most closely resembles Earth in size. The answer, of course, is Venus. From direct measurements, its diameter works out to 7,700 miles, while that of Earth is 7,900 miles. But note, please, that these 7,700 miles include the cloud layer or layers of Venus, so the planet proper must be somewhat smaller. And don't ask by how much – it isn't very polite to ask questions to which the answer is not known.

Now name the planet that comes closest to Earth of all full-fledged planets – which means discounting a few planetoids like Hermes, Albert, Icarus, etc., and naturally our own moon, too. The answer is again Venus. When both Earth and Venus are on the same side of their orbits, the distance between them amounts to about 26 million miles, which is a good 9 million miles closer than our neighbor on the other side, Mars, can ever manage. And even this is not the best Venus can do. On December 6, 1882, during a so-called transit – the transits will be discussed later – the distance was only 24,600,000 miles.

Now name the planet with the most nearly circular orbit. Venus, of course. Now the one which is the most nearly perfect sphere. Again Venus. And now name the planet about which least is known. The answer, disappointingly, is still Venus.

Though Venus can come closer than any other planet, we know as little about it as we know about Pluto, the planet which is farthest away. In fact, what we do know well (and reliably) is the same in both cases. We know their orbits.

That of Venus, as has been said, is very nearly circular. The differences in the distance of the closest approach between Venus and Earth are mostly caused by the fact that

119

the orbit of Earth is somewhat eccentric; Earth is closest to the Sun in January. As for Venus, the average distance from the Sun is 67,200,000 miles, and the planet, moving with an average orbital velocity of 21.7 miles per second – that of Earth is 18.5 miles per second – needs 224.7 days to go around the Sun once.

If the plane of the orbit of Venus coincided with that of Earth, which is the ecliptic, we would see the planet moving across the disk of the Sun every time Venus comes closest to us, overtaking the slower Earth in the permanent race around the Sun. But the plane of the orbit of Venus does *not* coincide with the plane of the orbit of Earth. There is a considerable tilt, amounting to 3 degrees, 23 minutes and 38 seconds of arc.

This is a stronger tilt than that of any other major planet, excepting only Mercury (with 7°0'12") and Pluto (with 17°8'38"). Because of it, Venus, as a rule, does not pass between us and the Sun, but is, as seen from Earth, "above" or "below" the Sun. Only rarely does it happen that the two planets pass each other in sections of their orbit which are situated in such a manner that a line from the center of the Sun through the centers of both planets would be a straight line, or very nearly so.

When that happens, we get a "transit". Venus, which mostly is the brightest planet in the sky, then moves across the Sun's disk as a black spot. The spacing of these transits in time is such that a man might either observe two of them within his lifetime or not live long enough to see even one. The generation born early in the present century will not live to see one, while the generation now being born will see two.

It works like this: supposing a Venus transit is due in the year X, the next transit will take place in X + 8. But the next one after that will not happen until 121½ years later. Then there is again an interval of only 8 years, but if somebody just happened to miss them, he would have to wait for 105½ years for his next opportunity. The cycle, then, runs 8, 121½, 8, 105½, 8, 121½ and so forth.

Actual years of Venus transits were 1761, 1769, 1874 and 1882, with the next two scheduled for 2004 and 2012.

By 2004, a Venus transit will assuredly have lost most of

its former importance, but in the past a transit was something that every astronomer was eager to observe – expeditions were sent halfway around the globe in order to obtain observations from as many points as possible. The main reason was what had first been pointed out by the Astronomer Royal Dr. Edmond Halley; namely, that the precise time required by Venus to cross the Sun's disk could be used to calculate the distance from the Earth to the Sun, something that was not yet established then.

In the course of these transit observations, it was found that Venus has an atmosphere. While Venus is crossing the Sun's disk, it appears simply as a round black spot, but while entering and leaving, the round dark spot is surrounded by a luminous ring, caused by the bending of the Sun's rays by the atmosphere.

It is one of the "believe-it-or-nots" of the history of science that the first two reports on this phenomenon were casually forgotten.

The first to see it and to draw the proper conclusions (and to write them up, which is important, too) was Mikhail Vasilyevitch Lomonósov, who observed it from his home in St. Petersburg, Russia, during the transit of May 26, 1761. Though his discovery was discussed with much animation at the Imperial Academy of Science, nobody outside Russia learned about this fact until another Russian scientist published a book about Lomonósov in Germany in 1910!

During the next transit of 1769, David Rittenhouse of Philadelphia made the same discovery. His report was also mislaid for more than a century and when it was again seen during the transit of 1874, it was considered a novelty!

After the next transit, that of 1882, it was established that the same phenomenon can sometimes be observed even when Venus is not in transit. As has been said before, Venus normally is "above" or "below" the Sun when the planet passes Earth. But on these occasions, Venus may be quite "near" the Sun along the line of sight and then one can spot the planet in the daylight sky as a very thin ring of light.

Unfortunately, this phenomenon only tells us that Venus has an atmosphere. It does not tell us how deep it is. The true diameter of Venus, therefore, is still unknown. Nor do

121

we know the mass of Venus. The books usually state that the mass of Venus is 80% of the mass of Earth and the surface gravity of the planet is also given as that of Earth minus 20 per cent. Well, it probably is near that value, but we can't be completely certain.

If Venus had a moon, the mass of the planet could be derived very readily from the time needed by that moon to swing around its primary. Since Venus is moonless, though, its mass has to be derived from its influence on the neighboring planets; you get the nice paradox that an astronomer may check on the movement of Mars with the utmost care *in order to find out how much Venus weighs!*

But since Mars is also pulled by Earth in one direction and by Jupiter in another, with Saturn exerting some influence, too, the final result has to be somewhat uncertain, although the masses of Earth, Mars, Jupiter and Saturn are well known because all of them do have moons.

That Venus might have a moon was believed for quite some time and, as late as 1870, the British astronomer Richard A. Proctor (in his book *Other Worlds Than Ours*) did not yet dare to say that the older observations of a moon of Venus had been mistakes. His attitude was more or less that there was so much historical evidence for a moon of Venus that its existence had to be accepted with some reservations even though it had not been seen recently.

The first to proclaim that Venus had a moon had been the Neapolitan astronomer Francesco Fontana in 1645. His report made his famous contemporary Jean Dominque Cassini watch for it. Cassini thought he saw it in 1666 and in 1672 he felt sure and published his observation.

But a long time went by until somebody else went on record as having observed the moon of the evening star. In 1740, the English astronomer Short announced his seeing it, whereupon Mayer in Griefswald in Germany started looking and succeeded in 1759. In 1761, Montaigne in Limoges, France, and Rödkier of Copenhagen corroborated the findings of Mayer and in 1764, Horrebow in Copenhagen and Montbarron in Auxerre, France, corroborated Rödkier and Montaigne.

To everybody's chagrin, that moon had failed to show up during the actual transit in 1761. Efforts to spot it were quadrupled during the transit of 1769, but except for one doubtful assertion, the evidence proved negative.

This failure had been predicted by Father Maximilian Hell, S.J., of Vienna in 1766. Father Hell – fortunately for his calling, the word *hell* merely means "bright" or "luminous" in German – had said that the moon of Venus was merely an optical illusion. The bright image of the planet is reflected back into the telescope from the cornea of the observer's eye and then "seen" as a smaller image of the same phase near the main image.

Still, people kept looking and the two transits of 1874 and 1882 were again checked for signs of a satellite of Venus. The result was negative and a Belgian astronomer, P. Stroobant, set himself the task of finding out what the various observers had seen, if they had seen anything other than Father Hell's secondary image. And he discovered that whenever the moon of Venus had been reported, the planet had been near a small fixed star, one just bright enough to be seen without a telescope as a faint star. In the telescope, it would be rather bright, though, of course, just a pinpoint of light.

The stars that have doubled for a moon of Venus were found to have been *64 Orionis, 71 Orionis* and *mu Tauri*.

With an object like Venus which becomes invisible – meaning that all we can see is the night side – just when closest to us, one has to be grateful for any definite bit of information. The discovery of the atmosphere by Lomonósov, Rittenhouse and Schroeter was one of these definite bits. The final disproof of the existence of a moon by Stroobant was another one.

A third one has been added just recently, more than half a century later, by Gerald P. Kuiper of Yerkes, and McDonald Observatories, who at long last succeeded in establishing the position of the axis of Venus. The inclination of the equator of Venus to the plane of its orbit turned out to be 32 degrees, with a possible error of 2 degrees either way. The axis of Venus points in the direction of the constellation of Cepheus.

Now for the markings.

They are quite faint and indistinct and consist mainly in the fact that the polar regions look somewhat brighter than the equatorial areas. Bianchini, after many observations, came to the conclusion that there were a number of interconnected equatorial seas which he named *Mare Galilei, Mare Columbi, Mare Vespucci* and so forth.

The German Schroeter centered his attention on the polar areas and announced that he had caught glimpses of an enormous mountain near the south pole, a mountain that had to be about 45 miles high. Since no mountain of such height is possible – its own weight could cause it to "settle" – Schroeter was probably deceived by an isolated high cloud.

In 1891, just after Schiaparelli had published his conclusions about the rotation of Venus, the astronomer Niesten, who did not agree with him at all, published a map of Venus which has remained the only one of its kind after Bianchini's.

Some seven or eight years later, W. Villiger, an astronomer in Munich, took a few rubber balls, dipped them in flat white paint and made a few spheres of plaster of Paris. Then he placed them at such a distance that, when observed through a small telescope, they would show the same angular diameter as Venus does in a larger telescope. And he illuminated them in the manner in which Venus is illuminated by the Sun. After that, he had some graduate students make drawings of them and also produced a few of his own. The featureless white spheres looked much brighter around their "poles" and acquired some vaguely elliptical grayish areas near their middle.

It was quite evident then that no astronomer had ever succeeded in seeing the surface of Venus. Even though definite indentations in the terminator have been seen, such irregularities in the cloud layer did not open a vista of the surface.

I said on one occasion in the past that Venus seems to be at least triple-veiled, for every overcast develops a hole once in a while, and even in a double overcast the holes should occasionally match. With a triple layer of clouds, the probability of the matching of holes – which are evidently rare events to begin with – becomes invisibly small. In short, the clouds of Venus are, as one writer phrased it, as opaque as marshmallows.

But what are they? For many years, they were taken to be water vapour without question and, at the beginning of this century, the surface of Venus was universally considered "dripping wet". If there was a difference in opinion, it was merely about the degree of wetness. When asked, most astronomers would haul a book on geology off the shelf, point at a picture depicting a carboniferous forest and say, "This is how it must look."

Only a few considered the possibility that Venus was a *panthalassa*, meaning that it was covered by a shoreless ocean without any considerable land masses at all, or possibly just a few islands.

The view of a dripping wet Venus was still held by as important a scientist as Svante Arrhenius in 1918.

Just one decade later, opinion had completely reversed itself, largely as the result of a long series of pictures taken by F. E. Ross at Mt. Wilson Observatory in 1927. The new view was that Venus was completely dry, that violent storms picked up dust from the endless desert, forming a dust-cloud layer beneath the other cloud layers.

One of the results of this work was that, while the markings seen with the telescope might be optical illusions, there were markings that could be photographed, provided you photographed them in violet and ultra-violet, for they do not show up in light of the wave-lengths the eye can see best. (Dr. Kuiper's determination of the position of Venus' axis is also based on such photographs.' The reason for postulating absolute dryness was that neither water nor oxygen could be detected spectroscopically, but that another set of lines showed up well which was then identified as belonging to carbon dioxide.

But negative evidence is often insufficient grounds for building conclusions. The statement that neither water nor oxygen has been found in the atmosphere of Venus should really read that neither water nor oxygen *has been found above the clouds*. And one can easily explain why there couldn't be any above the clouds.

The spectroscope can only detect water vapor, not water, and the highest clouds of Venus must be quite high up. If, for the sake of discussion, we compare the atmosphere of Venus with that of Earth, the clouds might be 10 miles from the surface, but in the terrestrial atmosphere, the temperature ten miles up is *minus* 67° Fahrenheit. Any water at ten miles would be in the form of ice crystals, so the clouds themselves would be ice crystals. And ice crystals do not show up in the spectroscope.

Likewise, any oxygen present would be past the stage of oxygen molecules, but would be single oxygen atoms because of the powerful solar radiation. I don't know where the bands caused by oxygen atoms would be in a spectrogram, but certainly not in or near the place where one looks for the bands of oxygen – that is to say, oxygen molecules.

So, while the picture of the bone-dry planet fits what observations there are, it is not necessarily the truth. In fact, Donald H. Menzel and Fred L. Whipple of Harvard Observatory have shown recently that the existing observations would also fit a *panthalassa,* incidentally one where the oceans consist of carbonated water – seltzer!

In short, Venus is either completely dry or completely wet. But can we ever find out which it is? Probably not until a new factor enters into the picture – space travel.

Just to observe from outside our own atmosphere would be an incredible boon to astronomers; the constitution of the atmosphere of Venus above its highest cloud layer could indubitably be established from the space station. The precise mass of Venus could be established by means of a slightly more elaborate experiment. One could fire a missile from the space station in such a manner that its path would be bent by the gravitational field of Venus. Careful observation of the path of this missile would settle the problem once and for all.

But to learn what is below the cloud layer, we would have to go a bit closer. A method that comes to mind without much deliberation is to fire sampling missiles into the atmosphere of Venus from a nearby ship. In the end, it might be possible to lower a reporting missile all the way to the ground.

And then we'll know.

Section IV

'Venus is Hell!'

WILLY LEY'S article of 1955 prepares us for the sober truths we encounter in this section, neatly encapsulated in Carl Sagan's final dictum, "Venus is Hell!"

Imaginative writers accepted the verdict, it seems, with reluctance; this may explain why they were unwilling to speculate about the Menzel-Whipple model with a seltzer ocean-cover. Or it may be that like the sceptical astronomer V. A. Firsoff, they were wary of too many models.

The extract from Firsoff's chapter, "The Baffling Venus", comes as a useful hors d'oeuvre to the items following, although, as it was first published in 1964, in his volume *Exploring the Planets*, it succeeds them chronologically. Firsoff gives a succinct outline of various Venus models and of how these ideas affect the intended function of space-probes – a point that could, I feel, be more widely disseminated.

Firsoff also makes mention of Mariner II. This is not intended to be a textbook; but, since we are now entering the realm of science as opposed to imagination, a few reminders of a few simple facts may be in order – for even President Johnson has become confused at times between rockets and probes. As Alfred Bester reminds us in his book, *The Life and Death of a Satellite*, the Mariner *rocket* to which the President once proudly referred was then under three miles of water in the South Atlantic, while the *probe* was serenely on course for Mars.

Mariners III and IV headed away on Martian mission

I and II were the Cytherean ones. Mariner I, launched in July 1962, went off course immediately and was immediately destroyed. Mariner II, launched only a month later, made a successful passage close to Venus and telemetered back such disconcerting information as that the planet has no magnetic field and that surface temperatures might reach as high as 800° F. It is this latter datum which Carl Sagan, the final contributor to this section, mainly discusses.

Even in the dawn of this period, when we were gaining a knowledge of Venus more thorough than any telescope could provide, the dictum of Flammarion's quoted on the title page still holds good – and forms, indeed, the essence of Firsoff's complaint. Flammarion goes on to ask – or rather, to say that he will *not* ask "with the good Father Kircher, whether the water of that world would be good for baptising*, and whether the wine would be fit for the sacrifice of the Mass; nor, with Huygens, whether the musical instruments of Venus resemble the harp or the flute; nor, with Swedenborg, whether the young girls walk about without clothing; etc.... As to imagining it desert or sterile, this is an hypothesis which could not arise in the brain of any naturalist."

These were not exactly the questions that vexed the minds of science fiction writers in the forties and fifties of this century.

When A. E. van Vogt visited the planet, his mind was on *A Can of Paint*, and the world is only vaguely sketched as one of grassy plains. Later, in *World of Null-A*, van Vogt's hero, Gosseyn, is sent to Venus and finds there the galactic base of The Greatest Empire.

Other characteristic preoccupations of writers might include John Russell Fearn (known also as Vargo Statten and Volsted Gridban) and his "slug-like hordes of evil Venusians" which rule the Earth in *Phantom from Space*. The wide oceans might be reckoned to hold particular appeal for sea-going Bertram Chandler, and so it proved in his *Special Knowledge*. His *Fire Brand* is all sailing ships and fungus and rot and the reeking swamps; while it was possibly a culinary interest that prompted Frederick Arnold Kummer Jun. to open his *White Land of Venus* with the

* A question to be taken up later in another context by the good Father James Blish in *A Case of Conscience* (1953).

memorable line, "The thick Venusian jungle was like a steaming stewing pot of spinach . . ." Swamps appear again, not surprisingly, in Jerry Shelton's *Swamper* – as do furry aliens. Ray Bradbury's child-like men spend all the story looking for shelter in a Sun Dome in *The Long Rain* ("How many million years since the rain stopped raining here on Venus?")

Other authors who ventured to Venus include C. L. Moore in *There Shall Be Darkness* and Clifford Simak in *Tools*. James Blish also made a few investigations there in his earlier days – with Damon Knight (who wore a pen-name for the occasion) in *Two Worlds in Peril*, using an all-water model; and with Robert Lowndes in *The Duplicated Man*, using a model in which the planet was swept with dust-storms, the dust containing formaldehyde crystals, so that people lived underground. In *The Bounding Crown*, Blish was back on Venus on his own, beginning his story thus: "Few people are single-minded enough to walk down the central avenues of the Venerian pleasure-city of Etoin without gawping to right and left . . . the only beautifull city on Venus . . . After eleven years on the level expanse of baked mud which is the sunward side of the planet."

Authors in the fifties, however, mostly gave an affirmative answer to the last part of Flammarions dramatic question regarding the Cytherean inhabitants: "Do they pass their life in pleasure, as Bernardin de St. Pierre* said, or, rather, are they so tormented by the inclemency of their seasons that they have no delicate perception, and are incapable of any scientific or artistic attention?"

One of the most striking of these answers was Frederick Pohl and Cyril Kornbluth's *Gravy Planet* (1952), later to be known as *The Space Merchants*. In this novel, Venus is hell, a drab planet scoured by tornadoes of ammonia and formaldehyde, which American advertising plans cynically to sell to American tourists and colonists. "It's something like the inside of a cave, sort of – only not dark," says one of the characters. "But the light is – funny. Nobody ever saw light like that on Earth. Orangey-brownish light, brilliant, *very* brilliant, but sort of threatening. Like the way

---

* Jacques Henri Bernardin de Saint-Pierre, eighteenth century author of *Paul et Virginie,* who described a terrestrial paradise on the Cytherean globe.

the sky is threatening in the summer around sunset just before a smasher of a thunderstorm. Only there never is any thunderstorm because there isn't a drop of water around ... There is lightning. Plenty of it, but never any rain."

An observation which is echoed by the second contributor to this section, Poul Anderson; whose stark short novel, *The Big Rain*, first appeared in 1955.

V. A. FIRSOFF: Exploring the Planets

THE futility of scholastic thought in the Middle Ages is traditionally typified by the problem of how many angels can dance on the point of a needle. We are assured that Francis Bacon has not wrought in vain, and in our empirical times the wrangle between the Realists and the Nominalists and other spurious problems that agitated the scholastic mind rest 5 fathoms deep beneath a sediment of mathematical papers. And so they do, but I am not at all so sure that the attitudes of mind have changed to the same extent as the labels.

We no longer count angels on needle points. Our modern scholastic "angels" are called "models". A model is an artificial mental construction which is supposed to portray the reality in its essential features. The method seems to consist in plucking a few data out of a complicated and ofttimes bewildering context and deducing from them, step by step, conclusions preconceived from the start. A few "reasonable interpretations" and "simplifying assumptions" are helpful on the way. The use of "advanced" mathematics and copious references to the "literature", especially the "difficult", if obscure, publications, add weight to paper and give it an "authoritative" look, never mind if the result is completely divorced from any conceivable reality.

Models, no doubt, have their uses, but at least in planetary astronomy they are more conspicious by their abuses.

We have three main models of the Venusian atmosphere intended to account for the microwave "brightness temperature": (1) Ionosphere, (2) Aeolospheric, (3) Greenhouse.

In the ionospheric model the whole of the microwave emission is generated by free-free transitions of electrons in the ionosphere. Otherwise an atmospheric structure similar to that described in the preceding section is assumed, with ground pressures of the order of one atmosphere and no special postulates with regard to chemical composition. The usual objection is that an electron density of about 1,000 times that in our ionosphere would be required to account for the observed microwave emission of Venus. This is considered improbable.

In the aeolospheric model, advocated chiefly by E. J. Opik, the surface of Venus is devoid of water and heated to the microwave brightness temperature by friction, generated in a deep atmosphere of nitrogen and carbon dioxide by fierce winds which are caused by the great temperature differences due to synchronized rotation, as one side of Venus is permanently facing towards and the other away from the Sun. The material of the clouds is, of course, dust or finely-ground quartz sand.

Quite apart from the fact that these assumptions do not satisfy the requirements set by the observational data, no mechanism will work without an adequate supply of energy. Being given the albedo and the effective radiation temperature of Venus, clouds of whatever composition will not admit to the ground more than 30 per cent of our Solar Constant, and 30 per cent of the Solar Constant can no more heat it up to 600°K. by friction than by any other means. This amount of energy will be insufficient to stir up those dense and deep atmospheric masses into fierce winds. In fact, the base of a deep waterless atmosphere would be a calm untroubled pool, with no agency to convey the dust and sand from the surface to higher altitudes which could be agitated by the differences in temperature between the dark and sunlit hemisphere – and no such have been discovered.

The greenhouse model is the most advertised at the time of writing. Once more the microwave radiation of Venus is assumed to be thermal and to correspond to the temperature of the planet's surface. It is said to be produced on the
131

slowly rotating planet by the intense greenhouse effect of a deep and dense atmosphere, composed chiefly of carbon dioxide with or without a proportion of water vapour.

... So there we are: a bunch of hypotheses, some less, some more plausible, but few certainties. Mariner II, successful as it was in its mission, has not cast any "blinding shaft of light" on the problems of Venus. Perhaps the programming of the probe was too narrow, too pegged down to particular hypotheses, which it has neither proved nor disproved. Further probes may be more effective in this respect, while extra-atmospheric spectroscopy should bring new information on the composition of the Venusian atmosphere.

The inconclusiveness of the Mariner observations provides a striking demonstration of the natural limitations of an unmanned automatic probe. Human observers could vary their programme according to the circumstances they encountered, and there is no real substitute for a close-up visual and photographic examination of the planet from a satellitic orbit. Thus, while in the present state of our ignorance, it would be very unwise to attempt a landing on Venus, a manned satellite mission would be both highly desirable and probably feasible in the "foreseeable future".

The requirements of flight to Venus have already been considered. The duration of a two-way trip in a Hohmann orbit is 762 days, but this is only a theoretical figure and could be shortened considerably by a judicious choice of the time of departure.

POUL ANDERSON: The Big Rain

I

THE room was small and bare, nothing but a ventilator grill to relieve the drabness of its plastic walls, no furniture except a table and a couple of benches. It was hot, and the cold light of fluoros glistened off the sweat which covered the face of the man who sat there alone.

He was a big man, with hard bony features under closed cropped reddish-brown hair; his eyes were gray, with something chilly in them, and moved restlessly about the chamber to assess its crude homemade look. The coverall which draped his lean body was a bit too colorful. He had fumbled a cigarette out of his belt pouch and it smoldered between his fingers, now and then he took a heavy drag on it. But he sat quietly enough, waiting.

The door opened and another man came in. This one was smaller, with bleak features. He wore only shorts to whose waistband was pinned a star-shaped badge, and a needle-gun holstered at his side, but somehow he had a military look.

"Simon Hollister?" he asked unnecessarily.

"That's me," said the other, rising. He loomed over the newcomer, but he was unarmed; they had searched him thoroughly the minute he disembarked.

"I am Captain Karsov, Guardian Corps." The English was fluent, with only a trace of accent. "Sit down." He lowered himself to a bench. "I am only here to talk to you."

Hollister grimaced. "How about some lunch?" he complained. "I haven't eaten for" – he paused a second – "thirteen hours, twenty-eight minutes."

His precision didn't get by Karsov, but the officer ignored it for the time being. "Presently," he said. "There isn't much time to lose, you know. The last ferry leaves in forty hours, and we have to find out before then if you are acceptable or must go back on it."

"Hell of a way to treat a guest," grumbled Hollister.

"We did not ask you to come," said Karsov coldly. "If you wish to stay on Venus, you had better conform to the regulations. Now, what do you think qualifies you?"

"To live here? I'm an engineer. Construction experience in the Amazon basin and on Luna. I've got papers to prove it, and letters of recommendation, if you'd let me get at my baggage."

"Eventually. What is your reason for emigrating?"

Hollister looked sullen. "I didn't like Earth."

"Be more specific. You are going to be narcoquizzed later, and the whole truth will come out. These questions

133

are just to guide the interrogators, and the better you answer me now the quicker and easier the quiz will be for all of us."

Hollister bristled. "That's an invasion of privacy."

"Venus isn't Earth," said Karsov with an attempt at patience. "Before you were even allowed to land, you signed a waiver which puts you completely under our jurisdiction as long as you are on this planet. I could kill you, and the UN would not have a word to say. But we do need skilled men, and I would rather O.K. you for citizenship. Do not make it too hard for me."

"All right." Hollister shrugged heavy shoulders. "I got in a fight with a man. He died. I covered up the traces pretty well, but I could never be sure – sooner or later the police might get on to the truth, and I don't like the idea of corrective treatment. So I figured I'd better blow out whilst I was still unsuspected."

"Venus is no place for the rugged individualist, Hollister. Men have to work together, and be very tolerant of each other, if they are to survive at all."

"Yes, I know. This was a special case. The man had it coming." Hollister's face twisted. "I have a daughter – Never mind. I'd rather tell it under narco than consciously. But I just couldn't see letting a snake like that get 'corrected' and then walk around free again." Defensively: "I've always been a rough sort, I suppose, but you've got to admit this was extreme provocation."

"That is all right," said Karsov, "if you are telling the truth. But if you have family ties back on Earth, it might lessen your usefulness here."

"None," said Hollister bitterly. "Not any more."

The interview went on. Karsov extracted the facts skillfully: Hollister, Simon James; born Frisco Unit, U.S.A., of good stock; chronological age, thirty-eight Earth-years; physiological age, thanks to taking intelligent advantage of biomedics, about twenty-five; Second-class education, major in civil engineering with emphasis on nuclear-powered construction machines; work record; psych rating at last checkup; et cetera, et cetera, et cetera. Somewhere a recorder took sound and visual impressions of every nuance for later analysis and filing.

At the end, the Guardian rose and stretched. "I think

you will do," he said. "Come along now for the narcoquiz. It will take about three hours, and you will need another hour to recover, and then I will see that you get something to eat."

The city crouched on a mountainside in a blast of eternal wind. Overhead rolled the poisonous gray clouds; sometimes a sleet of paraformaldehyde hid the grim red slopes around, and always the scudding dust veiled men's eyes so they could not see the alkali desert below. Fantastically storm-gnawed crags loomed over the city, and often there was the nearby rumble of an avalanche, but the ledge on which it stood had been carefully checked for stability.

The city was one armored unit of metal and concrete, low and rounded as if it hunched its back against the shrieking, steady gale. From its shell protruded the stacks of hundreds of outsize Hilsch tubes, swivel-mounted so that they always faced into the wind. It blew past filters which caught the flying dust and sand and tossed them down a series of chutes to the cement factory. The tubes grabbed the rushing air and separated fast and slow molecules; the cooler part went into a refrigeration system which kept the city at a temperature men could stand – outside, it hovered around the boiling point of water; the smaller volume of super-heated air was conducted to the maintenance plant where it helped run the city's pumps and generators. There were also nearly a thousand windmills, turning furiously and drinking the force of the storm.

None of this air was for breathing. It was thick with carbon dioxide; the rest was nitrogen, inert gases, formaldehyde vapor, a little methane and ammonia. The city devoted many hectares of space to hydroponic plants which renewed its oxygen and supplied some of the food, as well as to chemical purifiers, pumps and blowers. "Free as air" was a joke on Venus.

Near the shell was the spaceport where ferries from the satellite station and the big interplanetary ships landed. Pilots had to be good to bring down a vessel, or even take one up, under such conditions as prevailed here. Except for the landing cradles, the radio mast and the GCA shack in the main shell, everything was underground, as most of the city was.

Some twenty thousand colonists lived there. They were

135

miners, engineers, laborers, technicians in the food and maintenance centers. There were three doctors, a scattering of teachers and librarians and similar personnel, a handful of police and administrators. Exactly fifteen people were employed in brewing, distilling, tavern-running, movie operation, and the other non-essential occupations which men required as they did food and air.

This was New America, chief city of Venus in 2051 A.D.

Hollister didn't enjoy his meal. He got it, cafeteria style, in one of the big plain messhalls, after a temporary ration book had been issued him. It consisted of a few vegetables, a lot of potato, a piece of the soggy yeast synthetic which was the closest to meat Venus offered – all liberally loaded with a tasteless basic food concentrate – a vitamin capsule, and a glass of flavored water. When he took out one of his remaining cigarettes, a score of eyes watched it hungrily. Not much tobacco here either. He inhaled savagely, feeling the obscure guilt of the have confronted with the have-not.

There were a number of people in the room with him, eating their own rations. Men and women were represented about equally. All wore coveralls of the standard shorts, and most looked young, but hard too, somehow – even the women. Hollister was used to female engineers and technicians at home, but here *everybody* worked.

For the time being, he stuck to his Earthside garments.

He sat alone at one end of a long table, wondering why nobody talked to him. You'd think they would be starved for a new face and word from Earth. Prejudice? Yes, a little of that, considering the political situation; but Hollister thought something more was involved.

Fear. They were all afraid of something.

When Karsov strolled in, the multilingual hum of conversation died, and Hollister guessed shrewdly at the fear. The Guardian made his way directly to the Earthling's place. He had a blocky, bearded man with a round smiling face in tow.

"Simon Hollister ... Heinrich Gebhardt," the policeman introduced them. They shook hands, sizing each other up. Karsov sat down. "Get me the usual," he said, handing over his ration book.

Gebhardt nodded and went over to the automat. It scanned the books and punched them when he had dialled his orders. Then it gave him two trays, which he carried back.

Karsov didn't bother to thank him. "I have been looking for you," he told Hollister. "Where have you been?"

"Just wandering around," said the Earthling cautiously. Inside he felt muscles tightening, and his mind seemed to tilt forward, as if sliding off the hypnotically imposed pseudo-personality which had been meant as camouflage in the narcoquiz. "It's quite a labyrinth here."

"You should have stayed in the barracks," said Karsov. There was no expression in his smooth-boned face; there never seemed to be. "Oh, well, I wanted to say you have been found acceptable."

"Good," said Hollister, striving for imperturbability.

"I will administer the oath after lunch," said Karsov. "Then you will be a full citizen of the Venusian Federation. We do not hold with formalities, you see – no time." He reached into a pocket and got out a booklet which he gave to Hollister. "But I advise you to study this carefully. It is a resumé of the most important laws, insofar as they differ from Earth's. Punishment for infraction is severe."

Gebhardt looked apologetic. "It has to be," he added. His bass voice had a slight blur and hiss of German accent, but he was good at the English which was becoming the common language of Venus. "This planet was made in hell. If ve do not all work together, ve all die."

"And then, of course, there is the trouble with Earth," said Karsov. His narrow eyes studied Hollister for a long moment. "Just how do people back there feel about our declaration of independence?"

"Well –" Hollister paused. Best to tell the unvarnished truth, he decided. "Some resentment, of course. After all the money we ... they ... put into developing the colonies –"

"And all the resources they took out," said Gebhardt. "Men vere planted on Venus back in the last century to mine fissionables, vich vere getting short efen then. The colonies vere made self-supporting because that vas cheaper than hauling supplies for them, vich vould haff been an impossible task anyvay. Some of the colonies vere penal, some vere manned by arbitrarily assigned personnel; the so-called democracies often relied on broken men,

137

who could not find vork at home or who had been displaced by var. No, ve owe them notting."

Hollister shrugged. "I'm not arguing. But people do wonder why, if you wanted national status, you didn't at least stay with the UN. That's what Mars is doing."

"Because we are ... necessarily ... developing a whole new civilization here, something altogether remote from anything Earth has ever seen," snapped Karsov. "We will still trade our fissionables for things we need, until the day we can make everything here ourselves, but we want as little to do with Earth as possible. Never mind, you will understand in time."

Hollister's mouth lifted in a crooked grin. There hadn't been much Earth could do about it; in the present stage of astronautics, a military expedition to suppress the nationalists would cost more than anyone could hope to gain even from the crudest imperialism. Also, as long as no clear danger was known to exist, it wouldn't have sat well with a planet sick of war; the dissension produced might well have torn the young world government, which still had only limited powers, apart.

But astronautics was going to progress, he thought grimly. Spaceships wouldn't have to improve much to carry, cheaply, loads of soldiers in cold sleep, ready to land when thermo-nuclear bombardment from the skies had smashed a world's civilization. And however peaceful Earth might be, she was still a shining temptation to the rest of the System, and it looked very much as if something was brewing here on Venus which could become ugly before the century was past.

Well –

"Your first assignment is already arranged," said Karsov. Hollister jerked out of his reverie and tried to keep his fists unclenched. "Gebhardt will be your boss. If you do well, you can look for speedy promotion. Meanwhile" – he flipped a voucher across – "here is the equivalent of the dollars you had along, in our currency."

Hollister stuck the sheet in his pouch. It was highway robbery, he knew, but he was in no position to complain and the Venusian government wanted the foreign exchange. And he could only buy trifles with it anyway; the essentials were issued without payment, the size of the ration depending on rank. Incentive bonuses were money, though, permitting you to amuse yourself but not to consume more of the scarce food or textiles or living space.

He reflected that the communist countries before World War Three had never gone this far. Here, everything was government property. The system didn't call itself communism, naturally, but it was, and probably there was no choice. Private enterprise demanded a fairly large economic surplus, which simply did not exist on Venus.

Well, it wasn't his business to criticize their internal arrangements. He had never been among the few fanatics left on Earth who still made a god of a particular economic set-up.

Gebhardt cleared his throat. "I am in charge of the atmosphere detail in this district," he said. "I am here on leafe, and vill be going back later today. Very glad to haff you, Hollister, ve are alvays short of men. Ve lost two in the last rock storm."

"Cheerful news," said the Earthman. His face resumed its hard woodenness. "Well, I didn't think Venus was going to be any bed of roses."

"It vill be," said Gebhardt. Dedication glowed on the hairy face. "Some day it vill be."

II

The oath was pretty drastic: in effect, Hollister put himself completely at the mercy of the Technic Board, which for all practical purposes was the city government. Each colony, he gathered, had such a body, and there was a federal board in this town which decided policy for the entire planet.

Anyone who wished to enter the government had to pass a series of rigid tests, after which there were years of apprenticeship and study, gradual promotion on the recommendation of seniors. The study was an exhausting course of history, psychotechnics, and physical science: in principle, thought Hollister, remembering some of the blubberheads who still got themselves elected at home, a good idea. The governing boards combined legislative, executive, and judicial functions, and totaled only a couple of thousand people for the whole world. It didn't seem like much for a nation of nearly two million, and the minimal paperwork surprised him – he had expected an omnipresent bureaucracy.

But of course they had the machines to serve them, recording everything in electronic files whose computers could find and correlate any data and were always checking up. And he was told pridefully that the schools were inculcating the rising generation with a tight ethic of obedience.

Hollister had supper, and returned to the Casual barracks to sleep. There were only a few men in there with him, most of them here on business from some other town. He was awakened by the alarm, whose photocells singled him out and shot forth a supersonic beam; it was a carrier wave for the harsh ringing in his head which brought him to his feet.

Gebhardt met him at an agreed-on locker room. There was a wiry, tough-looking Mongoloid with him who was introduced as Henry Yamashita. "Stow your fancy clothes, boy," boomed the chief, "and get on some TBI's." He handed over a drab, close-fitting coverall.

Hollister checked his own garments and donned the new suit wordlessly. After that there was a heavy plasticord outfit which, with boots and gloves, decked his whole body. Yamashita helped him strap on the oxygen bottles and plug in the Hilsch cooler. The helmet came last, its shoulderpiece buckled to the airsuit, but all of them kept theirs hinged back to leave their heads free.

"If somet'ing happens to our tank," said Gebhardt, "you slap that helmet down fast. Or maybe you like being embalmed. Haw!" His cheerfulness was more evident when Karsov wasn't around.

Hollister checked the valves with the caution taught him on Luna – his engineering experience was not faked. Gebhardt grunted approvingly. Then they slipped the packs containing toilet kits, change of clothes, and emergency rations; clipped ropes, batteries and canteens to their belts – the latter with the standard sucker tubes by which a man could drink directly even in his suit; and clumped out of the room.

A descending ramp brought them to a garage where the
140

tanks were stored. These looked not unlike the sandcarts of Mars, but were built lower and heavier, with a refrigerating tube above and a grapple in the nose. A mechanic gestured at one dragging a covered steel wagon full of supplies, and the three men squeezed into the tiny transparent cab.

Gebhardt gunned the engine, nodding as it roared. "O.K.," he said. "On ve go."

"What's the power source?" asked Hollister above the racket.

"Alcohol," answered Yamashita. "We get it from the formaldehyde. Bottled oxygen. A compressor and cooling system to keep the oxy tanks from blowing up on us – not that they don't once in a while. Some of the newer models use a peroxide system."

"And I suppose you save the water vapour and CO_2 to get the oxygen back," ventured Hollister.

"Just the water. There's always plenty of carbon dioxide." Yamashita looked out, and his face set in tight lines.

The tank waddled through the great air lock and up a long tunnel toward the surface. When they emerged, the wind was like a blow in the face. Hollister felt the machine shudder, and the demon howl drowned out the engine. He accepted the earplugs Yamashita handed him with a grateful smile.

There was dust and sand scudding by them, making it hard to see the mountainside down which they crawled. Hollister caught glimpses of naked fanglike peaks, raw slashes of ocher and blue where minerals veined the land, the steady march of dunes across the lower ledges. Overhead, the sky was an unholy tide of ragged, flying clouds, black and gray and sulfurous yellow. He could not see the sun, but the light around him was a weird hard brass color, like the light on Earth just before a thunderstorm.

The wind hooted and screamed, banging on the tank walls, yelling and rattling and groaning. Now and then a dull quiver ran through the land and trembled in Hollister's bones, somewhere an avalanche was ripping out a mountain's flanks. Briefly, a veil of dust fell so thick around them that they were blind, grinding through an elemental night with hell and the furies loose outside. The control

141

board's lights were wan on Gebhardt's intent face, most of the time he was steering by instruments.

Once the tank lurched into a gully. Hollister, watching the pilot's lips, thought he muttered: "Damn! That vasn't here before!" He extended the grapple, clutching rock and pulling the tank and its load upward.

Yamashita clipped two small disks to his larynx and gestured at the same equipment hanging on Hollister's suit. His voice came thin but fairly clear: "Put on your talkie unit if you want to say anything." Hollister obeyed, guessing that the earplugs had a transistor arrangement powered by a piece of radioactive isotope which reproduced the vibrations in the throat. It took concentration to understand the language as they distorted it, but he supposed he'd catch on fast enough.

"How many hours till nightfall?" he asked.

"About twenty." Yamashita pointed to the clock on the board, it was calibrated to Venus' seventy-two hour day. "It's around one hundred thirty kilometres to the camp, so we should just about make it by sunset."

"That isn't very fast," said Hollister. "Why not fly, or at least build roads?"

"The aircraft are all needed for speed travel and impassable terrain, and the roads will come later," said Yamashita. "These tanks can go it all right – most of the time."

"But why have the camp so far from the city?"

"It's the best location from a supply standpoint. We get most of our food from Little Moscow, and water from Hellfire, and chemicals from New America and Roger's Landing. The cities more or less specialize, you know. They have to: there isn't enough iron ore and whatnot handy to any one spot to build a city big enough to do everything by itself. So the air camps are set up at points which minimize the total distance over which supplies have to be hauled."

"You mean action distance, don't you? The product of the energy and time required for hauling."

Yamashita nodded, with a new respect in his eyes. "You'll do," he said.

The wind roared about them. It was more than just the slow rotation of the planet and its nearness to the sun which created such an incessant storm; if that had been all, there would never have been any chance of making it habitable. It was the high carbon dioxide content of the air, and its greenhouse effect; and in the long night, naked, arid rock cooled off considerably. With plenty of water and vegetation, and an atmosphere similar to Earth's, Venus would have a warm but rather gentle climate on the whole, the hurricanes moderated to trade winds; indeed, with the lower Corialis force, the destructive cyclones of Earth would be unknown.

Such, at least, was the dream of the Venusians. But looking out, Hollister realized that a fraction of the time and effort they were expending would have made the Sahara desert bloom. They had been sent here once as miners, but there was no longer any compulsion on them to stay; if they asked to come back to Earth, their appeal could not be denied however expensive it would be to ship them all home.

Then why didn't they?

Well, why go back to a rotten civilization like – Hollister caught himself. Sometimes his pseudomemories were real enough in him to drown out the genuine ones, rage and grief could nearly overwhelm him till he recalled that the sorrow was for people who had never existed. The anger had had to be planted deep, to get by a narcoquiz, but he wondered if it might not interfere with his mission, come the day.

He grinned sardonically at himself. One man, caught on a planet at the gates of the Inferno, watched by a powerful and ruthless government embracing that entire world, and he was setting himself against it.

Most likely he would die here, and the economical Venusians would process his body for its chemicals as they did other corpses, and that would be the end of it as far as he was concerned.

Well, he quoted to himself, *a man might try.*

Gebhart's camp was a small shell, a radio mast, and a shed sticking out of a rolling landscape of rock and sand; the rest was underground. The sun was down on a ragged horizon, dimly visible as a huge blood-red disk, when he arrived. Yamashita and Hollister had taken their turns piloting; the Earthman found it exhausting work, and his

143

head rang with the noise when he finally stepped out into the subterranean garage.

Yamashita led him to the barracks. "We're about fifty here," he explained. "All men." He grinned. "That makes a system of minor rewards and punishments based on leaves to a city *very* effective."

The barracks was a long room with triple rows of bunks and a few tables and chairs; only Gebhardt rated a chamber of his own, though curtains on the bunks did permit some privacy. An effort had been made to brighten the place up with murals, some of which weren't bad at all, and the men sat about reading, writing letters, talking, playing games. They were the usual conglomerate of races and nationalities, with some interesting half-breeds, hard work and a parsimonious diet had made them smaller than the average American or European, but they looked healthy enough.

"Simon Hollister, our new sub-engineer," called Yamashita as they entered. "Just got in from Earth. Now you know as much as I do." He flopped onto a bunk while the others drifted over. "Go ahead. Tell all. Birth, education, hobbies, religion, sex life, interests, prejudices – they'll find it out anyway, and God knows we could use a little variety around here."

A stocky blond man paused suspiciously. "From Earth?" he asked slowly. "We've had no new people from Earth for thirty years. What did you want to come here for?"

"I felt like it," snapped Hollister. "That's enough!"

"So, a jetheading snob, huh? We're too good for you, I guess."

"Take it easy, Sam," said someone else.

"Yeah," a Negro grinned, "he might be bossin' you, you know."

"That's just it," said the blond man. "I was born here. I've been studying, and I've been on air detail for twenty years, and this bull walks right in and takes my promotion the first day.

Part of Hollister checked off the fact that the Venusians used the terms "year" and "day" to mean those periods for their own world, one shorter and one longer than Earth's. The rest of him tightened up for trouble, but others intervened. He found a vacant bunk and sat down on it, swinging his legs and trying to make friendly conversation. It wasn't easy. He felt terribly alone.

Presently someone got out a steel and plastic guitar and strummed it, and soon they were all singing. Hollister listened with half an ear.

"When the Big Rain comes, all the air will be good,
   and the rivers all flow with beer,
With the cigarets bloomin' by the beefsteak bush,
   and the ice-cream-bergs right here.
When the Big Rain comes, we will all be a-swillin'
   of champagne, while the violin tree
Plays love songs because all the gals will be willin',
   and we'll all have a Big Rain spree! —"

Paradise, he thought. *They can joke about it, but it's still the Paradise they work for and know they'll never see. Then why* do *they work for it? What is it that's driving them?*

After a meal, a sleep, and another meal, Hollister was given a set of blueprints to study. He bent his mind to the task, using all the powers which an arduous training had given it, and in a few hours reported to Gebhardt. "I know them," he said.

"Already?" The chief's small eyes narrowed. "It iss not vort' vile trying to bluff here, boy. Venus alvays calls it."

"I'm not bluffing," said Hollister angrily. "If you want me to lounge around for another day, O.K., but I know those specs by heart."

The bearded man stood up. There was muscle under his plumpness. "O.K., by damn," he said. "You go out vit me next trip."

That was only a few hours off. Gebhardt took a third man, a quiet grizzled fellow they called Johnny, and let Hollister drive. The tank hauled the usual wagonload of equipment, and the rough ground made piloting a harsh task. Hollister had used multiple transmissions before, and while the navigating instruments were complicated, he caught on to them quickly enough; it was the strain and muscular effort that wore him out.

Venus' night was not the pitchy gloom one might have
145

expected. The clouds diffused sunlight around the planet, and there was also a steady flicker of aurora even in these middle latitudes. The headlamps were needed only when they went into a deep ravine. Wind growled around them, but Hollister was getting used to that.

The first airmaker on their tour was only a dozen kilometers from the camp. It was a dark, crouching bulk on a stony ridge, its intake funnel like the rearing neck of some archaic monster. They pulled up beside it, slapped down their helmets, and went one by one through the air lock. It was a standard midget type, barely large enough to hold one man, which meant little air to be pumped out and hence greater speed in getting through. Gebhardt had told Hollister to face the exit leeward; now the three roped themselves together and stepped around the tank, out of its shelter.

Hollister lost his footing, crashed to the ground, and went spinning away in the gale. Gebhardt and Johnny dug their cleated heels in and brought the rope up short. When they had the new man back on his feet, Hollister saw them grinning behind their faceplates. Thereafter he paid attention to his balance, leaning against the wind.

Inspection and servicing of the unit was a slow task, and it was hard to see the finer parts even in the headlights' glare. One by one, the various sections were uncovered and checked, adjustments made, full gas bottles removed and empty ones substituted.

It was no wonder Gebhardt had doubted Hollister's claim. The airmaker was one of the most complicated machines in existence. A thing meant to transform the atmosphere of a planet had to be.

The intake scooped up the wind and drove it, with the help of wind-powered compressors, through a series of chambers; some of them held catalysts, some electric arcs or heating coils maintaining temperature – the continuous storm ran a good-sized generator – and some led back into others in a maze of interconnections. The actual chemistry was simple enough. Paraform was broken down and yielded its binding water molecules; the formaldehyde, together with that taken directly from the air, reacted with ammonia and methane – or with itself – to produce a whole series of hydrocarbons, carbohydrates, and more complex

146

compounds for food, fuel and fertilizer; such carbon dioxide as did not enter other reactions was broken down by sheer brute force in an arc to oxygen and soot. The oxygen was bottled for industrial use; the remaining substances were partly separated by distillation – again using wind power, this time to refrigerate – and collected. Further processing would take place at the appropriate cities.

Huge as the unit loomed, it seemed pathetically small when you thought of the fantastic tonnage which was the total planetary atmosphere. But more of its kind were being built every day and scattered around the surface of the world; over a million already existed, seven million was the goal, and that number should theoretically be able to do the job in another twenty Earth-years.

That was theory, as Gebhardt explained over the helmet radio. Other considerations entered, such as the law of diminishing returns; as the effect of the machines became noticeable, the percentage of the air they could deal with would necessarily drop; then there was stratospheric gas, some of which apparently never got down to the surface; and the chemistry of a changing atmosphere had to be taken into account. The basic time estimate for this work had to be revised upward another decade.

There was oxygen everywhere, locked into rocks and ores, enough for the needs of man if it could be gotten out. Specially mutated bacteria were doing that job, living off carbon and silicon, releasing more gas than their own metabolisms took up; their basic energy source was the sun. Some of the oxygen recombined, of course, but not enough to matter, especially since it would only act on or near the surface and most of the bacterial gnawing went on far down. Already there was a barely detectable percentage of the element in the atmosphere. By the time the airmakers were finished, the bacteria would also be.

Meanwhile giant pulverizers were reducing barren stone and sand to fine particles which would be mixed with fertilizers to yield soil; and the genetic engineers were evolving still other strains of life which could provide a balanced ecology; and the water units were under construction.

These would be the key to the whole operation. There was plenty of water on Venus, trapped down in the body of

147

the planet, and the volcanoes brought it up as they had done long ago on Earth. Here it was quickly snatched by the polymerizing formaldehyde, except in spots like Hellfire where machinery had been built to extract it from magma and hydrated minerals. But there was less formaldehyde in the air every day.

At the right time, hydrogen bombs were to be touched off in places the geologists had already selected, and the volcanoes would all wake up. They would spume forth plenty of carbon dioxide – though by that time the amount of free gas would be so low that this would be welcomed – but there would be water too, unthinkable tons of water. And simultaneously aircraft would be sowing platinum catalyst in the skies, and with its help Venus' own lightning would attack the remaining poisons in the air. They would come down as carbohydrates and other compounds, washed out by the rain and leached from the sterile ground.

That would be the Big Rain. It would last an estimated ten Earth-years, and at the end there would be rivers and lakes and seas on a planet which had never known them. And the soil would be spread, the bacteria and plants and small animal life released. Venus would still be mostly desert, the rains would slacken off but remain heavy for centuries, but men could walk unclothed on this world and they could piece by piece make the desert green.

A hundred years after the airmen had finished their work, the reclaimed sections might be close to Earth conditions. In five hundred years, all of Venus might be Paradise.

To Hollister it seemed like a long time to wait.

III

He didn't need many days to catch on to the operations and be made boss of a construction gang. Then he took out twenty men and a train of supplies and machinery, to erect still another airmaker.

It was blowing hard then, too hard to set up the sealtents which ordinarily provided a measure of comfort. Men rested in the tanks, side by side, dozing uneasily and smelling each other's sweat. They griped loudly, but endured. It was a lengthy trip to their site; eventually the whole camp was to be broken up and re-established in a better location, but meanwhile they had to accept the monotony of travel.

Hollister noticed that his men had evolved an Asian ability just to sit, without thinking, hour after hour. Their conversation and humor also suggested Asia: acrid, often brutal, though maintaining a careful surface politeness most of the time. It was probably more characteristic of this particular job than of the whole planet, though, and maybe they sloughed it off again when their hitches on air detail had expired and they got more congenial assignments.

As boss, he had the privilege of sharing his tank with only one man; he chose the wizened Johnny, whom he rather liked. Steering through a yelling sandstorm, he was now able to carry on a conversation – and it was about time, he reflected, that he got on with his real job.

"Ever thought of going back to Earth?" he asked casually.

"Back?" Johnny looked surprised. "I was born here."

"Well . . . going to Earth, then."

"What'd I use for passage money?"

"Distress clause of the Space Navigation Act. They'd have to give you a berth if you applied. Not that you couldn't repay your passage, with interest, in a while. With your experience here, you could get a fine post in one of the reclamation projects on Earth."

"Look," said Johnny in a flustered voice, "I'm a good Venusian. I'm needed here and I know it."

"Forget the Guardians," snapped Hollister, irritated. "I'm not going to report you. Why you people put up with a secret police anyway, is more than I can understand."

"You've got to keep people in line," said Johnny. "We all got to work together to make a go of it."

"But haven't you ever thought it'd be nice to decide your own future and not have somebody to tell you what to do next?"

"It ain't just 'somebody'. It's the Board. They know how you and me fit in best. Sure, I suppose there are subversives, but I'm not one of them."

"Why don't the malcontents just run away, if they don't
149

dare apply for passage to Earth? They could steal materials and make their own village. Venus is a big place."

"It ain't that easy. And supposin' they could and did, what'd they do then? Just sit and wait for the Big Rain? We don't want any freeloaders on Venus, mister."

Hollister shrugged. There was something about the psychology that baffled him. "I'm not preaching revolution," he said carefully. "I came here of my own free will, remember, I'm just trying to understand the set-up."

Johnny's faded eyes were shrewd on him. "You've always had it easy compared to us, I guess. It may look hard to you here. But remember, we ain't never had it different, except that things are gettin' better little by little. The food ration gets upped every so often, and we're allowed a dress suit now as well as utility clothes, and before long there's goin' to be broadcast shows to the outposts – and some day the Big Rain is comin'. Then we can all afford to take it free and easy." He paused. "That's why we broke with Earth. Why should we slave our guts out to make a good life for our grandchildren, if a bunch of freeloaders are gonna come from Earth and fill up the planet then? It's *ours*. It's gonna be the richest planet men ever saw, and it belongs to us what developed it."

Official propaganda line, thought Hollister. It sounded plausible enough till you stopped to analyze. For one thing, each country still had the right to set its own immigration policies. Furthermore, at the rate Earth was progressing, with reclamation, population control, and new resources from the oceans, by the time Venus was ripe there wouldn't be any motive to leave home – an emigration which would be too long and expensive anyway. "For their own reasons, which he still had to discover, the rulers of Venus had not mentioned all the facts and had instead built up a paranoid attitude in their people. The new airmaker site was the top of a ridge thrusting from a boulder-strewn plain. An eerie copper-colored light seemed to tinge the horizon with blood. A pair of bulldozers had already gone ahead and scooped out a walled hollow in which seal-tents could be erected; Hollister's gang swarmed from the tanks and got at that job. Then the real work began – blasting and carving a foundation, sinking piers, assembling the unit on top.

On the fourth day the rock storm came. It had dawned

with an angry glow like sulfur, and as it progressed the wind strengthened and a dirty rack of clouds whipped low overhead. On the third shift, the gale was strong enough to lean against, and the sheet steel which made the unit's armor fought the men as if it lived.

The blond man, Sam Robbins, who had never liked Hollister, made his way up to the chief. His voice came over the helmet radio, dim beneath static and the drumming wind: "I don't like this. Better we take cover fast."

Hollister was not unwilling, but the delicate arc electrodes were being set up and he couldn't take them down again; nor could he leave them unprotected to the scouring drift of sand. "As soon as we get the shielding up," he said.

"I tell you, there's no time to shield 'em!"

"Yes, there is." Hollister turned his back. Robbins snarled something and returned to his labor.

A black wall, rust-red on the edges, was lifting to the east, the heaviest sandstorm Hollister had yet seen. He hunched his shoulders and struggled through the sleetlike dust to the unit. Tuning up his radio: "Everybody come help on this. The sooner it gets done, the sooner we can quit."

The helmeted figures swarmed around him, battling the thunderously flapping metal sheets, holding them down by main force while they were welded to the frame. Hollister saw lightning livid across the sky. Once a bolt flamed at the rod which protected the site. Thunder rolled and banged after it.

The wind slapped at them, and a sheet tore loose and went sailing down the hill. It struck a crag and wrapped itself around. "Robbins, Lewis, go get that!" cried Hollister, and returned attention to the piece he was clutching. An end ripped loose from his hands and tried to slash his suit.

The wind was so deafening that he couldn't hear it rise still higher, and in the murk of sand whirling about him he was nearly blind. But he caught the first glimpse of gale-borne gravel whipping past, and heard the terror in his earphones: "Rock storm!"

The voice shut up; orders were strict that the channel be kept clear. But the gasping men labored still more frantically while struck metal rang and boomed.

151

Hollister peered through the darkness. "That's enough!" he decided. "Take cover!"

Nobody dropped his tools, but they all turned fast and groped down toward the camp. The way led past the crag, where Robbins and Lewis had just quit wrestling with the stubborn plate.

Hollister didn't see Lewis killed, but he did see him die. Suddenly his airsuit was flayed open, and there was a spurt of blood, and he toppled. The wind took his body, rolling it out of sight in the dust. *A piece of rock,* though Hollister wildly. *It tore his suit, and he's already embalmed* —

The storm hooted and squealed about him as he climbed the sand wall. Even the blown dust was audible, hissing against his helmet. He fumbled through utter blackness, fell over the top and into the comparative shelter of the camp ground. On hands and knees, he crawled toward the biggest of the self-sealing tents.

There was no time for niceties. They sacrificed the atmosphere within, letting the air lock stand open while they pushed inside. Had everybody made it to some tent or other? Hollister wasn't sure, but sand was coming in, filling the shelter. He went over and closed the lock. Somebody else started the pump, using bottled nitrogen to maintain air pressure and flush out the poisons. It seemed like a long time before the oxygen containers could be opened.

Hollister took off his helmet and looked around. The tent was half filled by seven white-faced men standing in the dust. The single fluorotube threw a cold light on their sweating bodies and barred the place with shadows. Outside, the wind bellowed.

"Might as well be comfortable," said Johnny in a small voice, and began shucking his airsuit. "If the tent goes, we're all done for anyhow." He sat down on the ground and checked his equipment methodically. Then he took a curved stone and spat on it and began scouring his face-plate to remove the accumulated scratches in its hard plastic. One by one the others imitated him.

"You there!"

Hollister looked up from his own suit. Sam Robbins stood before him. The man's eyes were red and his mouth worked.

"You killed Jim Lewis."

There was murder here. Hollister raised himself till he looked down at the Venusian. "I'm sorry he's dead," he replied, trying for quietness. "He was a good man. But these things will happen."

Robbins shuddered. "You sent him down there where the gravel got him. I was there, too, was it meant for me?"

"Nobody could tell where that chunk was going to hit," said Hollister mildly. "I could just as easily have been killed."

"I *told* you to quit half an hour before the things started."

"We couldn't quit then without ruining all our work. Sit down, Robbins. You're overtired and scared."

The men were very still sitting and and watching in the thick damp heat of the tent. Thunder crashed outside.

"You rotten Earthling —" Robbin's fist lashed out. It caught Hollister on the cheekbone and he stumbled back, shaking a dazed head. Robbins advanced grinning.

Hollister felt a cold viciousness of rage. It was his pseudo-personality he realized dimly but no time to think of that now. As Robbins closed in, he crouched and punched for the stomach.

Hard muscle met him. Robbins clipped him on the jaw. Hollister tried an uppercut, but it was skulfully blocked. This man knew how to fight.

Holister gave him another fusillade in the belly. Robbins grunted and rabbit-punched. Hollister caught it on his shoulder, reached up, grabbed an arm, and whirled his enemy over his head. Robbins hit a bunkframe that buckled under him.

He came back, dizzy but game. Hollister was well trained in combat. But it took him a good ten minutes to stretch his man bleeding on the ground.

Panting, he looked about him. There was no expression on the faces that ringed him in. "Anybody else?" he asked hoarsely.

"No, boss," said Johnny. "You're right, o' course. I don't think nobody else here wants twenty lashes back at base."

"Who said —" Hollister straightened, blinking. "Lashes?"

"Why, sure. This was mutiny, you know. It's gotta be punished."

153

Hollister shook his head. "Too barbaric. Correction –"

"Look, boss," said Johnny, "you're a good engineer but you don't seem to understand much about Venus yet. We ain't got the time or the manpower or the materials to spend on them there corrective jails. A bull what don't keep his nose clean gets the whip or the sweatbox, and then back to the job. The really hard cases go to the uranium mines at Lucifer.' He shivered, even in the dense heat.

Hollister frowned. "Not a bad system," he said, to stay in character. "But I think Robbins here has had enough. I'm not going to report him if he behaves himself from now on, and I'll trust the rest of you to cooperate."

They mumbled assent. He wasn't sure whether they respected him for it or not, but the boss was boss. Privately, he suspected that the Boards must frame a lot of men, or at least sentence them arbitrarily for minor crimes, to keep the mines going; there didn't seem to be enough rebellion in the Venusian character to supply them otherwise.

Chalk up another point for the government. The score to settle was getting rather big.

IV

Time was hard to estimate on Venus; it wasn't only that they had their own calendar here, but one day was so much like another. Insensibly and despite himself, Hollister began sliding into the intellectual lethargy of the camp. He had read the few books – and with his trained memory, he could only read a book once – and he knew every man there inside out, and he had no family in one of the cities to write to and think about. The job itself presented a daily challenge, no two situations were ever quite the same and occasionally he came near death, but outside of it there was a tendency to stagnate.

The two other engineers, Gebhardt and Yamashita, were pleasant company. The first was from Hörselberg, which had been a German settlement and still retained some character of its own, and he had interesting stories to tell of it; the second, though of old Venus-American stock, was mentally agile for a colonist, had read more than most and had a lively interest in the larger world of the Solar

System. But even the stimulation they offered wore a little thin in six months or so.

The region spun through a "winter" that was hardly different from summer except in having longer nights, and the sterile spring returned, and the work went on. Hollister's time sense ticked off days with an accuracy falling within a few seconds, and he wondered how long he would be kept here and when he would get a chance to report to his home office. That would be in letters ostensibly to friends, which one of the spaceships would carry back; he knew censors would read them first, but his code was keyed to an obscure eighteenth-century book he was certain no one on Venus had ever heard of.

Already he knew more about this planet than anyone on Earth. It had always been too expensive to send correspondents here, and the last couple of UN representatives hadn't found much to tell. The secretiveness toward Earthmen might be an old habit, going back to the ultra-nationalistic days of the last century. Colony A and Colony B, of two countries which at home might not be on speaking terms, were not supposed to give aid and comfort to each other; but on Venus such artificial barriers had to go if anyone was to survive. Yamashita told with relish how prospectors from Little Moscow and Trollen had worked together and divided up their finds. But of course, you couldn't let your nominal rulers know—

Hollister was beginning to realize that the essential ethos of Venus was indeed different from anything which existed on Earth. It had to be, the landscape had made it so. Man was necessarily a more collective creature than at home. That helped explain the evolution of the peculiar governmental forms and the patience of the citizenry toward the most outrageous demands. Even the dullest laborer seemed to live in the future.

Our children and grandchildren will build the temples, read the books, write the music. Ours is only to lay the foundation.

And was that why they stuck here, instead of shipping back and turning the whole job over to automatic machinery and a few paid volunteers? They had been the lonely, the rejected, the dwellers in outer darkness, for a long time; now they could not let go of their fierce and

155

angry pride, even when there was no more need for it. Hollister thought about Ireland. Man is not a logical animal.

Still, there were features of Venusian society that struck him as unnecessary and menacing. Something would have to be done about them, though as yet he wasn't sure what it would be.

He worked, and he gathered impressions and filed them away, and he waited. And at last the orders came through. This camp had served its purpose, it was to be broken up and replanted elsewhere, but first its personnel were to report to New America and get a furlough. Hollister swung almost gaily into the work of dismantling everything portable and loading it in the wagons. Maybe he finally was going to get somewhere.

He reported at the Air Control office with Gebhardt and Yamashita, to get his pay and quarters assignment. The official handed him a small card. "You've been raised to chief engineer's rank," he said. "You'll probably get a camp of your own next time."

Gebhardt pounded him on the back. "Ach, *sehr gut!* I recommended you, boy, you did fine, but I am going to miss you."

"Oh ... we'll both be around for a while, won't we?" asked Hollister uncomfortably.

"Not I! I haff vife and kids, I hop the next rocket to Hörselberg."

Yamashita had his own family in town, and Hollister didn't want to intrude too much on them. He wandered off, feeling rather lonesome.

His new rating entitled him to private quarters, a tiny room with minimal furniture, though he still had to wash and eat publicly like everyone else except the very top. He sat down and began composing the planned letters.

There was a knock at the door. He fumbled briefly, being used to scanners at home and not used to doors on Venus, and finally said: "Come in."

A woman entered. She was young, quite good-looking, with a supple tread and spectacularly red hair. Cool green eyes swept up and down his height. "My name is Barbara Brandon," she said. "Administrative assistant in Air Control."

156

"Oh ... hello." He offered her the chair. "You're here on business?"

Amusement tinged her impersonal voice. "In a way. I'm going to marry you."

Hollister's jaw did not drop, but it tried. "Come again?" he asked weakly.

She sat down. "It's simple enough. I'm thirty-seven years old, which is almost the maximum permissible age of celibacy except in special cases." With a brief, unexpectedly feminine touch: "That's Venus years, of course! I've seen you around, and looked at your record; good heredity there, I think. Pops O.K.'d it genetically – that's Population Control – and the Guardians cleared it, too."

"Um-m-m ... look here." Hollister wished there were room to pace. He settled for sitting on the table and swinging his legs. "Don't I get any say in the matter?"

"You can file any objections, of course, and probably they'd be heeded; but you'll have to have children by someone pretty soon. We need them. Frankly, I think a match between us would be ideal. You'll be out in the field so much that we won't get in each other's hair, and we'd probably get along well enough while we are together."

Hollister scowled. It wasn't the morality of it – much. He was a bachelor on Earth, secret service UN-men really had no business getting married; and in any case the law would wink at what he had done on Venus if he ever got home. But something about the whole approach annoyed him.

"I can't see where you need rules to make people breed," he said coldly. "They'll do that anyway. You don't realize what a struggle it is on Earth to bring the population back down toward a sensible figure."

"Things are different here," answered Barbara Brandon in a dry tone. "We're going to need plenty of people for a long time to come, and they have to be of the right stock. The congenitally handicapped can't produce enough to justify their own existence; there's been a program of euthanasia there, as you may know. But the new people are also needed in the right places. This town, for instance, can only accommodate so much population increase per year. We can't send surplus children off to a special crèche because there aren't enough teachers or doctors – or anything, so the mothers have to take care of all their own

157

kids; or the fathers, if they happen to have a job in town and the mother is a field worker. The whole process has *got* to be regulated."

"Regulations!" Hollister threw up his hands. "Behold the bold frontiersman!"

The girl looked worried. "Careful what you say." She smiled at him with a touch of wistfulness. "It needn't be such a hindrance to you. Things are ... pretty free except where the production of children is involved."

"I – this is kind of sudden." Hollister tried to smile back. "Don't think I don't appreciate the compliment. But I need time to think, adjust myself – Look, are you busy right now?"

"No, I'm off."

"All right. Put on your party clothes and we'll go out and have some drinks and talk the matter over."

She glanced shyly at the thin, colored coverall she wore. "These are my party clothes," she said.

Hollister's present rank let him visit another bar than the long, crowded room where plain laborers caroused. This one had private tables, decorations, music in the dim dusky air. It was quiet, the engineer aristocracy had their own code of manners. A few couples danced on a small floor.

He found an unoccupied table by the curving wall, sat down, and dialed for drinks and cigarettes. Neither were good enough to justify their fantastic cost but it had been a long time since he had enjoyed any luxuries at all. He felt more relaxed with them. The girl looked quite beautiful in the muted light.

"You were born here, weren't you, Barbara?" he asked after a while.

"Of course," she said. "You're the first immigrant in a long time. Used to be some deportees coming in every once in a while, but –"

"I know. 'Sentence suspended on condition you leave Earth.' That was before all countries had adopted the new penal code. Never mind. I was just wondering if you wouldn't like to see Earth – sometime."

"Maybe. But I'm needed here, not there. And I like it." There was a hint of defiance in the last remark.

He didn't press her. The luminous murals showed a soft

unreal landscape of lakes and forests, artificial stars twinkled gently in the ceiling. "Is this what you expect Venus to become?" he asked.

"Something like this. Probably not the stars, it'll always be cloudy here but they'll be honest rain clouds. We should live to see the beginning of it."

"Barbara," he asked, "do you believe in God?"

"Why, no. Some of the men are priests and rabbis and what-not in their spare time, but – No, not I. What about it?"

"You're wrong," he said. "Venus is your god. This is a religious movement you have here, with a slide rule in its hand."

"So –?" She seemed less assured, he had her off balance and the green eyes were wide and a little frightened.

"An Old Testament god," he pursued, "merciless, all-powerful, all-demanding. Get hold of a Bible if you can, and read Job and Ecclesiastes. You'll see what I mean. When is the New Testament coming ... or even the prophet Micah?"

"You're a funny one," she said uncertainly. Frowning, trying to answer him on his own terms: "After the Big Rain, things will be easier. It'll be –" She struggled through vague memories. "It'll be the Promised Land."

"You've only got this one life," he said. "Is there any sound reason for spending it locked in these iron boxes, with death outside, when you could lie on a beach on Earth and everything you're fighting for is already there?"

She grabbed his hand where it lay on the table. Her fingers were cold, and she breathed fast. "No! Don't say such things! You're here too. You came here –"

Get thee behind me, Satan.

"Sorry." He lifted his glass. "Here's freefalling."

She clinked with him smiling shakily.

"There isn't any retirement on Venus, is there?" he asked.

"Not exactly. Old people get lighter work, of course. When you get too old to do anything ... well, wouldn't you want euthanasia?"

He nodded, quite sincerely, though his exact meaning had gone by her. "I was just thinking of ... shall we say us ... rose-covered cottages, sunset of life. Darby and Joan stuff."

159

She smiled, and reached over to stroke his cheek lightly. "Thanks," she murmured. "Maybe there will be rose-covered cottages by the time we're that old."

Hollister turned suddenly, aware with his peripheral senses of the man who approached. Or maybe it was the sudden choking off of the low-voiced conversation in the bar. The man walked very softly up to their table and stood looking down on them. Then he pulled out the extra chair for himself.

"Hello, Karsov," said Hollister dully.

The Guardian nodded. There was a ghostly smile playing about his lips. "How are you?" he asked, with an air of not expecting a reply. "I am glad you did so well out there. Your chief recommended you very highly."

"Thanks," said Hollister, not hiding the chill in his voice. He didn't like the tension he could see in Barbara.

"I just happened by and thought you would like to know you will have a crew of your own next trip," said the policeman. "That is, the Air Control office has made a recommendation to me." He glanced archly at Barbara. "Did you by any chance have something to do with that, Miss Brandon? Could be!" Then his eyes fell to the cigarettes, and he regarded them pointedly till Barbara offered him one.

"Pardon me." Hollister held his temper with an effort and kept his voice urbane. "I'm still new here, lot of things I don't know. Why does your office have to pass on such a matter?"

"My office has to pass on everything," said Karsov.

"Seems like a purely technical business as long as my own record is clean."

Karsov shook his sleek head. "You do not understand. We cannot have someone in a responsible position who is not entirely trustworthy. It is more than a matter of abstaining from criminal acts. You have to be with us all the way. No reservations. That is what Psych Control and the Guardians exist for."

He blew smoke through his nose and went on in a casual tone: "I must say your attitude has not been entirely pleasing. You have made some remarks which could be ... misconstrued. I am ready to allow for your not being used to

Venusian conditions, but you know the law about sedition."

For a moment, Hollister savored the thought of Karsov's throat between his fingers. "I'm sorry," he said.

"Remember, there are recorders everywhere, and we make spot checks directly on people, too. You could be narcoquizzed again any time I order it. But I do not think that will be necessary just yet. A certain amount of grumbling is only natural, and if you have any genuine complaints you can file them with your local Technic Board."

Hollister weighed the factors in his mind. Karsov packed a gun, and – But too sudden a meekness could be no less suspicious. "I don't quite understand why you have to have a political police," he ventured. "It seems like an ordinary force should be enough. After all ... where would an insurrectionist go?"

He heard Barbara's tiny gasp, but Karsov merely looked patient. "There are many factors involved," said the Guardian. "For instance some of the colonies were not quite happy with the idea of being incorporated into the Venusian Federation. They preferred to stay with their mother countries, or even to be independent. Some fighting ensued, and they must still be watched. Then, too, it is best to keep Venusian society healthy while it is new and vulnerable to subversive radical ideas. And finally, the Guardian Corps is the nucleus of our future army and space navy."

Hollister wondered if he should ask why Venus needed military forces, but decided against it. The answer would only be some stock phrase about terrestrial imperialists, if he got any answer at all. He'd gone about far enough already.

"I see," he said. "Thanks for telling me."

"Would you like a drink, sir?" asked Barbara timidly.

"No," said Karsov. "I only stopped in on my way elsewhere. Work, always work." He got up. "I think you are making a pretty good adjustment, Hollister. Just watch your tongue ... and your mind. Oh, by the way. Under the circumstances, it would be as well if you did not write any letters home for a while. That could be misunderstood. You may use one of the standard messages. They are much cheaper, too." He nodded and left.

161

Hollister's eyes followed him out. *How much does he know?*

"Come on," said Barbara. There was a little catch in her voice. "Let's dance."

Gradually they relaxed, easing into the rhythm of the music. Hollister dismissed the problem of Karsov for the time being, and bent mind and senses to his companion. She was lithe and slim in his arms, and he felt the stirrings of an old hunger in him.

The next day he called on Yamashita. They had a pleasant time together, and arranged a party for later; Hollister would bring Barbara. But as he was leaving, the Venusian drew him aside.

"Be careful, Si," he whispered. "They were here a few hours after I got back, asking me up and down about you. I had to tell the truth, they know how to ask questions and if I'd hesitated too much it would have been narco. I don't think you're in any trouble, but be careful!"

Barbara had arranged her vacation to coincide with his – efficient girl! They were together most of the time. It wasn't many days before they were married. That was rushing things, but Hollister would soon be back in the field for a long stretch and – well – they had fallen in love. Under the circumstances, it was inevitable. Curious how it broke down the girl's cool self-possession, but that only made her more human and desirable.

He felt a thorough skunk, but maybe she was right. *Carpe diem.* If he ever pulled out of this mess, he'd just have to pull her out with him; meanwhile, he accepted the additional complication of his assignment. It looked as if that would drag on for years, anyhow; maybe a lifetime.

They blew themselves to a short honeymoon at a high-class – and expensive – resort by Thunder Gorge, one of Venus' few natural beauty spots. The atmosphere at the lodge was relaxed, not a Guardian in sight and more privacy than elsewhere on the planet. Psych Control was shrewd enough to realize that people needed an occasional surcease from all duty, some flight from the real world of sand and stone and steel. It helped keep them sane.

Even so, there was a rather high proportion of mental disease. It was a taboo subject, but Hollister got a doctor

162

drunk and wormed the facts out of him. The psychotic were not sent back to Earth, as they could have been at no charge; they might talk too much. Nor were there facilities for proper treatment on Venus. If the most drastic procedures didn't restore a patient to some degree of usefulness in a short time – they had even revived the barbarism of prefontal lobotomy! – he was quietly gassed.

"But it'll all be diff'rent af'er uh Big Rain," said the doctor. "My son ull have uh real clinic, he will."

More and more, Hollister doubted it.

A few sweet crazy days, and vacation's end was there and they took the rocket back to New America. It was the first time Hollister had seen Barbara cry.

He left her sitting forlornly in the little two-room apartment they now rated, gathering herself to arrange the small heap of their personal possessions, and reported to Air Control. The assistant super gave him a thick bound sheaf of papers.

"Here are the orders and specs," he said. "You can have two days to study them." Hollister, who could memorize the lot in a few hours, felt a leap of gladness at the thought of so much free time. The official leaned back in his chair. He was a gnarled old man, retired to a desk after a lifetime of field duty. One cheek was puckered with the scars of an operation for the prevalent HR cancer; Venus had no germs, but prepared her own special death traps. "Relax for a minute and I'll give you the general idea."

He pointed to a large map on the wall. It was not very complete or highly accurate: surveying on this planet was a job to break a man's heart, and little had been done. "We're establishing your new camp out by Last Chance. You'll note that Little Moscow, Trollen, and Roger's Landing cluster around it at an average distance of two hundred kilometers, so that's where you'll be getting your supplies, sending men on leave, and so forth. I doubt if you'll have any occasion to report back here till you break camp completly in a couple of years."

And Barbara will be here alone, Barbara and our child whom I won't even see –

"You'll take your wagon train more or less along this route," went on the super, indicating a dotted line that ran from New America. "It's been gone over and is safe. Notice
163

the eastward jog to Lucifer at the halfway point. That's to refuel and take on fresh food stores."

Hollister frowned, striving for concentration on the job. "I can't see that. Why not take a few extra wagons and omit the detour?"

"Orders," said the super.

Whose orders? Karsov's? I'll bet my air helmet! – but why?

"Your crew will be ... kind of tough," said the old man. "They're mostly from Ciudad Alcazar, which is on the other side of the world. It was one of the stubborn colonies when we declared independence, had to be put down by force, and it's still full of sedition. These spigs are all hard cases who've been assigned to this hemisphere so they won't stir up trouble at home. I saw in your dossier that you speak Spanish, among other languages, which is one reason you're being given this bunch. You'll have to treat them rough, remember. Keep them in line."

I think there was more than one reason behind this.

"The details are all in your assignment book," said the super. "Report back here in two days, this time. O.K. – have fun!" He smiled, suddenly friendly now that his business was completed.

V

Darkness and a whirl of poison sleet turned the buildings into crouching black monsters, hardly to be told from the ragged snarl of crags which ringed them in. Hollister brought his tank to a grinding halt before a tower which fixed him with a dazzling floodlight eye. "Sit tight, Diego," he said, and slapped his helmet down.

His chief assistant, Fernandez, nodded a sullen dark head. He was competent enough, and had helped keep the unruly crew behaving itself, but remained cold toward his boss. There was always a secret scorn in his eyes.

Hollister wriggled through the airlock and dropped to the ground. A man in a reinforced, armorlike suit held a tommy-gun on him, but dropped the muzzle as he advanced. The blast of white light showed a stupid face set in lines of habitual brutality.

"You the airman come for supplies?" he asked.

"Yes. Can I see your chief?"

The guard turned wordlessly and led the way. Beyond the lock of the main shell was a room where men sat with rifles. Hollister was escorted to an inner office, where a middle-aged, rather mild-looking fellow in Guardian uniform greeted him. "How do you do? We had word you were coming. The supplies were brought to our warehouse and you can load them when you wish."

Hollister accepted a chair. "I'm Captain Thomas," the other continued. "Nice to have you. We don't see many new faces at Lucifer – not men you can talk to, anyway. How are things in New America?"

He gossiped politely for a while. "It's quite a remarkable installation we have here," he ended. "Would you like to see it?"

Hollister grimaced. "No, thanks."

"Oh, I really must insist. You and your chief assistant and one or two of the foremen. They'll all be interested, and can tell the rest of your gang how it is. There's so little to talk about in camp."

Hollister debated refusing outright and forcing Thomas to show his hand. But why bother? Karsov had given orders, and Thomas would conduct him around at gun point if necessary. "O.K., thanks," he said coldly. "Let me get my men bunked down first, though."

"Of course. We have a spare barracks for transients. I'll expect you in two hours ... with three of your men, remember."

Diego Fernandez only nodded when Hollister gave him the news. The chief skinned his teeth in a bleak sort of grin. "Don't forget to 'oh' and 'ah'," he said. "Our genial host will be disappointed if you don't, and he's a man I'd hate to disappoint."

The smoldering eyes watched him with a quizzical expression that faded back into blankness. "I shall get Gomez and San Rafael," said Fernandez. "They have strong stomachs."

Thomas received them almost punctuously and started walking down a series of compartments. "As engineers, you will be most interested in the mine itself," he said. "I'll show you a little of it. This is the biggest uranium deposit known in the Solar System."

He led them to the great cell block, where a guard with

165

a shock gun fell in behind them. "Have to be careful," said Thomas. "We've got some pretty desperate characters here, who don't feel they have much to lose."

"All lifers, eh?" asked Hollister.

Thomas looked surprised. "Of course! We couldn't let them go back after what the radiation does to their germ plasm."

A man rattled the bars of his door as they passed. "I'm from New America!" His harsh scream bounded between steel walls. "Do you know my wife? Is Martha Riley all right?"

"Shut up!" snapped the guard, and fed him a shock beam. He lurched back into the darkness of his cell. His mate, whose face was disfigured by a cancer, eased him to his bunk.

Someone else yelled, far down the long white-lit rows. A guard came running from that end. The voice pleaded: "It's a nightmare. It's just a nightmare. The stuff's got intuh muh brain and I'm always dreamin' nightmares –"

"They get twitchy after a while," said Thomas. "Stuff *will* seep through the suits and lodge in their bodies. Then they're not much good for anything but pick-and-shovel work. Don't be afraid, gentlemen, we have reinforced suits for the visitors and guards."

These were donned at the end of the cell block. Beyond the double door, a catwalk climbed steeply, till they were on the edge of an excavation which stretched farther than they could see in the gloom.

"It's rich enough yet for open pit mining," said Thomas, "though we're driving tunnels, too." He pointed to a giant scooper. Tiny shapes of convicts scurried about it. "Four-hour shifts because of the radiation down there. Don't be-lieve those rumors that we aren't careful with our boys. Some of them live for thirty years."

Hollister's throat felt cottony. It would be so easy to rip off Thomas' air hose and kick him down into the pit! "What about women prisoners?" he asked slowly. "You must get some."

"Oh, yes. Right down there with the men. We believe in equality on Venus."

There was a strangled sound in the earphones, but Hol-lister wasn't sure which of his men had made it.

166

"Very essential work here," said Thomas proudly. "We refine the ore right on the spot too, you know. It not only supplies such nuclear power as Venus needs, but exported to Earth it buys the things we still have to have from them."

"Why operate it with convict labor?" asked Hollister absently. His imagination was wistfully concentrated on the image of himself branding his initials on Thomas' anatomy. "You could use free men, taking proper precautions, and it would be a lot more efficient and economical of manpower."

"You don't understand." Thomas seemed a bit shocked. "These are enemies of the state."

I've read that line in the history books. Some state, if it makes itself that many enemies!

"The refinery won't interest you so much," said Thomas. "Standard procedure, and it's operated by nonpolitical prisoners under shielding. They get skilled, and become too valuable to lose. But no matter who a man is, how clever he is, if he's been convicted of treason he goes to the mine."

So this was a warning – or was it a provocation?

When they were back in the office, Thomas smiled genially. "I hope you gentlemen have enjoyed the tour," he said. "Do stop in and see me again sometime." He held out his hand. Hollister turned on his heel, ignoring the gesture, and walked out.

Even in the line of duty, a man can only do so much.

Somewhat surprisingly Hollister found himself getting a little more popular with his crew after the visit to Lucifer. The three who were with him must have seen his disgust and told about it. He exerted himself to win more of their friendship, without being too obstrusive about it: addressing them politely, lending a hand himself in the task of setting up camp, listening carefully to complaints about not feeling well instead of dismissing them all as malingering. That led to some trouble. One laborer who was obviously faking a stomach-ache was ordered back to the job and made an insulting crack. Hollister knocked him to the floor with a single blow. Looking around at the others present, he said slowly: "There will be no whippings in this camp, because I do not believe men should be treated thus. But I intend to remain chief and to get this business done."

167

Nudging the fallen man with his foot: "Well, go on back to your work. This is forgotten also in the records I am supposed to keep."

He didn't feel proud of himself – the man had been smaller and weaker than he. But he had to have discipline, and the Venusians all seemed brutalized to a point where the only unanswerable argument was force. It was an inevitable consequence of their type of government, and boded ill for the future.

Somewhat later, his radio-electronics technie, Valdez – a soft-spoken little fellow who did not seem to have any friends in camp – found occasion to speak with him. "It seems that you have unusual ideas about running this operation, señor," he remarked.

"I'm supposed to get the airmakers installed," said Hollister. "That part of it is right on schedule."

"I mean with regard to your treatment of the men, señor. You are the mildest chief they have had. I wish to say that it is appreciated, but some of them are puzzled. If I may give you some advice, which is doubtless not needed, it would be best if they knew exactly what to expect."

Hollister felt bemused. "Fairness, as long as they do their work. What is so strange about that?"

"But some of us ... them ... have unorthodox ideas about politics."

"That is their affair, Senor Valdez." Hollister decided to make himself a little more human in the technie's eyes. "I have a few ideas of my own, too."

"Ah, so. Then you will permit free discussion in the barracks?"

"Of course."

"I have hidden the recorder in there very well. Do you wish to hear the tapes daily, or shall I just make a summary?"

"I don't want to hear any tapes," stated Hollister. "That machine will not be operated."

"But they might plan treason!"

Hollister laughed and swept his hand around the wall. "In the middle of *that*? Much good their plans do them!" Gently: "All of you may say what you will among yourselves. I am an engineer, not a secret policeman."

"I see, señor. You are very generous. Believe me, it is appreciated." Three days later, Valdez was dead.

Hollister had sent him out with a crew to run some performance tests on the first of the new airmakers. The men came back agitatedly, to report that a short, sudden rock storm had killed the technie. Hollister frowned, to cover his pity for the poor lonely little guy. "Where is the body?" he asked.

"Out there, señor – where else?"

Hollister knew it was the usual practice to leave men who died in the field where they fell; after Venusian conditions had done their work, it wasn't worthwhile salvaging the corpse for its chemicals. But – "Have I not announced my policy?" he snapped. "I thought that you people, of all, would be glad of it. Dead men will be kept here, so we can haul them into town and have them properly buried. Does not your religion demand that?"

"But Valdez, señor –"

"Never mind! Back you go, at once, and this time bring him in." Hollister turned his attention to the problem of filling the vacancy. Control wasn't going to like him asking for another so soon; probably he couldn't get one anyway. Well, he could train Fernandez to handle the routine parts, and do the more exacting things himself.

He was sitting in his room that night, feeling acutely the isolation of a commander – too tired to add another page to his letter to Barbara, not tired enough to go to sleep. There was a knock on the door. His start told him how thin his nerves were worn. "Come in!"

Diego Fernandez entered. The chill white fluorolight showed fear in his eyes and along his mouth. "Good evening, Simon," he said tonelessly. They had gotten to the stage of first names, though they still addressed each other with the formal pronoun.

"Good evening, Diego. What is it?"

The other bit his lip and looked at the floor. Hollister did not try to hurry him. Outside, the wind was running and great jags of lightening sizzed across an angry sky, but this room was buried deep and very quiet.

Fernandez's eyes rose at last. "There is something you ought to know, Simon. Perhaps you already know it."

"And perhaps not, Diego. Say what you will. There are no recorders here."

"Well, then, Valdez was not accidentally killed. He was murdered."

Hollister sat utterly still.

"You did not look at the body very closely, did you?" went on Fernandez, word by careful word. "I have seen suits torn open by flying rocks. This was not such a one. Some instrument did it . . . a compressed-air drill, I think."

"And do you know why it was done?"

"Yes." Fernandez's face twisted. "I cannot say it was not a good deed. Valdez was a spy for the government."

Hollister felt a knot in his stomach. "How do you know this?"

"One can be sure of such things. After the . . . Venusians had taken Alcazar, Valdez worked eagerly with their police. He had always believed in confederation and planetary independence. Then he went away, to some engineering assignment it was said. But he had a brother who was proud of the old hidalgo blood, and this brother sought to clear the shame of his family by warning that Valdez had taken a position with the Guardians. He told it secretly, for he was not supposed to, but most of Alcazar got to know it. The men who had fought against the invaders were sent here, to the other side of the world, and it is not often we get leave to go home even for a short while. But we remembered, and we knew Valdez when he appeared on this job. So when those men with him had a chance to revenge themselves, they took it."

Hollister fixed the brown eyes with his own. "Why do you tell me this?" he asked.

"I do not – quite know. Except that you have been a good chief. It would be best for us if we could keep you, and this may mean trouble for you."

I'll say! First I practically told Valdez how I feel about the government, then he must have transmitted it with the last radio report, and now he's dead. Hollister chose his words cautiously: "Have you thought that the best way I can save myself is to denounce those men?"

"They would go to Lucifer, Simon."

"I know." He weighed the factors, surprised at his own detached calm. On the one hand there were Barbara and himself, and his own mission; on the other hand were half a dozen men who would prove most valuable come the day – for it was becoming more and more clear that the sovereign state of Venus would have to be knocked down, the sooner the better.

Beyond a small ache, he did not consider the personal element; UN-man training was too strong in him for that. A melody skipped through his head. *"Here's a how-de do –"* It was more than a few men, he decided; this whole crew, all fifty or so, had possibilities. A calculated risk was in order.

"I did not hear anything you said," he spoke aloud. "Nor did you ever have any suspicions. It is obvious that Valdez died accidentally – too obvious to question."

Fernandez's smile flashed through the sweat that covered his face. "Thank you, Simon!"

"Thanks to *you,* Diego." Hollister gave him a drink – the boss was allowed a few bottles – and sent him on his way.

The boss was also allowed a .45 magnum automatic, the only gun in camp. Hollister took it out and checked it carefully. What was that classic verdict of a coroner's jury, a century or more ago in the States? "An act of God under very suspicious circumstances." He grinned to himself. It was not a pleasant expression.

VI

The rocket landed three days later. Hollister, who had been told by radio to expect it but not told why, was waiting outside. A landing space had been smoothed off and marked, and he had his men standing by and the tanks and bulldozers parked close at hand. Ostensibly that was to give any help which might be needed; actually, he hoped they would mix in on his side if trouble started. Power-driven sand blasts and arc welders were potentially nasty weapons, and tanks and 'dozers could substitute for armored vehicles in a pinch. The gun hung at his waist.

There was a mild breeze, for Venus, but it drove a steady sound of sand across the broken plain. The angry storm-colored light was diffused by airborne dust till it seemed to pervade the land, and even through his helmet and earphones Hollister was aware of the wind-yammer and the remote banging of thunder.

A new racket grew in heaven, stabbing jets and then the downward hurtle of sleek metal. The rocket's glider wings were fully extended, braking her against the updraft, and the pilot shot brief blasts to control his yawing vessel and bring her down on the markings. Wheels struck the hard-packed sand, throwing up a wave of it; landing flaps strained, a short burst from the nose jet arched its back against the flier's momentum, and then the machine lay still.

Hollister walked up to it. Even with the small quick-type air lock, he had to wait a couple of minutes before two suited figures emerged. One was obviously the pilot; the other –

"Barbara!"

Her face had grown thin, he saw through the helmet plate, and the red hair was disordered. He pulled her to him, and felt his faceplate clank on hers. "Barbara! What brings you here? Is everything all right?"

She tried to smile. "Not so public. Let's get inside."

The pilot stayed, to direct the unloading of what little equipment had been packed along; a trip was never wasted. Fernandez could do the honors afterward. Hollister led his wife to his own room, and no words were said for a while.

Her lips and hands felt cold.

"What is it, Barbara?" he asked when he finally came up for air. "How do we rate this?"

She didn't quite meet his eyes. "Simple enough. We're not going to have a baby after all. Since you'll be in the field for a long time, and I'm required to be a mother soon, it ... it wasn't so hard to arrange a leave for me. I'll be here for ten days."

That was almost an Earth month. The luxury was un-heard-of. Hollister sat down on his bunk and began to think.

"What's the matter?" She rumpled his hair. "Aren't you glad to see me? Maybe you have a girl up in Trollen?"

Her tone wasn't quite right, somehow. In many ways she was still a stranger to him, but he knew she wouldn't ban-ter him with just that inflection. Or did she really think –

"I'd no such intention," he said.

172

"Of course not, you jethead! I trust you." Barbara stretched herself luxuriously. "Isn't this wonderful?"

Yeah . . . too wonderful. "Why do we get it?"

"I told you." She looked surprised. "We've got to have a child."

He said grimly, "I can't see that it's so all-fired urgent. If it were, it'd be easier, and right in line with the Board's way of thinking, to use artificial insemination." He stood up and gripped her shoulders and looked straight at her. "Barbara, why are you really here?"

She began to cry, and that wasn't like her either. He patted her and mumbled awkward phrases, feeling himself a louse. But something was very definitely wrong, and he had to find out what.

He almost lost his resolution as the day went on. He had to be outside most of that time, supervising and helping; he noticed that several of the men had again become frigid with him. Was that Karsov's idea – to drive a wedge between him and his crew by giving him an unheard-of privilege? Well, maybe partly, but it could not be the whole answer. When he came back, Barbara had unpacked and somehow, with a few small touches, turned his bleak little bedroom-office into a home. She was altogether gay and charming and full of hope.

The rocket had left, the camp slept, they had killed a bottle to celebrate and now they were alone in darkness. In such a moment of wonder, it was hard to keep a guard up.

"Maybe you appreciate the Board a little more," she sighed. "They aren't machines. They're human, and know that we are too."

" 'Human' is a pretty broad term," he murmured, almost automatically. "The guards at Lucifer are human, I suppose."

Her hand stole out to stroke his cheek. "Things aren't perfect on Venus," she said. "Nobody claims they are. But after the Big Rain –"

"Yeah. The carrot in front and the stick behind, and on the burro trots. He doesn't stop to ask where the road is leading. I could show it by psycho-dynamic equations, but even an elementary reading of history is enough once a group gets power, it *never* gives it up freely."

"There was Kemal Ataturk, back around 1920, wasn't there?"

"Uh-huh. A very exceptional case: the hard-boiled, practical man who was still an idealist, and built his structure so well that his successors – who'd grown up under him – neither could nor wanted to continue dictatorship. It's an example which the UN Inspectorate on Earth has studied closely and tried to adapt, so that its own power won't some day be abused.

"The government of Venus just isn't that sort. Their tactics prove it. Venus has to be collective till the Big Rain, I suppose, but that doesn't give anyone the right to collectivize the minds of men. By the time this hell-hole is fit for human life, the government will be unshakeably in the saddle. Basic principle of psychology: survival with least effort. In human society, one of the easiest ways to survive and grow fat is to rule your fellow men.

"It's significant that you've learned about Ataturk. How much have they told you about the Soviet Union? The state was supposed to wither away there, too."

"Would you actually . . . conspire to revolt?" she asked.

He slammed the brakes so hard that his body jerked. *Danger! Danger! Danger! How did I get into this? What am I saying? Why is she asking me?* With a single bound, he was out of bed and had snapped on the light.

Its glare hurt his eyes, and Barbara covered her face. He drew her hands away, gently but using his strength against her resistance. The face that looked up at him was queerly distorted; the lines were still there, but they had become something not quite human.

"Who put you up to this?" he demanded.

"No one . . . what are you talking about, what's wrong?"

"The perfect spy," he said bitterly. "A man's own wife."

"What do you mean?" She sat up, staring wildly through her tousled hair. "Have you gone crazy?"

"*Could* you be a spy?"

"I'm not," she gasped. "I swear I'm not."

"I don't ask if you were. What I want to know is could you be a spy?"

"I'm not. It's impossible. I'm not –" She was screaming now, but the thick walls would muffle that.

"Karsov is going to send me to Lucifer," he flung at her. "Isn't he?"

"I'm not, I'm not, I'm not –"

He stabbed the questions at her, one after another, slapping when she got hysterical. The first two times she fainted, he brought her around again and continued; the third time, he called it off and stood looking down on her.

There was no fear or rage left in him, not even pity. He felt strangely empty. There seemed to be a hollowness inside his skull, the hollow man went through the motions of life and his brain still clicked rustily, but there was nothing inside, he was a machine.

The perfect spy, he thought. *Except that Karsov didn't realize UN-men have advanced psych training. I know such a state as hers when I see it.*

The work had been cleverly done, using the same drugs and machines and conditioning techniques which had given him his own personality mask. (No – not quite the same. The Venusians didn't know that a mind could be so deeply verbal-conditioned as to get by a narcoquiz; that was a guarded secret of the Inspectorate. But the principles were there.) Barbara did not remember being taken to the laboratories and given the treatment. She did not know she had been conditioned; consciously, she believed everything she had said, and it had been anguish when the man she loved turned on her.

But the command had been planted, to draw his real thoughts out of him. Almost, she had succeeded. And when she went back, a quiz would get her observations out of her in detail.

It would have worked, too, on an ordinary conspiratory. Even if he had come to suspect the truth, an untrained man wouldn't have known just how to throw her conscious and subconscious minds into conflict, wouldn't have recognized her symptomatic reactions for what they were.

This tears it, thought Hollister. *This rips it wide open.* He didn't have the specialized equipment to mask Barbara's mind and send her back with a lie that could get past the Guardian psychotechnies. Already she knew enough to give strong confirmation to Karsov's suspicions. After he had her account, Hollister would be arrested and they'd try to wring his secrets out of him. That might or might not be possible, but there wouldn't be anything left of Hollister.

Not sending her back at all? No, it would be every bit as

much of a giveaway, and sacrifice her own life to boot. Not that she might not go to Lucifer anyhow.

Well –

The first thing was to remove her conditioning. He could do that in a couple of days by simple hypnotherapy. The medicine chest held some drugs which would be useful. After that –

First things first. Diego can take charge for me while I'm doing it. Let the men think what they want. They're going to have plenty to think about soon.

He became aware of his surroundings again and of the slim form beneath his eyes. She had curled up in a fetal position, trying to escape. Emotions came back to him, and the first was an enormous compassion for her. He would have wept, but there wasn't time.

Barbara sat up in bed, leaning against his breast. "Yes," she said tonelessly. "I remember it all now."

"There was a child coming, wasn't there?"

"Of course. They ... removed it." Her hand sought his. "You might have suspected something otherwise. I'm all right, though. We can have another one sometime, if we live that long."

"And did Karsov tell you what he thought about me?"

"He mentioned suspecting you were an UN-man, but not being sure. The Technic Board wouldn't let him have you unless he had good evidence. That – No, I don't remember any more. It's fuzzy in my mind, everything which happened in that room."

Hollister wondered how he had betrayed himself. Probably he hadn't; his grumblings had fitted in with his assumed personality, and there had been no overt acts. But still, it was Karsov's job to suspect everybody, and the death of Valdez must have decided him on drastic action.

"Do you feel all right, sweetheart?" asked Hollister.

She nodded, and turned around to give him a tiny smile. "Yes. Fine. A little weak, maybe, but otherwise fine. Only I'm scared."

"You have a right to be," he said bleakly. "We're in a devil of a fix."

"You *are* an UN-man, aren't you?"

"Yes. I was sent to study the Venusian situation. My

176

chiefs were worried about it. Seems they were justified, too. I've never seen a nastier mess."

"I suppose you're right," she sighed. "Only what else could we do? Do you want to bring Venus back under Earth?"

"That's a lot of comet gas, and you'd know it if the nationalist gang hadn't been censoring the books and spewing their lies out since before you were born. This whole independence movement was obviously their work from the beginning, and I must say they've done a competent job; good psychotechnies among them. It's their way to power. Not that all of them are so cynical about it – a lot must have rationalizations of one sort or another – but that's what it amounts to.

"There's no such thing as Venus being 'under' Earth. If ready for independence – and I agree she is – she'd be made a state in her own right with full UN membership. It's written into the charter that she could make her own internal policy. The only restrictions on a nation concern a few matters of trade, giving up military forces and the right to make war, guaranteeing certain basic liberties, submitting to inspection, and paying her share of UN expenses – which are smaller than the cost of even the smallest army. That's all. Your nationalists have distorted the truth as their breed always does."

She rubbed her forehead in a puzzled way. He could sympathize: a lifetime of propaganda wasn't thrown off overnight. But as long as she was with his cause, the rest would come of itself.

"There's no excuse whatsoever for this tyranny you live under," he continued. "It's got to go."

"What would you have us do?" she asked. "This isn't Earth. We do things efficiently here, or we die."

"True. But even men under the worst conditions can afford the slight inefficiency of freedom. It's not my business to write a constitution for Venus, but you might look at how Mars operates. They also have to have requirements of professional competence for public schools – deadwood gets flunked out fast enough – and the graduates have to stand for election if they want policy-making posts. Periodic elections do not necessarily pick better men than an appointive system, but they keep power from concentrating

177

in the leaders. The Martians also have to ration a lot of things, and forbid certain actions that would endanger a whole city, but they're free to choose their own residences, and families, and ways of thinking, and jobs. They're also trying to reclaim the whole planet, but they don't assign men to that work, they hire them for it."

"Why doesn't everyone just stay at home and do nothing?" she asked innocently.

"No work, no pay; no pay, nothing to eat. It's as simple as that. And when jobs are open in the field, and all the jobs in town are filled, men will take work in the field – as free men, free to quit if they wish. Not many do, because the bosses aren't little commissars.

"Don't you see, it's the *mass* that society has to regulate; a government has to set things up so that the statistics come out right. There's no reason to regulate individuals."

"What's the difference?" she inquired.

"A hell of a difference. Some day you'll see it. Meanwhile, though, something has to be done about the government of Venus – not only on principle, but because it's going to be a menace to Earth before long. Once Venus is strong, a peaceful, nearly unarmed Earth is going to be just too tempting for your dictators. The World Wars had this much value, they hammered it into our heads and left permanent memorials of destruction to keep reminding us that the time to cut out a cancer is when it first appears. Wars start for a variety of reasons, but unlimited national sovereignty is always the necessary and sufficient condition. I wish our agents had been on the ball with respect to Venus ten years ago; a lot of good men are going to die because they weren't."

"You might not have come here then," she said shyly.

"Thanks, darling." He kissed her. His mind whirred on, scuttling through a maze that seemed to lead only to his silent, pointless death.

"If I could just get a report back to Earth! That would settle the matter. We'd have spaceships landing UN troops within two years. An expensive operation, of doubtful legality perhaps, a tough campaign so far from home, especially since we wouldn't want to destroy any cities – but there'd be no doubt of the outcome, and it would surely be carried through; because it would be a matter of survival

178

for us. Of course, the rebellious cities would be helpful, a deal could be made there – and so simple a thing as seizing the food-producing towns would soon force a surrender. You see, it's not only the warning I've got to get home, it's the utterly priceless military intelligence I've got in my head. If I fail, the Guardians will be on the alert, they may very well succeed in spotting and duping every agent sent after me and flanging up something for Earth's consumption. Venus is a long way off –"

He felt her body tighten in his arms. "So you do want to take over Venus."

"Forget that hogwash, will you? What'd we want with this forsaken desert? Nothing but a trustworthy government for it. Anyway –" His exasperation became a flat hardness: "If you and I are to stay alive much longer, it has to be done."

She said nothing to that.

His mind clicked off astronomical data and the side rule whizzed through his fingers. "The freighters come regularly on Hohmann 'A' orbits," he said. "That means the next one is due in eight Venus days. They've only got four-man crews, they come loaded with stuff and go back with uranium and thorium ingots which don't take up much room. In short, they could carry quite a few passengers in an emergency, if those had extra food supplies."

"And the ferries land at New America," she pointed out.

"Exactly. My dear, I think our only chance is to take over the whole city!"

It was hot in the barracks room, and rank with sweat. Hollister thought he could almost smell the fear, as if he were a dog. He stood on a table at one end, Barbara next to him, and looked over his assembled crew. Small, thin, swarthy, unarmed and drably clad, eyes wide with frightened waiting, they didn't look like much of an army. But they were all he had.

"Señores," he began at last, speaking very quietly, "I have called you all together to warn you of peril to your lives. I think, if you stand with me, we can escape, but it will take courage and energy. You have shown me you possess these qualities, and I hope you will use them now."

He paused, then went on: "I know many of you have

been angry with me because I have had my wife here. You thought me another of these bootlickers to a rotten government" – that brought them to full awareness! – "who was being rewarded for some Judas act. It was not true. We all owe our lives to this gallant woman. It was I who was suspected of being hostile to the rulers, and she was sent to spy on me for them. Instead, she told me the truth, and now I am telling it to you.

"You must know that I am an agent from Earth. No, no, I am not an Imperialist. As a matter of fact, the Central American countries were worried about their joint colony, Ciudad Alcazar, your city. It was suspected she had not freely joined this confederation. There are other countries, too, which are worried. I came to investigate for them; what I have seen convinces me they were right."

He went on, quickly, and not very truthfully. He had to deal with their anti-UN conditioning, appeal to the nationalism he despised. (At that, it wouldn't make any practical difference if some countries on Earth retained nominal ownership of certain tracts on Venus; a democratic confederation would re-absorb those within a generation, quite peacefully.) He had to convince them that the whole gang was scheduled to go to Lucifer; all were suspected, and the death of Valdez confirmed the suspicion, and there was always a labor shortage in the mines. His psych training stood him in good stead, before long he had them rising and shouting, *I shoulda been a politician,* he thought sardonically.

"... And are we going to take this outrage? Are we going to rot alive in that hell, and let our wives and children suffer, forever? Or shall we strike back, to save our own lives and liberate Venus?"

When the uproar had subsided a little, he sketched his plan: a march on Lucifer itself, to seize weapons and gain some recruits, then an attack on New America. If it was timed right, they could grab the city just before the ferries landed, and hold it while all of them were embarked on the freighter – then off to Earth, and in a year or two a triumphant return with the army of liberation!

"If anyone does not wish to come with us, let him stay here. I shall compel no man. I can only use those who will be brave, and will obey orders like soldiers, and will set

180

lives which are already forfeit at hazard for the freedom of their homes. Are you with me? Let those who will follow me stand up and shout 'Yes'!"

Not a man stayed in his seat; the timid ones, if any, dared not do so while their comrades were rising and whooping about the table. The din roared and rolled, bunkframes rattled, eyes gleamed murder from a whirlpool of faces. The first stage of Hollister's gamble had paid off well indeed, he thought; now for the rough part.

He appointed Fernandez his second in command and organized the men into a rough corps; engineering discipline was valuable here. It was late before he and Barbara and Fernandez could get away to discuss concrete plans.

"We will leave two men here," said Hollister. "They will send the usual radio reports, which I shall write in advance for them, so no one will suspect; they will also take care of the rocket when it comes for Barbara, and I *hope* the police will assume it crashed. We will send for them when we hold New America. I think we can take Lucifer by surprise, but we can't count on the second place not being warned by the time we get there."

Fernandez looked steadily at him. "And will all of us leave with the spaceship?" he asked.

"Of course. It would be death to stay. And Earth will need their knowledge of Venus."

"Simon, you know the ship cannot carry fifty men – or a hundred, if we pick up some others at Lucifer."

Hollister's face was wintry. "I do not think fifty will survive," he said.

Fernandez crossed himself, then nodded gravely. "I see. Well, about the supply problem –"

When he had gone, Barbara faced her husband and he saw a vague fright in her eyes. "You weren't very truthful out there, were you?" she asked. "I don't know much Spanish, but I got the drift, and –"

"All right!" he snapped wearily. "There wasn't time to use sweet reasonableness. I had to whip them up fast."

"They aren't scheduled for Lucifer at all. They have no personal reason to fight."

"They're committed now," he said in a harsh tone. "It's fifty or a hundred lives today against maybe a hundred million in the future. That's an attitude which was drilled into me at the Academy, and I'll never get rid of it. If you want to live with me, you'll have to accept that."

"I'll . . . try," she said.

VII

The towers bulked black through a whirl of dust, under a sky the color of clotted blood. Hollister steered his tank close, speaking into its radio: "Hello, Lucifer. Hello, Lucifer. Come in."

"Lucifer," said a voice in his earphones. "Who are you and what do you want?"

"Emergency. We need help. Get me your captain."

Hollister ground between two high gun towers. They had been built and manned against the remote possibility that a convict outbreak might succeed in grabbing some tanks; he was hoping their personnel had grown lazy with uneventful years. Edging around the main shell of the prison, he lumbered toward the landing field and the nearby radio mast. One by one, the twenty tanks of his command rolled into the compound and scattered themselves about it.

Barbara sat next to him, muffled in airsuit and closed helmet. Her gauntleted hand squeezed his shoulder, he could just barely feel the pressure. Glancing around to her stiffened face, he essayed a smile.

"Hello, there! Captain Thomas speaking. What are you doing?"

"This is Hollister, from the Last Chance air camp. Remember me? We're in trouble and need help. Landslip damn near wiped our place out." The Earthman drove his machine onto the field.

"Well, what are you horsing around like that for? Assemble your tanks in front of the main lock."

"All right, all right, gimme a chance to give some orders. The boys don't seem to know where to roost."

Now! Hollister slapped down the drive switch and his tank surged forward. "Hang on!" he yelled. "Thomas, this thing has gone out of control – Help!"

It might have gained him the extra minute he needed. He wasn't sure what was happening behind him. The tank smashed into the radio mast and he was hurled forward against his safety webbing. His hands flew – extend the grapple, snatch that buckling strut, drag it aside, and *push*!

The frame wobbled crazily. The tank stalled. Hollister yanked off his harness, picked up the cutting torch whose fuel containers were already on his back, and went through the air lock without stopping to conserve atmosphere. Blue flame stabbed before him, he slid down the darkened extra faceplate and concentrated on his job. Get this beast down before it sent a call for help!

Barbara got the bull-like machine going again and urged it ahead, straining at the weakened skeleton. The mast had been built for flexibility in the high winds, not for impact strength. Hollister's torch roared, slicing a main support. A piece of steel clanged within a meter of him.

He dropped the torch and dove under the tank, just as the whole structure caved in.

"Barbara!" He picked himself out of the wreckage, looking wildly into the hurricane that blew around him. "Barbara, are you all right?"

She crawled from the battered tank and into his arms. "Our car won't go any more," she said shakily. The engine hood was split open by a falling beam and oil hissed from the cracked block.

"No matter. Let's see how the boys are doing –"

He led a run across the field, staggering in the wind. A chunk of concrete whizzed by his head and he dropped as one of the guard towers went by. Good boys! They'd gone out and dynamited it!

Ignoring the ramp leading down to the garage, Fernandez had brought his tank up to the shell's main air lock for humans. It was sturdily built, but his snorting monster walked through it. Breathable air gasped out. It sleeted a little as formaldehyde took up water vapor and became solid.

No time to check on the rest of the battle outside, you could only hope the men assigned to that task were doing their job properly. Hollister saw one of his tanks go up under a direct hit. All the towers weren't disabled yet. But he had to get into the shell.

"Stay here, Barbara!" he ordered. Men were swarming from their vehicles. He led the way inside. A group of uniformed corpses waited for him, dying and shriveling even as he watched. He snatched the carbines from them and

183

handed them out to the nearest of his followers. The rest would have to make do with their tools till more weapons could be recovered.

Automatic bulkheads had sealed off the rest of the shell. Hollister blasted through the first one. A hail of bullets from the smoking hull told him that the guards within had had time to put on their suits.

He waved an arm. "Bring up Marie Larga!"

It took a while, and he fumed and fretted. Six partisans trundled the weapon forth. It was a standard man-drawn cart for semiportable field equipment, and Long Mary squatted on it: a motor-driven blower connected with six meters of hose, an air blast. This one had had an oxygen bottle and a good-sized fuel tank hastily attached to make a super flame thrower. Fernandez got behind the steel plate which had been welded in front as armor, and guided it into the hole. The man behind whooped savagely and turned a handle. Fire blew forth, and the compartment was flushed out.

There were other quarters around the cell block, which came next, but Hollister ignored them for the time being. The air lock in this bulkhead had to be opened the regular way, only two men could go through at a time, and there might be guards on the other side. He squeezed in with San Rafael and waited until the pump cleaned out the chamber. Then he opened the inner door a crack, tossed a homemade shrapnel grenade, and came through firing.

He stumbled over two dead men beyond. San Rafael choked and fell as a gun spat farther down the corridor. Hollister's .45 bucked in his hand. Picking himself up, he looked warily down the cruelly bright length of the block. No one else. The convicts were yammering like wild animals.

He went back, telling off a few men to cut the prisoners out of their cells, issue airsuits from the lockers, and explain the situation. Then he returned to the job of cleaning out the rest of the place.

It was a dirty and bloody business. He lost ten men in all. There were no wounded: if a missile tore open a suit, that was the end of the one inside. A small hole would have given time to slap on an emergency patch, but the guards were using magnum slugs.

Fernandez sought him out to report that an attempt to get away by rocket had been stopped, but that an indeterminate number of holdouts were in the refinery, which was a separate building. Hollister walked across the field, dust whirling about smashed machines, and stood before the smaller shell.

Thomas' voice crackled in his earphones: "You there! What is the meaning of this?"

That was too much. Hollister began to laugh. He laughed so long he thought perhaps he was going crazy.

Sobering, he replied in a chill tone: "We're taking over. You're trapped in there with nothing but small arms. We can blast you out if we must, but you'd do better to surrender."

Thomas, threateningly: "This place is full of radioactivity, you know. If you break in, you'll smash down the shielding – or we'll do it for you – and scatter the stuff everywhere. You won't live a week."

It might be a bluff – "All right," said Hollister with a cheerful note, "you're sealed in without food or water. We can wait. But I thought you'd rather save your own lives."

"You're insane! You'll be wiped out –"

"That's our affair. Any time you want out, pick up the phone and call the office. You'll be locked in the cells with supplies enough for a while when we leave." Hollister turned and walked away.

He spent the next few hours reorganizing; he had to whip the convicts into line, though when their first exuberance had faded they were for the most part ready to join him. Suddenly his army had swelled to more than two hundred. The barracks were patched up and made habitable, munitions were found and passed about, the transport and supplies inventoried. Then word came that Thomas' handful were ready to surrender. Hollister marched them into the cell block and assigned some convicts to stand watch.

He had had every intention of abiding by his agreement, but when he was later wakened from sleep with the news that his guards had literally torn the prisoners apart, he didn't have the heart to give them more than a dressing down.

"Now," he said to his council of war, "we'd better get rolling again. Apparently we were lucky enough so that no word of this has leaked out, but it's a long way yet to New America."

"We have not transportation for more than a hundred," said Fernandez.

"I know. We'll take the best of the convicts; the rest will just have to stay behind. They *may* be able to pull the same trick on the next supply train that our boys in Last Chance have ready for the rocket – or they may not. In any event, I don't really hope they can last out, or that we'll be able to take the next objective unawares – but don't tell anyone that."

"I suppose not," said Fernandez somberly, "but it is a dirty business."

"War is always a dirty business," said Hollister.

He lost a whole day organizing his new force. Few if any of the men knew how to shoot, but the guns were mostly recoilless and automatic so he hoped some damage could be done; doctrine was to revert to construction equipment, which they did know how to use, in any emergency. His forty Latins were a cadre of sorts, distributed among the sixty convicts in a relationship equivalent to that between sergeant and private. The whole unit was enough to make any military man break out in a cold sweat, but it was all he had.

Supply wagons were reloaded and machine guns mounted on a few of the tanks. He had four Venusian days to get to New America and take over – and if the rebels arrived too soon, police reinforcements would pry them out again, and if the radio-control systems were ruined in the fighting, the ferries couldn't land.

It was not exactly a pleasant situation.

The first rocket was sighted on the fifth day of the campaign. It ripped over, crossing from horizon to horizon in a couple of minutes, but there was little doubt that it had spotted them. Hollister led his caravan off the plain, into broken country which offered more cover but would slow them considerably. Well, they'd just have to keep going day and night.

The next day it was an armored, atomic-powered monster which lumbered overhead, supplied with enough energy to go slowly and even to hover for a while. In an atmosphere

186

without oxygen and always riven by storms, the aircraft of Earth weren't possible – no helicopters, no leisurely air-boats; but a few things like this one had been built as emergency substitutes. Hollister tuned in his radio, sure it was calling to them.

"Identify yourselves! This is the Guardian Corps."

Hollister adapted his earlier lie, not expecting belief – but every minute he stalled, his tank lurched forward another hundred meters or so.

The voice was sarcastic: "And of course, you had nothing to do with the attack on Lucifer?"

"What attack?"

"That will do! Go out on the plain and set up camp till we can check on you."

"Of course," said Hollister meekly. "Signing off."

From now on, it was strict silence in his army. He'd gained a good hour, though, since the watchers wouldn't be sure till then that he was disobeying – and a lovely dust storm was blowing up.

Following plan, the tanks scattered in pairs, each couple for itself till they converged on New America at the agreed time. Some would break down, some would be destroyed en route, some would come late – a few might even arrive disastrously early – but there was no choice. Hollister was reasonably sure none would desert him; they were all committed past that point.

Ho looked at Barbara. Her face was tired and drawn, the red hair hung lusterless and tangled to her shoulders, dust and sweat streaked her face, but he thought she was very beautiful. "I'm sorry to have dragged you into this," he said.

"It's all right, dear. Of course I'm scared, but I'm still glad."

He kissed her for a long while and then slapped his helmet down with a savage gesture.

The first bombs fell toward sunset. Hollister saw them as flashes through the dust, and felt their concussion rumble in the frame of his tank. He steered into a narrow, overhung gulch, his companion vehicle nosing close behind. There were two convicts in it – Johnson and Waskowicz – pretty good men, he thought, considering all they had been through.

187

Dust and sand were his friends, hiding him even from the infrared 'scopes above which made nothing of mere darkness. The rough country would help a lot, too. It was simply a matter of driving day and night, sticking close to bluffs and gullies, hiding under attack and then driving some more. He was going to lose a number of his units, but thought the harassing would remain aerial till they got close to New America. The Guardians wouldn't risk their heavy stuff unnecessarily at any great distance from home.

VIII

The tank growled around a high pinnacle and faced him without warning. It was a military vehicle, and cannons swiveled to cover his approach.

Hollister gunned his machine and drove directly up the pitted road at the enemy. A shell burst alongside him, steel splinters rang on armor. Coldly, he noted for possible future reference the relatively primitive type of Venusian war equipment: no tracker shells, no Rovers. He had already planned out what to do in an encounter like this, and told his men the idea – now it had happened to him.

The Guardian tank backed, snarling. It was not as fast or as manoeuverable as his, it was meant for work close to cities where ground had been cleared. A blast of high-caliber machine-gun bullets ripped through the cab, just over his head. Then he struck. The shock jammed him forward even as his grapple closed jaws on the enemy's nearest tread.

"Out!" he yelled. Barbara snatched open the air lock and fell to the stones below. Hollister was after her. He flung a glance behind. His other tank was an exploded ruin, canted to one side, but a single figure was crawling from it, rising, zig-zagging toward him. There was a sheaf of dynamite sticks in one hand. The man flopped as the machine gun sought him and wormed the last few meters. Waskowicz. "They got Sam," he reported, huddling against the steel giant with his companions. "Shall we blast her?"

Hollister reflected briefly. The adversary was immobilized by the transport vehicle that clutched it bulldog fashion. He himself was perfectly safe this instant, just beneath the guns. "I've got a better notion. Gimme a boost."

188

He crawled up on top, to the turret lock. "O.K., hand me that torch. I'm going to cut my way in!"

The flame roared, biting into metal. Hollister saw the lock's outer door move. So – just as he had expected – the lads inside wanted out! He paused. A suited arm emerged with a grenade. Hollister's torch slashed down. Barbara made a grab for the tumbling missile and failed. Waskowicz tackled her, landing on top. The thing went off.

Was she still alive –? Hollister crouched so that the antenna of his suit radio poked into the lock. "Come out if you want to live. Otherwise I'll burn you out."

Sullenly, the remaining three men appeared, hands in the air. Hollister watched them slide to the ground, covering them with his pistol. His heart leaped within him when he saw Barbara standing erect. Waskowicz was putting an adhesive patch on his suit where a splinter had ripped it.

"You O.K.?" asked Hollister.

"Yeah," grunted the convict. "Pure dumb luck. Now what?"

"Now we got us one of their own tanks. Somebody get inside and find some wire or something to tie up the Terrible Three here. And toss out the fourth."

"That's murder!" cried one of the police. "We've only got enough oxy for four hours in these suits –"

"Then you'll have to hope the battle is over by then," said Hollister unsympathetically. He went over and disentangled the two machines.

The controls of the captured tank were enough like those of the ordinary sort for Barbara to handle. Hollister gave Waskowicz a short lecture on the care and feeding of machine guns, and sat up by the 40mm. cannon himself; perforce, they ignored the 20. They closed the lock but didn't bother to replenish the air inside; however, as Hollister drove up the mountainside, Waskowicz recharged their oxygen bottles from the stores inside the vehicle.

The battle was already popping when they nosed up onto the ledge and saw the great sweep of the city. Drifting dust limited his vision, but Hollister saw his own machines and the enemy's. Doctrine was to ram and grapple the military tank, get out and use dynamite or torches, and then worm toward the colony's main air lock. It might have to

189

be blown open, but bulkheads should protect the civilians within.

An engineer tank made a pass at Hollister's. He turned aside, realizing that his new scheme had its own drawbacks. Another police machine came out of the dust; its guns spoke, the engineers went up in a flash and a bang, and then it had been hit from behind. Hollister wet his teeth and went on. It was the first time he had seen anything like war; he had an almost holy sense of his mission to prevent this from striking Earth again.

The whole operation depended on his guess that there wouldn't be many of the enemy. There were only a few Guardians in each town, who wouldn't have had time or reserves enough to bring in a lot of reinforcements; and tanks couldn't be flown in. But against their perhaps lesser number was the fact that they would fight with tenacity and skill. Disciplined as engineer and convicts were, they simply did not have the training – even the psychological part of it which turns frightened individuals into a single selfless unit. They would tend to make wild attacks and to panic when the going got rough – which it was already.

He went on past the combat, towards the main air lock. Dim shapes began to appear through scudding dust. Half a dozen mobile cannon were drawn up in a semicircle to defend the gate. That meant – all the enemy tanks, not more than another six or seven, out on the ledge fighting the attackers.

"All right," Hollister's voice vibrated in their earphones. "We'll shoot from here. Barbara, move her in a zigzag at 10 KPH, keeping about this distance; let out a yell if you think you have to take other evasive action. Otherwise I might hit the city."

He jammed his faceplate into the rubberite viewscope and his hands and feet sought the gun controls. Crosshairs – range – *fire one!* The nearest cannon blew up.

Fire two! Fire three! His 40 reloaded itself. Second gun broken, third a clean miss – *Fire four! Gotcha!*

A rank of infantry appeared, their suits marked with the Guardian symbol. They must have been flown here. Waskowicz blazed at them and they broke, falling like rag dolls, reforming to crawl in. They were good soldiers. Now the other three enemy mobiles were swiveling about, shooting through the dust. "Get us out of here, Barbara!"

The racket became deafening as they backed into the concealing murk. Another enemy tank loomed before them. Hollister fed it two shells almost point blank.

If he could divert the enemy artillery long enough for his men to storm the gate –

He saw a police tank locked with an attacker, broken and dead. Hollister doubted if there were any left in action now. He saw none of his own vehicles moving, though he passed by the remnants of several. And where were his men?

Shock threw him against his webbing. The echoes rolled and banged and shivered for a long time. His head swam. The motors still turned, but –

"I think they crippled us," said Barbara in a small voice.

"O.K. Let's get out of here." Hollister sighed; it had been a nice try, and had really paid off better than he'd had a right to expect. He scrambled to the lock, gave Barbara a hand, and they slid to the ground as the three fieldpieces rolled into view on their self-powered carts.

The stalled tank's cannon spoke, and one of the police guns suddenly slumped. "Waskowicz!" Barbara's voice was shrill in the earphones. "He stayed in there –"

"We can't save him. And if he can fight our tank long enough – Build a monument to him some day. Now come on!" Hollister led the way into curtaining gloom. The wind hooted and clawed at him.

As he neared the main lock, a spatter of rifle fire sent him to his belly. He couldn't make out who was there, but it had been a ragged volley – take a chance on their being police and nailing him – "Just as chickens, boss!" he shouted. Somewhere in a corner of his mind he realized that there was no reason for shouting over a radio system. His schooled self-control must be slipping a bit.

"Is that you, Simon?" Fernandez's voice chattered in his ears. "Come quickly now, we're at the lock but I think they will attack soon."

Hollister wiped the dust from his faceplate and tried to count how many there were. Latins and convicts, perhaps twenty – "are there more?" he inquired. "Are you the last?"

"I do not know, Simon," said Fernandez. "I had gathered

191

this many, we were barricaded behind two smashed cars, and when I saw their artillery pull away I led a rush here. Maybe there are some partisans left besides us, but I doubt it."

Hollister tackled the emergency control box which opened the gate from outside. It would be nice if he didn't have to blast – Yes, by Heaven! It hadn't been locked! He jammed the whole score into the chamber, closed the outer door and started the pumps.

"They can get in, too," said Fernandez dubiously.

"I know. Either here or by ten other entrances. But I have an idea. All of you stick by me."

The anteroom was empty. The town's civilians must be huddled in the inner compartments, and all the cops must be outside fighting. Hollister threw back his helmet, filling his lungs with air that seemed marvelously sweet, and led a quick cautious trot down the long halls.

"The spaceship is supposed to have arrived by now," he said. "What we must do is take and hold the radio shack. Since the police don't know exactly what our plans are, they will hesitate to destroy it just to get at us. It will seem easier merely to starve us out."

"Or use sleepy gas," said Fernandez. "Our suits' oxygen supply isn't good for more than another couple of hours."

"Yes ... I suppose that is what they'll do. That ship had better be up there!"

The chances were that she was. Hollister knew that several days of ferrying were involved, and had timed his attack for hours after she was scheduled to arrive. For all he knew, the ferries had already come down once or twice.

He didn't know if he or anyone in his band would live to be taken out. He rather doubted it; the battle had gone worse than expected, he had not captured the city as he hoped – but the main thing was to get some kind of report back to Earth.

A startled pair of techvies met the invaders as they entered. One of them began an indignant protest, but Fernandez waved a rifle to shut him up. Hollister glanced about the gleaming controls and meters. He could call the ship himself, but he didn't have the training to guide a boat down. Well –

He pulled off his gloves and sat himself at the panel. Keys

clattered beneath his fingers. When were the cops coming? Any minute.

"Hello, freighter. Hello, up there. Spaceship, this is New America calling. Come in."

Static buzzed and crackled in his earphones.

"Come in, spaceship. This is New America. Come in, damn it!"

Lights flashed on the board, the computer clicked, guiding the beam upward. It tore past the ionosphere and straggled weakly into the nearest of the tiny, equally spaced robot relay stations which circled the planet. Obedient to the keying signal, the robot amplified the beam and shot it to the next station, which kicked it farther along. The relayer closest to the spaceship's present position in her orbit focused the beam on her.

Or was the orbit empty?

". . . Hello, New America." The voice wavered, faint and distorted. "*Evening Star* calling New America. What's going on down there? We asked for a ferry signal three hours ago."

"Emergency," snapped Hollister. "Get me the captain — fast! Meanwhile, record this."

"But —"

"Fast, I said! And record. This is crash priority, condition red." Hollister felt sweat trickling inside his suit.

"Recording. Sending for the captain now."

"Good!" Hollister leaned over the mike. "For Main Office, Earth, United Nations Inspectorate. Repeat: Main Office, UN Inspectorate. Urgent, confidential. This is Agent A-431-240. Repeat, Agent A-431-240. Code Watchbird. Code Watchbird. Reporting on Venusian situation as follows —" He began a swift sketch of conditions.

"I think I hear voices down the hall," whispered Barbara to Fernandez.

The Latin nodded. He had already dragged a couple of desks into the corridor to make a sort of barricade; now he motioned his men to take positions; a few outside, the rest standing by, crowded together in the room. Hollister saw what was going on and swung his gun to cover the two technies. They were scared, and looked pathetically young, but he had no time for mercy.

A voice in his earphones, bursting through static: "This is Captain Brackney. What d'you want?"

"UNI business, captain. I'm beseiged in the GCA shack here with a few men. We're to be gotten out at all costs if it's humanly possible."

He could almost hear the man's mouth fall open. "God in space – is that the truth?"

Hollister praised the foresight of his office. "You have a sealed tape aboard among your official records. All spaceships, all first-class public conveyances, do. It's changed by an UN-man every year or so. O.K., that's an ID code, secret recognition signal. It proves my right to commandeer everything you've got."

"I know that much. What's on the tape?"

"This year it will be, 'Twas brillig and the slithy toves give me liberty or give me pigeons on the grass alas'. Have your radioman check that at once."

Pause, then: "O.K. I'll take your word for it till he does. What do you want?"

"Bring two ferries down, one about fifty kilometres behind the other. No arms on board, I suppose? . . . No. Well, have just the pilots aboard, because you may have to take twenty or so back. How long will this take you? . . . Two hours? That long? . . . Yes, I realize you have to let your ship get into the right orbital position and – All right, if you can't do it in less time. Be prepared to embark anyone waiting out there and lift immediately. Meanwhile stand by for further instructions . . . Hell, yes, you can do it!"

Guns cracked outside.

"O.K. I'll start recording again in a minute. Get moving, captain!" Hollister turned back to the others.

"I have to tell Earth what I know, in case I don't make it," he said. "Also, somebody has to see that these technies get the boats down right. Diego, I'll want a few men to defend this place. The rest of you retreat down the hall and pick up some extra oxy bottles for yourselves and all the concentrated food you can carry; because that ship won't have rations enough for all of us. Barbara will show you where it is."

"And how will you get out?" she cried when he had put it into English.

"I'll come to that. You've got to go with them, dear, be-

194

cause you live here and know where they can get the supplies. Leave a couple of suits here for the technies, pick up others somewhere along the way. When you get outside, hide close to the dome. When the ferry lands, some of you make a rush to the shack here. It's right against the outer wall. I see you're still carrying some dynamite, Garcia. Blow a hole to let us through ... Yes, it's risky, but what have we got to lose?"

She bent to kiss him. There wasn't time to do it properly. A tommy-gun was chattering in the corridor.

Hollister stood up and directed his two prisoners to don the extra suits. "I've no grudge against you boys," he said, "and in fact, if you're scared of what the cops might do to you, you can come along to Earth – but if those boats don't land safely, I'll shoot you both down."

Fernandez, Barbara, and a dozen others slipped out past the covering fire at the barricade and disappeared. Hollister hoped they'd make it. They'd better! Otherwise, even if a few escaped, they might well starve to death on the trip home.

The food concentrate would be enough. It was manufactured by the ton at Little Moscow – tasteless, but pure nourishment and bulk, normally added to the rest of the diet on Venus. It wouldn't be very palatable, but it would keep men alive for a long time.

The technies were at the board, working hard. The six remaining rebels slipped back into the room; two others lay dead behind the chewed-up barricade. Hollister picked up an auxiliary communication mike and started rattling off everything about Venus he could think of.

A Guardian stuck his head around the door. Three guns barked, and the head was withdrawn. A little later, a white cloth on a rifle barrel was wavered past the edge.

Hollister laid down his mike. "I'll talk," he said. "I'll come out, with my arms. You'll have just one man in sight, unarmed." To his men he gave an order to drag the dead into the shack while the truce lasted.

Karsov met him in the hall. He stood warily, but there was no fear on the smooth face. "What are you trying to do?" he asked in a calm voice.

"To stay out of your mines," said Hollister. It would

help if he could keep up the impression that was an ordinary revolt.

"You have called that ship up there, I suppose?"

"Yes. They're sending down a ferry."

"The ferry could have an accident. We would apologize profusely, explain that a shell went wild while we were fighting you gangsters, and even pay for the boat. I tell you this so that you can see there is no hope. You had better give up."

"No hope if we do that either," said Hollister. "I'd rather take my chances back on Earth; they can't do worse there than treat my mind."

"Are you still keeping up that farce?" inquired Karsov. But he wasn't sure of himself, that was plain. He couldn't understand how an UN-man could have gotten past his quiz. Hollister had no intention of enlightening him.

"What have you got to lose by letting us go?" asked the Earthman. "So we tell a horror story back home. People there already know you rule with a rough hand."

"I am not going to release you," said Karsov. "You are finished. That second party of yours will not last long, even if they make it outside as I suppose they intend – they will suffocate. I am going to call the spaceship captain on the emergency circuit and explain there is a fight going on and he had better recall his boat. That should settle the matter; if not, the boat will be shot down. As for your group, there will be sleep gas before long."

"I'll blow my brains out before I let you take me," said Hollister sullenly.

"That might save a lot of trouble," said Karsov. He turned and walked away. Hollister was tempted to kill him, but decided to save that pleasure for a while. No use goading the police into a possible use of high explosives.

He went back to the shack and called the *Evening Star* again. "Hello, Captain Brackney? UNI speaking. The bosses down here are going to radio you with a pack of lies. Pretend to believe them and say you'll recall your ferry. Remember, they think just one is coming down. Then –" He continued his orders.

"That's murder!" said the captain. "Pilot One won't have a chance –"

"Yes, he will. Call him now, use spacer code; I don't think
196

any of these birds know it, if they should overhear you. Tell him to have his spacesuit on and be ready for a crash landing, followed by a dash to the second boat."

"It's still a long chance."

"What do you think I'm taking? These are UNI orders, captain. I'm boss till we get back to Earth, if I live so long. All right, got everything? Then I'll continue recording."

After a while he caught the first whiff and said into the mike: "The gas is coming now, I'll have to close my helmet. Hollister signing off."

His men and the technies slapped down their cover. It would be peaceful here for a little time, with this sector sealed off while gas poured through its ventilators. Hollister tried to grin reassuringly, but it didn't come off.

"Last round," he said. "Half of us, the smallest ones, are going to go to sleep now. The rest will use their oxygen, and carry them outside when we go."

Someone protested. Hollister roared him down. "Not another word! This is the only chance for all of us. No man has oxygen for much more than an hour; we have at least an hour and a half to wait. How else can we do it?"

They submitted unwillingly, and struggled against the anaesthetic as long as they could. Hollister took one of the dead men's bottles to replace the first of his that gave out. His band was now composed of three sleeping men and three conscious but exhausted.

He was hoping the cops wouldn't assault them quickly. Probably not; they would be rallying outside, preparing to meet the ferry with a mobile cannon if it should decide to land after all. The rebels trapped in here would keep.

The minutes dragged by. A man at the point of death was supposed to review his whole life, but Hollister didn't feel up to it. He was too tired. He sat watching the telescreen which showed the space field. Dust and wind and the skeleton cradles, emptiness, and a roiling gloom beyond.

One of the wakeful men, a convict, spoke into the helmet circuit: "So you are UNI. Has all this been just to get you back to Earth."

"To get my report back," said Hollister.

"There are many dead," said one of the Latins, in Eng-

197

lish. "You have sacrificed us, played us like pawns, no? What of those two we left back at Last Chance?"

"I'm afraid they're doomed," said Hollister tonelessly, and the guilt which is always inherent in leadership was heavy on him.

"It was worth it," said the convict. "If you can smash this rotten system, it was well worth it." His eyes were haunted. They would always be haunted.

"Better not talk," said Hollister. "Save your oxygen."

One hour. The pips on the radarscopes were high and strong now. The spaceboats weren't bothering with atmospheric braking, they were spending fuel to come almost straight down.

One hour and ten minutes. Was Barbara still alive?

One hour and twenty minutes.

One hour and thirty minutes. Any instant –

"There, señor! There!"

Hollister jumped to his feet. Up in a corner of the screen, a white wash of fire – here she came!

The ferry jetted slowly groundward, throwing up a blast of dust as her fierce blasts tore at the field. Now and then she wobbled, caught by the high wind, but she had been built for just these conditions. Close, close – were they going to let her land after all? Yes, now she was entering the cradle, now the rockets were still.

A shellburst struck her hull amidships and burst it open. The police were cautious, they hadn't risked spilling her nuclear engine and its radioactivity on the field. She rocked in the cradle. Hollister hoped the crash-braced pilot had survived. And he hoped the second man was skilful and had been told exactly what to do.

That ferry lanced out of the clouds, descending fast. She wasn't very manoeuverable, but the pilot rode her like a horseman, urging, pleading, whipping and spurring when he had to. She slewed around and fell into a shaky curve out of screen range.

If the gods were good, her blast had incinerated the murderers of the first boat.

She came back into sight, fighting for control. Hollister howled. "Guide her into a cradle!" He waved his gun at the seated technies. "Guide her safely in if you want to live!"

She was down.

Tiny figures were running towards her heedless of earth still smoking underfoot. Three of them veered and approached the radio shack. "O.K.!" rapped Hollister. "Back into the corridor!" He dragged one of the unconscious men himself; stooping, he sealed the fellow's suit against the poison gases outside. There would be enough air within it to last a sleeper a few minutes.

Concussion smashed at him. He saw shards of glass and wire flying out the door and ricocheting nastily about his head. Then the yell of Venus' wind came to him. He bent and picked up his man. "Let's go."

They scrambled through the broken wall and out onto the field. The wind was at their backs, helping them for once. One of the dynamiters moved up alongside Hollister. He saw Barbara's face, dim behind the helmet.

When he reached the ferry, the others were loading the last boxes of food. A figure in space armor was clumping unsteadily toward them from the wrecked boat. Maybe their luck had turned. Sweeping the field with his eyes, Hollister saw only ruin. There were still surviving police, but they were inside the city and it would take minutes for them to get out again.

He counted the men with him and estimated the number of food boxes. Fifteen all told, including his two erstwhile captives – Barbara's party must have met opposition – but *she* still lived, God be praised! There were supplies enough, it would be a hungry trip home but they'd make it.

Fernandez peered out of the air lock. "Ready," he announced. "Come aboard. We have no seats, so we must rise at low acceleration, but the pilot says there is fuel to spare."

Hollister helped Barbara up the ladder and into the boat. "I hope you'll like Earth," he said awkwardly.

"I know I will – with you there," she told him.

Hollister looked through the closing air lock at the desolation which was Venus. Some day it would bloom, but –

"We'll come back," he said.

BECAUSE Venus is enshrouded by clouds, direct telescopic examination of its surface was beyond the ability of the early planetary observers. In the absence of direct observations, they adduced a variety of differing and mutually inconsistent environments. Since only water clouds were familiar, the apparent thickness of the Cytherean cloud layer seemed to argue for a great abundance of water. From there, it was only a step to the assertion, seriously put forth in 1918 by Svante Arrhenius, that

> everything on Venus is dripping wet ... a very great part of the surface of Venus is no doubt covered with swamps ... The constantly uniform climatic conditions which exist everywhere result in an entire absence of adaptation to changing exterior conditions. Only low forms of life are therefore represented, mostly no doubt, belonging to the vegetable kingdom; and the organisms are nearly of the same kind all over the planet.

Arrhenius, it will be remembered, had criticized Lowell for deducing too much about Mars from too little data.

Spectroscopic observations of such a wet world should easily demonstrate, one would think, the presence of atmospheric water vapour. Thus, it was with some surprise that observers in the 1920s found that they were unable to detect any water vapour above the clouds of Venus at all. Thus, the Carboniferous swamp model was generally abandoned, and replaced by the arid, planetary desert model. The clouds could not then be water; they were instead attributed to a permanent pall of dust, raised from the windswept surface.

Unsatisfied with such an explanation of the brilliant white clouds of Venus as dust, the American astronomers Donald H. Menzel and Fred L. Whipple, of Harvard

University, pointed out in 1955 that the absence of spectroscopically detectable water vapour was not a good argument against water clouds. The situation can be demonstrated by the simple analogy of a pan of water whose temperature can be controlled. At a given moment, some fast-moving H_2O molecules have broken the weak chemical bonds which bind them to their neighbors and are escaping from the pan. At the same moment, some other H_2O molecules are re-entering the pan from the overlying atmosphere. Just as in the atmosphere of Mercury, the amount of water vapor above the pan depends on the equilibrium between two processes. As we reduce the temperature of the pan, there are far fewer fast-moving molecules in the liquid and therefore far fewer water vapor molecules in the atmosphere above. If the temperature of the water is sufficiently low – say, many tens of degrees below 0°C., so that the water has frozen to ice – then the amount of water vapor above the pan will be very small indeed.

From the infrared emission of Venus, it was determined that the temperature of the clouds of Venus is about – 40°C (by coincidence, this is also – 40°F). If the clouds of Venus were made of ice crystals at a temperature of – 40°C, the amount of water vapor above them would be undetectable, and no contradiction with the spectroscopic results would be implied. Menzel and Whipple then went on to argue that if large amounts of water existed in the clouds, even larger amounts must exist on the surface. In the previous unsuccessful searches for water vapor, it had been found, quite by accident, that great quantities of carbon dioxide existed in the atmosphere of Venus. Menzel and Whipple proposed, in effect, that the surface of Venus was largely covered by carbonated oceans – seltzer water.

As a final example of the variety of descriptions of Venus which could be derived from the very limited data then available, let us consider the model proposed, also in 1955, by Fred Hoyle. In the early history of any planet, there will be a certain amount of water and other materials outgassed from the planetary interior. In the upper atmosphere of the planet, the water vapor tends to be photo-dissociated by solar ultraviolet radiation; the hydrogen escapes to space, and the oxygen remains behind to oxidize the atmosphere. If the plant initially has much more water than hydrocarbons, all the hydrocarbons will eventually be oxidized, and an aqueous, oxidizing environment will result as on Earth. But if the initial complement of hydrocarbons greatly exceeds the amount of water, all the water will be used up in partially oxidizing the hydrocarbons to CO_2 and a CO_2 atmosphere with a large residue of surface hydrocarbons will result. While the atmosphere of Venus is thought to be largely composed of N_2, by the same argument from default that we encountered for Mars, the proportion of CO_2 is perhaps a hundred times greater than in the Earth's atmosphere. Hoyle therefore proposed that the surface of Venus was covered with oil, or other hydrocarbons, and that the cloud layer was smog.

The state of our knowledge of Venus in 1956 is amply illustrated by the fact that the Carboniferous swamp, the windswept desert, the planetary oilfield, and the global seltzer ocean each had its serious proponents. Those optimists planning, in 1956, eventual manned missions to Venus must have had considerable difficulties in deciding whether to send along a paleobotanist, a mineralogist, a petroleum geologist, or a deep-sea diver. We now know that none of these models is correct, and that a proper description of Venus incorporates features from several of the early models ...

In 1956, a team of American radioastronomers at the U.S. Naval Research Laboratory, headed by Cornell H. Mayer, first turned a large radiotelescope towards Venus. The observations were made near inferior conjunction, the time when Venus is nearest the Earth, and when, also, we are looking almost exclusively at the dark hemisphere of the planet. Mayer and his colleagues were astounded to find that Venus radiated as if it were a hot object at a temperature of about 300°C. Subsequent observations at a variety of wavelengths have confirmed these observations and have shown that the deduced temperature of Venus increases away from inferior conjunction – that is, as we see more and more of the illuminated hemisphere. The most natural explanation of these observations is that the surface of Venus is hot – far hotter than anyone had previously imagined. Venus is about 0.7 A.U. from the Sun. By the inverse square law it should therefore receive $1/(0.7)^2$, or about twice as much solar energy as does the Earth. On the

202

other hand, its clouds are very highly reflecting. When both effects are considered, it turns out that despite its smaller distance from the Sun, Venus absorbs less sunlight than the Earth. Ordinarily, it should not even be as hot as the Earth; yet it was 300° warmer.

Some early difficulties in providing a detailed explanation of the high surface temperatures led to an alternative explanation of the intense radio radiation from Venus. Douglas E. Jones, an American physicist at the Jet Propulsion Laboratory of the National Aeronautics and Space Administration, proposed that the high temperatures apply not to the surface of Venus, but to a dense ionized layer, or ionosphere, high in the Cytherean atmosphere.

... A distinction between the hot ionosphere and hot surface models can be gained if we imagine a radiotelescope scanning across the disk of Venus, tuned to a wavelength of about one centimeter. In the hot surface model, the atmosphere and clouds are slightly absorbing at 1 cm wavelength. Thus, when the radiotelescope looks towards the edge of the disk, there is more absorbing material in the light path than when the radiotelescope points to the center of the disk. Thus, in the hot surface model, there should be less radiation coming from the edges, or limbs, of Venus than from the center, a circumstance known as limb-darkening.

In contrast, consider the hot ionosphere model. Here, the semitransparent ionosphere is the primary source of emission at 1 cm wavelength. At the center of the disk, the radiotelescope sees a smaller thickness of the emitting ionosphere than at the limbs. Where there is more emitting material, there should be more emission. Thus the hot ionosphere model predicts limb-brightening. Unfortunately, the available radiotelescopes on Earth are unable to resolve, or scan across, Venus. At 1 cm wavelength, they could only determine the average emission over the entire disk. A relatively small radiotelescope, flown to the vicinity of Venus, could distinguish between limb-brightening and limb-darkening by scanning the Cytherean disk; this was a primary mission of the United States spacecraft Mariner II.

Its extended horizontal panels are solar cells for the conversion of sunlight into electricity. At the very bottom is a directional antenna for radioing scientific results back to Earth. The radiotelescope used to scan the disk of Venus is the small disk sitting just above the main hexagonal electronics housing.

On 14 December, 1962, Mariner II passed within 35,000 to 40,000 km of Venus, and scanned across the disk at two wavelengths near 1 cm. Mariner II found no limb-brightening. Instead, a distinct limb-darkening was observed. These results contradict the ionospheric model and provide support for the hot surface model.

This Mariner II experiment is an excellent example of the role of space vehicles in the investigation of planetary environments. A specific model of Venus had been proposed which explained most of the observations then available. The model had predictable consequences, which were different from the consequences of other models, but which could not be tested from the vicinity of the Earth. A space vehicle was needed. The spacecraft and the radiotelescope were designed and built together. Despite the fact that some expectations for the mission were not fulfilled, both the spacecraft and the radiotelescope worked well enough to provide the critical tests of the theoretical model . . .

If, then, the ionospheric model is invalid, what makes Venus hot? From a variety of observations at visual, infrared, and radio frequencies, it has recently been established that the clouds of Venus are indeed made of water: ice crystals in the colder cloudtops, which are seen in ordinary photographs; and water droplets in the bottom of the clouds, which are "seen" at long wavelengths. The CO_2 and H_2O in the Cytherean atmosphere, plus the water in the clouds, combine to produce a very efficient greenhouse effect. The atmosphere is in convective motion. Sunlight is deposited either in the clouds or directly on the surface. The sunlight which is deposited on the surface heats it immediately; the sunlight which is deposited in the clouds or atmosphere is transported by the downward convective motions, to heat the surface. The hot surface attempts to radiate in the infrared, but the absorption by the atmospheric CO_3 and H_2O and the water clouds is so great that very little heat from the surface or lower atmosphere escapes directly to space. The surface temperature must then be sufficiently high so that the small fraction of radiation which does escape to space equals the intensity of the sunlight which is absorbed by Venus.

The American astronomer James B. Pollack of the Smithsonian Astrophysical Observatory and I have explored the role which water clouds can play in determining the characteristic features of the Venus environment. We find that a fairly thick layer of ice crystal clouds with water droplets below can explain in detail the spectrum of infrared and microwave radiation emitted from the planet, the limb-darkening at microwave frequencies observed by Mariner II, the variations of the centimeter wavelength temperatures with the phase of Venus, the limb-darkening observed in the infrared, and the polarization properties of the Venus clouds at optical frequencies. In addition, these clouds can explain, through the greenhouse effect, the high surface temperatures deduced from radio observations. While there are still a number of unsolved problems about Venus, the hypothesis that the clouds are water explains, in a straightforward way, a wide variety of observations.

When a radar pulse is sent to Venus at centimeter wavelengths, it is transmitted by the atmosphere and clouds and strikes the surface, where it is partially absorbed and partially reflected. The part which is reflected is then returned to Earth, where it can be detected with a large radiotelescope. The ability of Venus to reflect radar gives a clue to its surface composition, just as the brightness and color of an object in reflected visible light can be used for estimating its composition. For example, extensive oceans of water or hydrocarbons can be excluded. In addition, the rotation of Venus causes a Doppler broadening of monochromatic radar pulses reflected from the planet, and the rate of rotation of Venus can be deduced.

When the passive radio observations and these active radar observations are combined, some interesting conclusions about the body of Venus emerge. Venus is rotating very slowly, approximately once every 250 days; but more remarkable yet, it is rotating backwards. Except for Uranus, which is a marginal case, all the other planets in the solar system have direct rotation; that is, they are rotating in the same direction that they are revolving about the Sun. If we stand above the Earth's north pole and observe the Earth rotating from West to East beneath us, we will find that it is rotating in a counterclockwise direction. From the same vantage point, we would see the Earth revolve about the Sun, also counterclockwise. This is called direct rotation. But if we were able to make the same observation at Venus, we would find that while it revolves about the Sun in a counterclockwise sense, it rotates clockwise about its axis. This is called retrograde rotation. The cause of the retrograde rotation of Venus is unknown, but it and the slow rotation period are both probably related to tidal friction. The rotation and revolution of Venus together imply that the time from local sunrise to sunrise – the "day" on Venus – is about 116 of our days. The nights on Venus are long and hot.

The surface of Venus is not covered with liquid water or pools of hydrocarbons. But any one of a large number of pulverized common terrestrial minerals could account for the properties of the Cytherean surface as determined by radio measurements. The coldest temperature on Venus is about 200°C; the warmest, about 700°C. At these temperatures, any familiar terrestrial organisms would be scorched. It is perhaps premature to exclude the possibility of completely novel organisms, based on exotic chemistry, but, from our present vantage point, the prospects for life on the surface of Venus appear very bleak indeed.

The Cytherean water clouds are, perhaps, another story. They are at moderate temperatures, bathed in sunlight, abundantly supplied with water, and must contain small amounts of minerals convectively transported from the underlying surface. It is possible to imagine organisms carrying out their entire life cycle in such an environment. The clouds of Venus appear to be a possible habitat for micro-organisms from Earth, if not indigenous Cytherean organisms.

As for the surface of Venus, it is appallingly hot; because of the thick clouds, it is overcast and gloomy even in the daytime. The temperatures are so high that in some places the surface should glow with the deep ruby red of its own heat. Venus, the bright morning star, has for millennia been called and identified with Lucifer. The identification is curiously appropriate. Venus is very much like hell.

Section V

Big Sister

VENUS is very much like hell ... But in what respects? In this section, three authors concentrate on various aspects of that question and produce different answers.

Although *Escape to Venus,* first published in 1956, may not be one of the world's masterpieces, it holds an honourable place in the annals of Fantastic Venus, in that the author uses the Cytherean setting to establish an anti-utopia or dystopia carrying a flavour of George Orwell's *1984*; so Big Brother is imported to Little Sister. Lott also seems to be the only story-teller to speculate about the possibilities of a Cytherean calendar. The extract given here forms part of a briefing delivered to the escapees from Earth as they head towards Venus in their spaceship.

The atmosphere in Lott's Venus is being adapted so that mankind may breathe it: one of the preoccupations of the writers of the fifties, and one handled convincingly in Poul Anderson's *The Big Rain*. Mr. Anderson calls this short novel, too modestly, "a period piece", going on to say, "At least one reputable astronomer, Carl Sagan, has published speculations about making the planet habitable. His method is necessarily different from mine – which, by the way, resembles an approach used by Pohl and Kornbluth in *The Space Merchants* – but it too would lead to the Big Rain."

It may be that *The Big Rain* seems a period piece; but another few years, maybe another planet, could bring its subject matter back into topicality. That's the way it often is with science fiction. This applies even more strongly to

Mr. Anderson's *Sister Planet,* which first appeared in 1959. We can only hope that any alien life-forms mankind may encounter will be treated more scrupulously than we have treated most of our fellow life-forms on this planet – as scrupulously, in fact, as Hawthorne treats the splendid creatures in *Sister Planet* (thank goodness *one* science fiction writer finally used that inviting title!).

No apology is needed for using two Poul Anderson novelettes in one anthology – fortunate the anthologist who has my excuse for so doing! Although he would not claim to be the major stylist of the field, Poul Anderson has won his wide popularity by thinking hard from a solid basis of fact and developing his dreams from scientific conjectures. He clearly wins the Cytherean Memorial Prize for Quantity and Quality in this genre; his two stories, with opposed Cytherean models, only gain by being set together in one book.

Humanitarian principles also inform Arthur Clarke's *Before Eden.* The story, which first appeared in 1961, employs its strange Cytherean landscape adroitly, and, although some of its usage of facts may qualify it as a period piece, the ethical content of the story will always retain its relevance. Mr. Clarke had earned honours enough; here he claims the laurels awaiting the writer of the Best Short Story Set On Venus!

S. MAKEPEACE LOTT: Escape to Venus

"You have been given the details of conditions on Venus and the process of Acclimatization," announced the screen, *"and you've seen all that is known of the Geography of Venus ..."*

I turned to Diane, we were sitting in the warm comfort of the telecinema after lunch. "Yesterday," she whispered. "You missed it."

208

"... now we will show you some details of the domestic life. The communal living quarters are much what you are accustomed to, although the stress on Venus has to be on vertical living." The screen was suddenly full of towering blocks of apartments, glistening windowless high over their transparent connecting arcs of street roofing. "Every effort is made to keep all people under cover at all times as the temperature range is from – 40°C. to about 55°C., this being, of course, greater than in any one locality on Earth. Outdoor recreation is normally limited to the periods of twilight and dawn, each of which lasts for approximately twelve hours and occurs at sixteen Earth-day intervals. As intimated in our first film, life on the planet has been adapted to the altered length of Venus day and year. There are seven sidereal days in the Venus year and each day is treated in the same way as an Earth-month. This gives an error of exactly one Earth-day each Venus-year and so the last day of the Venus year is celebrated as Venus day, although it does not actually mark the day on which the first ship reached the planet.

"Similarly the numbering of the Venus-year runs from an arbitrary date," went on the telescreen above general panoramic effects, "that of inferior conjunction in the year the explorers landed, and the date on Venus at this moment is Tuesday the tenth of Jupiter, thirty-seven. There are four weeks of eight days in each month, the eighth day being called Earthday and coming between Sunday and Monday. Each month starts on Monday the first and the months are called after the planets other than Venus and Earth in the order of their distance from the Sun. Thus Mercury is the first month, then Mars, Jupiter, Saturn, Uranus, Neptune, with Pluto the last month. Owing to the fact that the eccentricity of the orbit of Venus is only 0.007 the greatest and least distances from the sun do not differ by as much as a million and a half kilometres and so the seasons are not as clearly defined as on Earth. The keeping of the four seasons, therefore, is merely a retained Earth-convention. Winter," the telescreen solemnly informed us, "is restricted to the month Pluto, whilst each of the other seasons lasts for two months."

Then the screen was full of agricultural pictures showing cultivation by the Berguson method, with infra-red fertilization and the usual electrical soil heating. And then there were the giant chlorophyll-factories which were producing the enormous stocks of the carbohydrates, forming the main bulk of our Venus diet, from the carbon dioxide that was the terror of the Venus atmosphere. It was hoped that in time the plants and the synthetic chlorophyll between them would reduce the volume of carbon dioxide to such an extent that normal life would be possible over an ever-widening proportion of the planet's surface, but at present all life was restricted to the small watershed which the first explorers had discovered.

"The political life on Venus," the telescreen told us, *"will be fully introduced to you when you have disembarked, but details of the trivialities will be given now to prepare the ground for later information. This film will, therefore, deal with the consumer goods that are available on the planet and the method of purchasing them."*

We leant back in our seats, this was going to be an advertising film.

"In view of the emphasis that must be placed on work on the new planet clothes are simple and functional ..." A male and female mannequin paraded the suits we were already wearing. *"For external use a heavy outer garment is provided ..."* This was an all-enveloping costume with transparent hood and emergency oxygen tanks. *"All clothes are issued on a standard basis and it is only possible to buy personal adornment in the form of jewellery ..."* A few bangles, necklaces and ear-rings floated across the translucent screen. *"Replacements of clothes and shoes are, of course, provided where necessary.*

"Communal dining-rooms are provided in all apartment blocks but it is possible to buy food on certain days, although the excellent café facilities make this really unnecessary ..." We were duly shown some cafés which certainly looked very comfortable and friendly.

"No furniture is available for private purchase but varying pieces may be obtained on a voucher system slightly different from that used in place of Earth-money. Details of this money system will be explained when the subject of Banking is dealt with on Venus itself. It must be remembered, however, that the prime consideration governing the production of any article is its importance to the economy

of the planet, bearing in mind the need to establish as high a standard of intellectual and physical life as possible."

"He sounds a typical civil servant," I whispered to Diane, but she only smiled and squeezed my hand.

"There is, at present, no equivalent to the conception of private property on the planet and hence no question of capital . . ."

I sat up with a jerk. Here was the fundamental political Ethic being tossed at us as if it didn't matter and I was curious to see how the others reacted. But it was dark in the telecinema and I could hardly see . . . and the screen droned on.

POUL ANDERSON: Sister Planet

Long afterward they found a dead man in shabby clothes adrift near San Francisco. The police decided he must have jumped from the Golden Gate bridge one misty day. That was an oddly clean and lonesome place for some obscure wino to die, but no one was very much interested. Beneath his shirt he carried a Bible with a bookmark indicating a certain passage which had been underlined. Idly curious, a member of the Homicide Squad studied the waterlogged pulp until he deduced the section: Ezekiel vii, 3-4.

The ferry left its orbiting mother ship and flashed down through clouds. When its destination gleamed far below, it extended wings and glided to the sea. Shorty McClellan taxied on to the dock with a single deftly-gauged snort of jetfire.

"End of the line." He stood up and began struggling into his air harness. Nat Hawthorne, whose mind had been turned outwardly, heard the pilot's voice as a harsh quack. And yet he had come to like McClellan. The stocky, sandy-haired man had begun the voyage from Earth with his usual bawdy limericks and bad puns; he had ended with shyly passing around stereos of his children.

"You know," continued McClellan, "I've been toting freight between Venus Station and the spaceships for six years now, and I still feel uneasy in one of these gizmos."

"Why so?" Hawthorne, hanging a tank on his own shoulders, gave the other a surprised look.

McClellan adjusted his mask. It covered nose and mouth with a tight airseal of celluplastic gasketing. Both men had already sipped ultraviolet-filtering contact lenses over their eyeballs. "I keep remembering, there isn't an oxygen molecule that's not manmade for 25 million miles," he said. The air-hose muffled his voice, giving it for Hawthorne a homelike accent. "I'd feel safer in a spacesuit."

"De gustibus non disputandum est," said Hawthorne, "which has been translated as, 'There is no disputing that Gus is in the east.' Me, I was never yet in a spacesuit that didn't smell of somebody else's garlic."

Through the port he saw a long blue back swirl in the waves. A grin tugged his hidden lips. "Why, there's Oscar," he said.

"Yeah. Your soul mate," grunted McClellan.

They went out the airlock. Ears popped, adjusting to a slight pressure difference. The masks strained out some water vapor for reasons of comfort, and nearly all the carbon dioxide, for there was enough to kill a man in three gulps. Nitrogen and inert gases passed, on to be blent with oxygen from the harness tanks and breathed.

The heat struck like a fist. Hawthorne had already donned the local custume: loose, flowing garments of synthetic material, designed to ward ultraviolet radiation off his skin and not absorb water. Now he paused, told himself that he was a mammal able to get along quite well at this temperature, and relaxed. The sea lapped his bare feet where he stood on a pontoon. It felt cool. Suddenly he stopped minding the heat; he forgot it.

Instead, his eyes sought remembered horizons. You would never have expected a landless planet-wide ocean to be so alive. But there were climatic zones, each with its own million restless hues – the color of light, the quality of living organisms – so that a sea on Venus was not an arbitrary cartographic division but an iridescent belt around the

212

globe. Now, at evening, this the Phosphor Sea had grown purple, streaked with white foam; but on the world's very edge it shaded to an infinitely clear green. A floating island, jungle supported on giant bladders, upbore flame yellows and a private mistiness, so that in its neighborhood the great wrinkled waves looked almost black. Turning skyward, Hawthorne saw the lower western clouds tinged copper. The permanent layer above ranged from pearl gray in the east to a still blinding white where the invisible sun burned and sank. A double rainbow arched a storm, blue-black wall far to the northeast.

Oscar frisked up. Yes, of course it was Oscar. The other cetoids, a dozen or so, were more interested in the ferry: rubbing sleek flanks along the metal or holding their calves up in their fore flippers for a good look. They seemed even more enthusiastic than the human crew clustered on the dock; but then, spaceship arrivals were months apart. Oscar paid attention only to Hawthorne. He lifted his blunt bulky head, nuzzled the ecologist's toes, and slapped flukes on water 20 feet away.

Hawthorne squatted. "Hi, Oscar," he said. "Didn't think I'd make it back, huh?" He chucked the creature under the chin. Be damned if the cetoids didn't have true chins. Oscar rolled belly-up and snorted. "Thought I'd pick up some dame Earthside and forget all about you, huh? Why, bless your ugly puss, I never dreampt of that, I just did it! C'mero, beast." He scratched the rubbery skin behind the blowhole. Oscar wriggled. "Okay, okay, I'm home. Let's not get sickening about it."

Oscar sounded. Hawthorne rose: a tall, rather bony man, with dark-blond hair and prematurely creased face. He was about to climb the dock ladder when the cetoid returned. Awkwardly, because this was not the regular trading pier, Oscar pushed something out of his mouth. It lay at Hawthorne's feet like a little ball of molten spectrum. After which Oscar sounded again and Hawthorne muttered total, profane astonishment. His eyes stung.

He had just been presented with one of the finest firegems on record.

After dark, the aurora bestowed by the near sun became visible. The night was royal blue, with rosy curtains and

213

silent white shuddering streamers. And the water itself shone, bioluminescence, each wave laced by cold fires. Where droplets struck the caissons on which the station floated, they glowed for minutes before evaporating, as if gold coals had been strewn.

Hawthorne looked out the transparent wall of the wardroom. "It's good to be back," he said.

"Get that," said Shorty McClellan. "From wine and women panting for the company of a glamorous interplanetary explorer, it is good to be back. This man is crazy."

The geophysicist, Wim Dykstra, nodded with seriousness. He was the tall swarthy somber breed of Dutchman. "I think I understand, Nat," he said. "I read between the lines of my mail. Is it that bad on Earth?"

"In some ways." Hawthorne continued gazing out, past cabins and tiered decks to the ocean. The cetoids were playing. Joyous torpedo shapes would hurtle from the water, streaming liquid radiance, arch over and come down in a fountain that burned.

"Ah, so. I do not know if I want to take my next furlough when it comes," said Dykstra.

McClellan looked bewildered. "What're you fellows talking about?" he asked. "What's wrong?"

Hawthorne sighed. "I don't know where to begin," he said. "The trouble is, Shorty, you see Earth continually. But we're gone three years at a stretch. We notice the changes."

"Oh, sure." McClellan shifted uneasily. "Sure, I suppose, well, more people and fewer resources every day – But you guys are well paid. You rate special privileges. What're *you* complaining about?"

"Call it the atmosphere," said Hawthorne. He sketched a smile. "If God existed, which thank God He doesn't, I'd say He has forgotten the human race."

Dykstra flushed. "God does not forget," he said. "Men do."

"Sorry, Wim," said Hawthorne. "But I've seen – not just Earth, Earth is too big to be anything but statistics – I visited my own country, the place I grew up. And the lake where I went fishing as a kid is an alga farm, and my mother has one room to share with a yattering old biddy she can't stand the sight of, and they've cut down Bobolink

214

Grove to put up still another slum mislabeled a housing project, and my kid brother was out on corvée – and the gangs are operating in broad daylight now, armed escort has become a major industry, and I walk into a bar and not a face is happy, they're just staring stupefied at a telescreen, and the show is usually one of these new-style gouge combats between women, and –" He pulled up short. "Never mind. I probably exaggerate."

"I'll say you do," declared McClellan. "Why, I can show you – You've never been to San Francisco, have you? Well, come with me to a pub I know in North Beach, and I'll give you the time of your life, among some of the most decent merry people God ever made."

"Could be," said Hawthorne. "But how much longer will such fragments survive?"

"The rich get richer," said Dykstra, "and the poor get poorer, and the middle class vanishes. Eventually there is the fossilized Empire. I have read history." He regarded Hawthorne out of dark, thoughtful eyes. "Medieval feudalism and monasticism evolved *within* the Roman domain: they were there when it fell apart. I wonder if a parallel development may not already be taking place. The feudalism of the large Terrestrial organizations; the monasticism of planetary stations like this."

"Complete with celibacy," grimaced McClellan. "I'll take the feudalism!"

Hawthorne sighed again. There was always a price. Sex-suppressive pills, and the memory of lips and arms on Earth, were often poor comfort. "We're not a very good analogy, Wim," he argued. "In the first place, we live entirely off the jewel trade. Because it's profitable, we're allowed also to carry on the scientific work which interests us personally: in effect, that's part of our wage. But if the cetoids stopped bringing gems, we'd be hauled home so fast we'd meet ourselves coming. You know nobody will pay the fabulous cost of interplanetary freight for pure knowledge – only for luxuries."

Dykstra shrugged. "What of it? The economics is irrelevant. Have you never drunk Benedictine?"

"Uh ... yeah, I get it. But also, we're only celibate by necessity."

"I am not pressing the analogy too close," said Dykstra.

215

"My point is, however, that we feel ourselves serving a very large purpose. Science, in our case, rather than religion, but still a purpose worth all the isolation and other sacrifice. If, in our hearts, we really consider the isolation a sacrifice."

Hawthorne winced. Sometimes Dykstra was too analytical. Indeed, thought Hawthorne, the station personnel were monks. Wim, with his Roman Catholic background, fitted quite easily into such a pattern of life. Hawthorne, less lucky, had spent fifteen years shaking off a Puritan upbringing, and finally realized that he never would. He could try to make up for long self-denial by an Earthside leave which was one continuous orgy, but the sense of sin plagued him nonetheless, disguised as bitterness. I have been iniquitous upon Terra, ergo Terra is a sink of evil . . .

Dykstra continued, with a sudden unwonted tension in his voice: "The similarity to medieval monasteries holds good in yet another respect. They thought they were retreating from the world; instead, they became the nucleus of its next stage. And we too, unwittingly until now, may have changed history."

"Uh-uh," denied McClellan. "You can't have a history without a next generation, can you? And there's not a woman on all Venus."

Hawthorne said, quickly, to get away from his own thoughts: "I heard talk in the Company offices about that. They think maybe it'll be possible. If trade continues to expand, the station will have to be enlarged, and the new people could as well be female technicians and scientists. Which would give all of us more incentive to stay."

"Or lead to trouble," warned McClellan.

"Not if there were enough to go around," said Hawthorne. "Nobody signs on here who hasn't long ago given up any wish for romantic love, or fatherhood."

"They could have that," murmured Dykstra. "Fatherhood, at least." "Kids?" Hawthorne was startled. "On Venus? Is that a joke?"

Something flickered across Dykstra's mouth. Hawthorne, reverting to the sensitivity of intimate years, knew Dykstra had a secret, which he wanted to shout to the universe but could not yet. Dykstra had discovered something wonderful.

To give him a lead, Hawthorne said: "I've been so busy

swapping gossip, I've had no time for shop talk. What have you learned about this planet since I left?"

"Some promising things," evaded Dykstra. His tone was still not altogether steady.

"Found how the firegems are formed?"

"Heavens, no. That would scuttle us, would it not, if they could be synthesized?"

"Learn more about the life cycle?"

"Yes, Chris and Mamoru have some fresh clues to the detailed chemistry. It is over my head, Nat, but you will want to study it, and they have been anxious for your help as an ecologist. You know this business of the plants, if one may call them that, using solar energy to build up unsaturated compounds, which the creatures we call animals then oxidize? Oxidation need not involve oxygen, Shorty."

"I know that much chemistry," said McClellan, looking hurt.

"Well, there was the problem that the reactions involved did not seem energetic enough to power organisms the size of Oscar. But Mamoru got to thinking about fermentation, the closest Terrestrial analogy. And it seems that microorganisms really are involved. The Venusian enzymes are indistinguishable from ... shall we call them viruses, for lack of a better name? Certain forms even seem to have the function of genes. How is that for symbiosis, eh?"

Hawthorne whistled.

"As for myself – I may have a most important letter for you to deliver on Earth, Shorty," said Dykstra.

All at once he shivered with excitement.

When Hawthorne emerged into sunrise, where mists smoked along indigo waters, under a sky like nacre, the whole station seemed to explode outward around him. Wim Dykstra had already scooted off with his assistant, little Jimmy Chengtung of the hopeful grin; their two-man sub was over the horizon, picking up data-recording units off the sea bottom. Now boats left the wharf in every direction: Diehl and Matsumoto to gather pseudo-plankton, Vassiliev after some of the weird growths on Erebus Bank, Lafarge continuing his mapping of the currents, Glass heading straight up to investigate the clouds a bit more ...

The space ferry had been given its first loading during

the night. Shorty McClellan walked across a bare deck with Hawthorne and Captain Jevons. "Expect me back again about sundown," he said. "No use coming before then, with everyone out fossicking."

"I imagine not." Jevons, white-haired and dignified, looked wistfully at Lafarge's retreating craft. Five cetoids frisked after. Nobody had invited them, but by now few men would have ventured out of station view without such an escort. More than once, when accidents happened, the cetoids had kept men afloat, borne them home.

"I wish I too were, ah, fossicking," said Jevons. He chuckled. "But someone has to mind the store."

"Have you thought of any new trade goods we might bring in the next cargo?" asked McClellan. "Anything the Veenies might go for?"

"Well," said Hawthorne, "I've speculated about a saw, designed to be held in the mouth. To cut coralite blocks and make shelters on the ocean floor."

"Do you seriously think they would?" asked McClellan, astonished.

"I don't know," said Hawthorne. "How much do we know about Venus – a pocketful of men on an entire world?"

"It's at least an idea you have." Jevons smiled. "Good to have you back ideating, Nat. And, er, decent of you to volunteer to take your station watch the first thing, right after you return. That wasn't expected of you."

"Ah, he's got memories to soften the monotony," said McClellan. "I saw him in a hostess joint in Chicago. Whoo!"

The air masks hid most expression, but Hawthorne felt his ears redden. Jevons minded his own business, but he was old-fashioned, and more like a father than the implacable man in black whom Hawthorne unwillingly remembered.

"I want to mull over the new biochemical data and sketch out a research program in the light of it," said the ecologist hastily. "And, too, renew my acquaintance with Oscar. That really touched me, his giving me that gem. I feel like a louse, handing it over to the Company."

"At the price it'll command, I'd feel lousy too," said McClellan.

"No, I don't mean that. I mean – Oh, run along, jet-boy!"

Hawthorne and Jevons stood watching the spacecraft taxi off and ascend. Its rise was slow at first, much fire and noise, then a gradual acceleration. But by the time it had pierced the clouds, it was an upward meteor. And still it moved faster, Hawthorne knew: a streak through the planet's thick permanent overcast, until it was above and the clouds did not show as gray but as blinding white. So many miles high, even the air of Venus grew thin and piercingly cold, water vapor was frozen out. Thus absorption spectra had not revealed to Earthbound astronomers that this planet was a single vast ocean; the first explorers had expected desert. And instead they found wonder. But still McClellan rode his lightning horse, faster and higher, into a blaze of constellations.

When the sound had faded, Hawthorne came out of his reverie and said: "At least we've created one beautiful thing, the spaceship. I'm not sure how much destruction and ugliness that makes up for."

"You've been saddened by your furlough," said Jevons gravely. "That shouldn't be. You're too young for sadness."

"New England ancestors." Hawthorne tried to grin. "My chromosomes insist that I disapprove of something, and you know I don't believe in God." He added harshly: "Have you ever thought, though, Oscar's breed is better evidence for a divine purpose than our murderous idiotic race?"

"Don't romanticize the cetoids," advised Jevons. "They show a degree of intelligence, yes, but –"

"I know. They haven't got hands, and of course fire is impossible for them, so – I've heard it a hundred times before, Cap. But how can we tell what the cetoids do and don't do, the days on end they spend on the sea bottom? And up here, I've watched those games of 'tag' they play. I swear I see a pattern: an art form, like our ballet, but using the wind and currents and waves to dance to. And how do you account for their showing tastes in music, individual tastes, so that Oscar goes for those old jazz numbers and Sambo won't come near them but will pay you carat for carat if you give him some Buxtehude? Why trade at all?"

"Pack rats trade on Earth," said Jevons.

"Sure. And the first expedition rafting here thought it was pack rat psychology too, cetoids snatching oddments off the lower deck and leaving shells, coralite, finally jewels . . . sure. But by now it's developed into too intricate a price system. And anyway, why should mere animals go for music tapes, sealed in plastic and run off a thermionic cell? Or for waterproof reproductions of paintings? As for tools, they're often seen helped by schools of specialized 'fish', hunting or harvesting pseudo-kelp. They don't need hands, Cap. They use live tools! "

"I have been here a good many years," said Jeavons dryly.

Hawthorne flushed. "Sorry. I gave that lecture so often Earthside, to people who didn't even have the data, that it's become a reflex."

"I don't mean to denigrate our friends," said the captain. "But you know as well as I, all the years of trying to establish communication with them, symbols, signals, everything failed."

"Are you sure?" asked Hawthorne.

"What?"

"How do you know the cetoids have not learned our alphabet off those slates?"

"Well . . . after all –"

"They might have good reasons for not wanting to take our grease pencils in their mouths and scribble messages back at us. A degree of wariness, perhaps. Let's face it, Cap., we're the aliens here, the monsters. Or maybe they simply aren't interested: our goods are amusing enough to be worth trading for, but we ourselves seem drab. Or, of course – and I think this is the most probable – our behaviour is too strange. Consider the two planets, how different they are. How alike do you expect the two races' thinking to be?"

"An interesting speculation," said Jevons. "Not new, of course."

"Well, I'll go collect," said Hawthorne. He walked a few paces, then stopped and turned around. "You know," he said, "I'm being a fool. Oscar did communicate with us, only last evening. A perfectly unambiguous message, in the form of a firegem."

220

Jevons started. "I'll be damned," he said at last, slowly. "You're right."

Hawthorne went past a heavy machine gun, loaded with explosive slugs. He despised the rule that an entire arsenal must always be kept ready. When had Venus ever threatened men with anything but the impersonal consequences of ignorance? He continued on along the trading pier.

Its metal gleamed, nearly awash. Baskets had been lowered overnight, with goods from the ferry. These included records and pictures the cetoids already knew, but always seemed to want more of. (As individuals, or for some undersea equivalent of libraries, or –?) Then there were the little plastibulbs of sodium chloride, aqua ammonia, and other materials, whose taste the cetoids apparently enjoyed. Lacking continents to leach out, the Venusian ocean was less mineralized than Earth's, and these chemicals were exotic; tests on lower animals had eliminated the poisons. The standard articles also involved a few toys, like beach balls, which the cetoids used for some appallingly rough games; and specially devised dressings, to put on injuries ... Oh, nobody doubted Oscar was more intelligent than a chimpanzee, thought Hawthorne. The problem had always been, was he as much intelligent as a man?

He pulled up the baskets and took out the equally standardized payments which had been left in them. There were gems; particularly beautiful specimens of carolite, which would be made into ornaments on Earth; several kinds of shell. There were specimens of marine life for study, most of them never before seen by man; a few tools, lost overboard, recovered as if the cetoids knew what space freight cost per pound; a lump of something unidentifiable, light and yellow, maybe only of slight interest and maybe offering a clue to an entire new field of chemistry – The plunder of a world rattled into Hawthorne's collection boxes.

All novelties had a fixed small value; if the humans took the next such offering, its price would go up, and so on until the stable fee was reached, not too steep for the Earthmen or too low to be worth the cetoids' trouble. Amazing how detailed a bargain you could strike without language.

Hawthorne looked down at Oscar. The big fellow had nosed up close to the pier and lay idly swinging his tail.

The blue sheen along his upcurved back was lovely to watch. An expression crossed his face, doubtless one was very unscientific to call it a grin but Hawthorne felt sure that was what Oscar intended.

"Okay," said the man, "now let's see what you think of our gr-r-reat new products. Each and every one of these products has been tested in our spotless laboratories and don't think it was easy to test the patent spot remover there . . . and now –"

The music bubbles of Schönberg had been rejected, but a tape of traditional Japanese songs was gone and a two-carat smokepearl had been left, about twice the normal price for a novelty. In effect, some cetoid was asking for more of the same. As usual, every contemporary pictorial artist was refused, but Hawthorne agreed they were all rotten. Nor was Picasso (middle period) wanted, but Mondrian and Matisse had gone well. A doll had been accepted at low valuation, a mere bit of odd mineral: "Okay, we (I?) will take just this one, but don't bother bringing any more." Once again, all waterproof illustrated books had been ignored; the cetoids had never bought books, after the first few. It was an idiosyncrasy, among others, which had led many researchers to doubt their essential intelligence.

That doesn't follow, thought Hawthorne. *They haven't got hands, so text isn't natural for them. Because of sheer beauty – or interest, or humor, or whatever they get out of it – some of our best art is worth their trouble. But they might have their own method of keeping factual records. Such as what? How should I know? Maybe, by sheer telepathy, they build sentences into the crystal structure of stones.*

Oscar bustled along, following the man. Hawthorne squatted down and rubbed the cetoid's smooth wet brow. "Hey, what do you think about me?" he wondered aloud. "Do you wonder if *I* think? Sure, my people came down from the sky and built a floating metal settlement and brought all sorts of curious goodies – but bees and termites have pretty intricate behavior patterns, and you've got similar things on Venus."

Oscar snorted and nosed Hawthorne's ankles. "You have no right to be as smart as you are," said the man. "The sea isn't supposed to be a changeable enough environment to stimulate the evolution of intelligence. But this is Venus, and what do we know about the history of your ocean? Tell me, Oscar, are your dog-type and cattle-type "fish" just cases like aphids kept by ants, or are they real domestic animals, consciously trained? It's got to be the latter. I'll continue to insist it is, till ants develop a fondness for van Gogh and Beiderbecke."

Oscar plunged, drenching Hawthorne with carbonated sea water. It tingled on his skin. A small wind crossed the world, puffing the wetness out of his garments. He sighed. The cetoids were like children, never staying put, another reason why so many psychologists rated them only a cut above Terrestrial apes. A logically unwarranted conclusion. At the quick pace of Venusian life, urgent business might well arise on a second's notice. Or, even if the cetoids were merely being capricious, were they stupid on that account? They might just naturally have more joy in living than men ever felt.

I shouldn't run down my own species the way I do, Hawthorne forced himself to think. *We're different from Oscar, that's all. But by the same token, is he any worse than us? Even granting, which I do not, that he's only a sort of Pithecanthropus, won't his race keep on evolving, till it has as much brain and soul as man today? (And man may then be extinct, or degraded.) Perhaps more soul – more sense of beauty and mercy and laughter – if you extrapolate their present behavior.*

The pier quivered. Hawthorne glanced down again. Oscar had returned. He nosed the metal and made gestures with his flipper. Hawthorne stared at him. Oscar curved up his tail and whacked his own back.

"Hey, wait!" Hawthorne got the idea. He hoped; nothing like this had ever happened before. "You want me to come for a ride?"

The cetoid blinked both eyes. Was that the counterpart of a nod? And if so, had Oscar actually understood the English words?

Hawthorne hurried off to the oxygen electrolyzer, from which harness tanks were replenished. Skindiving equipment was stored beside it. He wriggled into a flexible heat-retaining Long John. Holding his breath, he unclipped his hose from tank and air mixer, discarded them, and substi-

223

tuted a couple of oxynitro flasks, thus converting the mask to an aqualung. For a moment he hesitated ... he should inform Jevons, or at least take the collection boxes inside ... to hell with it. This wasn't Earth, where you couldn't leave an empty beer bottle unwatched without having it stolen. Oscar might lose patience. Hawthorne's pulse beat loudly.

He ran back. Oscar lay level with the pier. Hawthorne straddled him, grasping a small cervical fin and leaning back against the muscular dorsal. The long body glided from the station. Water rippled sensuously around Hawthorne's legs. Oscar's flukes churned up foam like a snowstorm. A small polypoid went by, its keelfin submerged, its iridescent membrane-sail driving it on a broad reach. A nearby cetoid slapped the water with his tail. A greeting?

Presently Oscar submerged. Hawthorne had often dived. He was not surprised by the violet clarity of the first yards, nor the rich darkening as he went on down. The glowfish which passed him like comets were familiar. But he had never before felt the living play of muscles between his thighs; suddenly he knew why a few wealthy men on Earth still kept horses.

When he was in cool, silent, absolute blackness, Oscar began to travel. Almost, Hawthorne was torn off by the stream; he lost himself in the exhilaration of hanging on. With other senses than vision he was aware how they twisted through caves and canyons in buried mountains. An hour had passed when light gleamed before him. It took another half-hour to reach its source.

He had seen many luminous coralite banks. But never this one. A 20-mile radius sweeps out a big territory; men had not chanced by. And the usual reef was a good bit like its Terrestrial analogue, a ragged jumble of spires, bluffs, and grottos, eerie but unorganized beauty.

Here, a city of merfolk opened up before Hawthorne.

Afterward he did not remember just how it looked. His mind was not trained to register patterns so foreign. He knew there were fluted columns, arched chambers with arabesque walls, a piling of clean masses at one spot and a Gothic humoresque elsewhere; he saw towers enspiraled like a narwhal's tusk, arches and buttresses of delicate filigree, an overall unity of pattern at once as light as spin-

224

drift and as strong as the world-circling solar tide, immense, complex, and serene. A hundred coralite species, each with its own distinctive glow, were blended to make the place, so that there was a subtle play of color, hot reds and icy blues and living jades and bronzes, against ocean black. And from some source, he never knew what, came a thin crystal sound, a contrapuntal symphony which he did not understand but which recalled to him frost flowers on the windows of his mother's home.

Oscar let him swim about freely. He saw a few other cetoids, also drifting along, some accompanied by young. But plainly, they didn't live here. Was this a temple, a memorial, an art gallery, or – Hawthorne didn't know. It was huge, reaching farther downward than he could go before pressure killed him, half a mile down to the sea bottom. Yet this had never been made for any "practical" reason. Or had it? Perhaps the Venusians recognized what Earth had forgotten, though the ancient Greeks had known it, that the contemplation of loveliness is essential to thinking life.

This could not be a freak of nature. But no matter how closely he looked, and the flameless fire was adequate to see by, Hawthorne found no trace of chisel or mold. He could only decide that in some unknown way, Oscar's people had grown this thing.

He lost himself. It was Oscar who finally nudged him, a reminder that he had better go back before he ran out of air. When they reached the pier and Hawthorne had stepped off, Oscar nuzzled the man's foot, very briefly, like a kiss, and then he sounded in a tremendous splash.

Toward the close of the 43-hour daylight period, the boats came straggling in. Men landed wearily, unloaded their craft, stashed instruments and specimens, and went off for food and rest. Detailed study would come during the long night.

Wim Dykstra and Jimmy Cheng-tung had returned earlier than most, with armfuls of recording meters. Hawthorne knew in a general way what they were doing. By seismographs, sonic probes, mineral analyses, measurements of temperature and radioactivity and a hundred other facets, they tried to understand the planet's inner

225

structure. It was an old enigma. Venus had 80% of Earth's mass, and the chemical composition was almost identical. The two planets should have been equally similar. Instead, the Venusian magnetic field was a feeble ghost; there was no land surface; volcanic and seismic activity followed unaccountably different patterns; the rocks were of odd types and distributions; and there was a galaxy of other technicalities which Hawthorne did not pretend to follow.

Jevons had remarked that in the past weeks Dykstra had been getting more and more excited about something. The Dutchman was the cautious type of scientist, who said never a word about his results until they were nailed down past argument. But he had been spending Earth-days on end at the computer, as well as in the field. One gathered he was well on the way to solving the geological problem of Venus. "Or aphroditological?" Jevons had murmured. "But I know Wim. There's more behind this than curiosity or a chance at fame. He has something very big afoot, and very close to his heart. I hope it won't take him too blooming long!"

Today Dykstra had rused below decks and sworn nobody would get at the computer till he was through. Cheng-tung wandered up with the rest of the station to watch McClellan come in again.

Hawthorne sought him out. "Hey, Jimmy," he urged. "You don't have to keep up that mysterious act. You're among friends."

The Chinese grinned. "I'm practising my Oriental inscrutability," he answered.

"Hell, your project is obvious in general outline," said Hawthorne. "Wim's been calculating in advance what sort of data he ought to get if his theory is right. Now he's reducing those data for comparison. So okay, what *is* his theory?"

"There is nothing secret about its essence," said Cheng-tung. "The basic hypothesis was made more than a century ago. The idea is that Venus has a core unlike Earth's, and this accounts for the gross differences observed. Dr. Dykstra has been elaborating it, and data so far have confirmed his beliefs. Today we brought in what may be the crucial measurements: chiefly, seismic echoes from depth bombs exploded in wells drilled in the ocean floor."

"M-m, yeh." Hawthorne stared across surging waters. No cetoids were in sight. Had they gone down to their beautiful sanctuary? And if so, why? *It's a good thing the questions aren't answered,* he thought. *If there were no more riddles on Venus, I don't know what I'd do with my life.*

"I seem to've read somewhere that Venus ought by rights not to have a core at all," he went on. His curiosity was actually no more than mild, but he felt a need for conversation. He was still wondering how to break the news of what had happened. He should have reported it immediately to Jevons, but for hours after returning he had been dazed, and then the inadequacy of words reared a barrier. He was too conditioned against showing emotion to want to speak about such an experience; would Wim Dykstra care to give a blow-by-blow account of his own feelings during Communion?

"Not enough mass," finished Hawthorne, becoming aware he had dropped into silence. "The planet ought to have a continuous rocky character clear to the center, like Luna or Mars."

"Your memory is not quite infallible," said Cheng-tung. His sarcasm was gentle and inoffensive. "But then, the situation is a trifle complex. You see, if you use quantum laws to calculate the curve of pressure at a planet's center, versus the planet's mass, you do not get a simple figure. Up to about eight-tenths of an Earth-mass it rises smoothly, but there is a change at what is called the Y-point. The curve jogs back, and only after a certain interval, about 2% of Earth's mass, does the central pressure resume a steady rise."

"What happens at this Y-point?" asked Hawthorne absently.

"The force becomes great enough to collapse matter. First crystals, which had already assumed their densest possible form, break down completely. Then, as more mass is added to the planet, the electron shells of the atoms themselves are compressed. Only after this stage of quantum degeneracy has been reached – when the electrons can't get into lower energy states, and there is a true core, with a specific gravity of better than 10 – only then will increased mass again bring a steady rise in central pressure."

"Uh ... yes. I remember now Wim spoke of it, quite some time ago. I take it, then, that Venus has a core which is not in a state of ultimate collapse?"

"Yes. At its present internal temperature, Venus is just past the Y-point. If more mass should somehow be added to this planet, its radius would actually decrease. This accounts rather well for the observed peculiarities. You can see how the accretion of primordial material reached a point where Venus began to shrink; and then, as it happened, the accumulation of mass stopped, not going on to produce maximum core density and thereafter steadily increasing size, as in the case of Earth. This means a smooth planet, no upthrust above the hydrosphere to form continents. With no exposed rocks, there's nothing to take up CO_2 from the air: so life evolved for a different atmosphere. The relatively large mantle, as well as the low-density core, lead to a non-Terrestrial seismology, vulcanology, and mineralogy. The Venusian core is less conductive than Earth's – conductivity increases with degeneracy – so the currents circulating in it are smaller. Hence, the weak planetary magnetism."

"Very interesting," said Hawthorne. "But what's the big secret? I mean, it's a good job of work, but all you've shown is that Venusian atoms obey quantum laws. Hardly a surprise."

Cheng-tung's small body tensed. "It has been more difficult than one might suspect," he said. "But yes, our data now reveal unequivocally that Venus has just the type of core which it could have under present conditions."

Since he had asked Hawthorne to correct any mistakes in his excellent English, the ecologist answered, "You mean, the type of core it should have."

"I mean precisely what I said." The grin became dazzling. Cheng-tung hugged himself and did a few dance steps. "But let Dr. Dykstra bring forth his own brain child." Abruptly he changed the subject.

Hawthorne was puzzled, but dismissed the feeling. And presently McClellan's ferry blazed out of heaven and came to rest. It was a rather splendid sight, but Hawthorne found himself watching it with only half an eye. Most of him was still down under the ocean, in the living temple.

Several hours past nightfall, Hawthorne laid the collected

228

reports down on his desk. Chris Diehl and Mamoru Matsumoto had done a superb task; even in this earliest stage, their concept of enzymatic symbiosis offered possibilities beyond imagination. Here there was work for a century of science to come. And out of that work would be gotten a deeper insight into biological processes, including those of Earth, than men had yet hoped for. And who could tell what practical benefits? – But a person can only concentrate so long at a time. Hawthorne left his cubbyhole office and wandered down a passageway.

He glimpsed a number of the station's fifty men working. Some did their turn at routine chores, maintenance, sorting and baling of trade goods, and the rest. Others puttered happily with test tubes, microscopes, spectroscopes, and less understandable apparatus; or perched on lab benches, brewing coffee over a Bunsen burner while they argued; or sat feet on desk, pipe in mouth, hands behind head, and labored. Those who noticed Hawthorne hailed him as he passed. The station itself muttered familiarly, engines, ventilators, a faint quiver from the surrounding, forever unrestful waters.

Indeed it was good to be home again.

Hawthorne entered the wardroom. Jevons sat in a corner with his beloved Montaigne. McClellan and Cheng-tung were shooting dice. Otherwise it was deserted. The transparent wall overlooked a sea which tonight was black, roiled and laced with gold luminosity. A low haze diffused the aurora, so that the sky seemed made from infinite layerings of blue and ghostly green; a rainstorm approached from the west, blackness and lightning; a forty-foot ocean snake writhed from one horizon to another, its cresting jaws dripping phosphorescence.

McClellan looked up. "Hi, Nat," he said. "Want to sit in?"

"Right after Earth leave? What would I use for money?" Hawthorne went over to the samovar and tapped himself a cup.

"Eighter from Decatur," chanted Jimmy Cheng-tung. "Come on, boys, let's see that good old Maxwell distribution."

Hawthorne sat down at the table. His heartbeat sounded quick in his ears. No more delay: it was necessary that he share what he knew with all men. For the Venusians must be at least as intelligent as the builders of the Taj Mahal; they had finally decided the biped strangers were fit to be shown something; they would presumably have a whole planet's riches and mysteries to show on later occasions – Red bitterness scalded Hawthorne's tongue. "Cap," he said.

"Yes?" Jevons lowered his dogeared volume, patient as always at the interruption.

"Something happened today," said Hawthorne.

Jevons looked at him keenly. Cheng-tung finished a throw but did not move further, nor did McClellan. Outside there could be heard the heavy tread of waves and a rising wind.

"Go on," invited Jevons finally.

"I was on the trading pier and –"

Wim Dykstra entered. He did not walk, but strode. Hawthorne's voice stumbled into silence. The Dutchman dropped fifty clipped-together sheets of paper on the table. It seemed they should have clashed, like a sword thrown in challenge, but only the wind spoke. Dykstra's eyes blazed.

"I have it," he said.

"By God!" exploded Cheng-tung.

"What on Earth?" said Jevons' mild old voice.

"You mean off Earth," said McClellan. But tightness grew in him as he regarded Dykstra.

The geophysicist looked at them all for several seconds. He laughed curtly. "I was trying to think of a suitable phrase," he said. "None came to mind. So much for historic moments."

McClellan glanced at the papers and shuddered. "Let's keep the math within reason," he said. "What do those squiggles *mean*?"

Dykstra took out a cigarette and made a ceremony of lighting it. When smoke was in his lungs, he said shakily: "I have spent the past weeks developing the details of an old and little-known idea, first advanced by Ramsey in 1951. I have just completed the proof."

"We'd all like a Nobel Prize," said Jevons.

His trick of soothing dryness didn't work this time. Dykstra pointed at the glowing cigarette like a weapon and answered: "I do not care about that. I am interested in the largest and most significant engineering project of history."

230

They waited. Hawthorne began for no good reason to feel cold.

"The colonization of Venus," said Dykstra.

His words fell into silence as if into a well. And then, like the splash, Shorty McClellan said, "Huh? Isn't the Mindanao Deep closer to home?" But Hawthorne spilled hot tea over his own fingers.

Dykstra began to pace, up and down, smoking in short nervous drags. His words rattled out: "The basic reason for the steady decay of Terrestrial civilization is what one may call crampedness. If we had some place to go, what a difference! Oh, interplanetary emigration could not relieve much population pressure. But the fact that men *could* go, perhaps to hardship but surely to freedom and opportunity the fact of a frontier would be a liberating force even at home. And come worst to worst, if civilization on Earth must die, its best elements would survive on Venus. A second chance for humankind – do you see?"

"It's a pleasant theory," said Jevons slowly, "but I don't believe a permanent colony forced to live on elaborated rafts and wear masks every minute outdoors, could be successful."

"Of course not," said Dykstra. "That is why I spoke of an engineering project. The transformation of Venus to another Earth."

"Now wait a minute!" yelled Hawthorne, springing up.

No one noticed him. For them, in that moment, only the dark man who spoke like a prophet had reality. Hawthorne clenched his fists together and sat down, muscle by muscle, forcing himself.

Dykstra said through a veil of smoke: "Do you know the structure of this planet? Its mass puts it just beyond the Y-point –"

Even then, McClellan had to say, "No, I don't know. W'y point?"

But that was automatic, and ignored. Dykstra was watching Jevons, who nodded. The geophysicist went on, rapidly, "Now in the region where the mass-pressure curve jogs back, it is not a single-valued function. A planet of about 80% Earth's mass has three possible central pressures. There is the one Venus actually has, corresponding to a small score of comparatively low density and a large rocky

231

mantle. But there is also a higher-pressure situation, where the planet has a large degenerate core, hence a greater over-all density and smaller radius. And, on the other side of the Y-point, there is the case of lower central pressure: this means that the planet has no core at all but, like Mars, is merely built in layers of rock and magma.

"Now such an ambiguous condition makes it possible for the small core to change phase. This would not be true on Earth, which has too much mass, or Mars, which does not have enough; but Venus is very near the critical point. If the lower mantle collapsed, to make a larger and denser core, the released energy would appear as vibrations and ultimately as heat. If, on the other hand, the at-present degenerate atoms were to revert to a higher energy level, there would be blast waves traveling to the surface, dis-ruption on a truly astronomical scale – and, when things had quieted down, Venus would be larger and somewhat less dense than at present, without any true core."

He paused. McClellan exclaimed, "Hey! Do you mean this damn golf ball is liable to explode under us at any minute?"

"Oh, no," said Dykstra more calmly. "Venus does have a mass somewhat above the critical for existing temperatures. Its core is metastable, and there would be no reason to worry for billions of years. In any event, expansion would not be quite as violent as Ramsey believed, because Venus does lie beyond his Y-point. The explosion would not actu-ally throw much material into space. But it would, of course, raise continents."

"Wait!" That was from Jevons. He leaped up. (Haw-thorne sat slumped into nightmare. Outside, the wind lifted, and the storm moved closer.) "You mean ... increased planetary radius, magnifying surface irregularities –"

"And the upthrust of lighter rocks," nodded Dykstra. "It is all here in my calculations. I can predict that an area of dry land would result about equal to that on Earth. The newly exposed rocks will consume carbon dioxide in huge amounts, to form carbonates. At the same time, specially developed strains of Terrestrial photo-synthetic life – very like those now used to maintain the air on spaceships – can be sown. They will thrive, liberating oxygen in quan-

232

tity, until a balance is struck, which can be made identical with that now existing in Earth's atmosphere. The oxygen will form an ozone layer, thus blocking excessive ultraviolet radiation. Eventually, another Earth. Warmer, of course, and still cloudy, because of the near sun – a milder climate, nowhere too hot for man – but nevertheless, New Earth!"

Hawthorne shook himself, trying to find a strength which seemed drained from him. He thought dully that one good practical objection would end it all, and then he could wake up. "Hold on," he said in a stranger's voice. "It's a clever idea, but these processes – I mean, all right, perhaps continents could be raised in days, but changing the atmosphere would take millions of years."

"Ah, no," said Dykstra. "This also I have investigated. There are catalysts. And the growth of micro-organisms under favorable conditions, without any natural enemies, is exponential. Using only known techniques, I calculate that Venus could be made habitable in fifty years. To be sure, then must come the grinding of stone into soil, fertilizing, planting, the slow painful establishment of an ecology. But that, again, needs only to be started. Such a wealth of uranium and other minerals, now in short supply on Earth, would become available, that finance is no problem. The first settlers on Venus could make oases for themselves, miles wide, and enlarge these with automatic machinery till they covered the planet. Oceanic life would burgeon rapidly, without much human attention: hence the Venusians could soon carry on fishing and pelagiculture. I have estimates to show that the development of this world could exceed the population growth. The first-comers would have hope – their grandchildren will have wealth!"

Hawthorne sat back. "There are already Venusians," he mumbled.

Nobody heard him. "Say," objected McClellan, "how do you propose to blow up your balloon in the first place?"

"It is not obvious?" said Dykstra. "Increased core temperature can supply the energy to push a few tons of matter into a higher quantum state. This would lower the pressure enough to trigger the rest. We shall tap several thousand deep wells in the ocean floor, and touch off a

233

major nuclear explosion in each simultaneously. The instantaneous melting will safely contain most of the resulting radio-activity; what fallout does escape will be gone in a few decades. The bombs are available, they exist already in far larger amounts than needed for this project. Is this not a better use for them than waiting to give our sick civilization the deathblow?"

He walked over to the clear wall. The storm had reached them. Under the station caissons, the sea ramped and struck and shattered in radiant foam. The deep strong force of those impacts traveled up through steel and concrete like the play of muscles. Rain began to smash in great sheets on the decks. A continuous lightning flickered across Dykstra's lean countenance, and thunder toned.

"A world," he whispered.

Hawthorne stood up. He leaned forward, his fingertips resting on the table. They were cold. His voice still came to him like somebody else's. "No," he said.

"Eh?" Dykstra turned almost reluctantly from watching the storm. "What is wrong, Nat?"

"You'd sterilize a whole planet," said Hawthorne.

"Well ... true," admitted Dykstra. "Humanely, though. The first shock would destroy all organisms before they had time to feel it."

"But that's murder!" cried Hawthorne.

"Come, now," said Dykstra. "Let us not get sentimental. I admit it will be a pity to destroy life so interesting, but when children starve and one nation after another is driven to despotism –" He shrugged and smiled.

Jevons, still seated, stroked a thin hand across his book, as if he wanted to recall a friend five hundred years dead. There was trouble on his face. "This is too sudden, Wim," he said, very low. "Venus can teach us so much as it is. A thousand years is not too long to study everything here. We may gain a few continents at the price of something we cannot now imagine."

"Without some safety valve," warned Dykstra, "technological civilization may not last another century."

"You don't understand!"

Hawthorne shouted it at them, as if they were deaf men. "It isn't my job I'm worried about," he stammered, "or

234

science, or any such thing. It's the murder of an entire intelligent race."

"Oh, no!" muttered McClellan. "Lecture 28-B. I listened to it all the way from Earth."

"Please," said Cheng-tung. "The issue is important."

"The cetoids do pose an embarrassing problem," said Jevons. "Still, if there is a real human benefit to be gained, not even the most highly developed animals can –"

"The cetoids are more human than you are!" screamed Hawthorne.

"Wait a minute," said Dykstra. He moved from his vision of lightning, toward the ecologist. His face had lost its glory, it was concerned. "I realize you have opinions about this, Nat, but after all, you have no more evidence –"

"I do!" gasped Hawthorne. "I've got it at last. I've been wondering all day how to tell you, but now I must."

What Oscar had showed him came out in words, between shouts of thunder.

At the end, only rain, and wind, and the *brroom-brroom* of waves far below, continued to speak. McConnell stared at his hands, which turned a die between the fingers. Cheng-tung rubbed his chin and smiled with scant mirth. Jevons, however, became resolute; in an odd way, he looked relieved. Dykstra was harder to read, his mouth flickered from one expression to the next, Finally he got very busy lighting a new cigarette.

When the silence had become too much, Hawthorne said, "Well?" in a cracked tone.

"This does indeed put another complexion on the matter," said Cheng-tung.

"It isn't proof," snapped Dykstra. "Look at what social insects do on Earth."

"Hey," said McClellan, "be careful, Wim, or you'll prove we're just glorified ants ourselves."

"Exactly," said Hawthorne. "I'll take you out in a submarine tomorrow; I can find the temple, now that I know what direction to go. Add this to all the other hints we've had, and damn it, you know the cetoids are intelligent. They don't think identically with us, but they think at least as well."

"And could doubtless teach us a great deal," said Cheng-tung.

235

Jevons nodded. "I wish you had told me this earlier, Nat," he said. "Of course there would have been no argument."

"Oh, well," said McClellan, "I guess I'll have to settle for blowing up firecrackers on the Fourth of July."

The rain, wind-flung, hissed against the wall. Lightning still flared, blue-white, but the thunder wagon was rolling off. The sea ran with wild frosty fires.

Hawthorne looked at Dykstra. The Dutchman was tense as a wire. Hawthorne felt his own briefly relaxing sinews grow taut again.

"Well, Wim?" he said.

"Certainly, certainly!" said Dykstra. He had grown pale. The cigarette fell unnoticed from his lips. "I am still not absolutely convinced, but that may be only my own disappointment. I agree, the chance of genocide must not be taken."

"Good boy," smiled Jevons.

Dykstra smote a fist into his palm. "But my report," he said. "What shall I do with my report?"

So much pain was in his voice that Hawthorne felt shock, even though the ecologist had known this question must arise. Cheng-tung spoke the horror.

"I am afraid we must suppress it, Dr. Dykstra. Regrettably, our species cannot be trusted with the information."

Jevons bit his lip. "I hate to believe we'd exterminate a billion or more sentient beings," he said. "For our own ... convenience."

"We have done similar things often enough in the past," said Dykstra woodenly.

I've read enough history myself, Wim, to give a very partial roll call, thought Hawthorne. And he began to tick off on his fingers. *Jericho. Troy. Carthage. Jerusalem. The Albigensians. Bo-Russia. Tasmania. Andersonville. Wounded Knee. Buchenwald. Hiroshima. Budapest. New York. Moscow.*

That's enough for now, he thought, feeling a wish to vomit.

"But surely," began Jevons, "modern times –"

"It is barely possible that moral considerations may stay Earth's hand for a decade or two," said Dykstra. "But how long can we live in our growing, brutalizing poverty with such a temptation?"

"It it came to a choice between taking over Venus and watching our civilization go under," said McClellan, "frankly, I myself would say too bad for Venus. I've got a wife and kids."

"Be glad, then, that the choice will not be so clear-cut in your lifetime," said Cheng-tung.

Jevons nodded. He had suddenly become an old man, whose work neared an end. "You must destroy that report, Wim," he said. "Totally. None of us here can ever speak a word about it."

And now Hawthorne wanted to weep, but could not. There was a barrier in him, like fingers closed on his throat.

Dykstra drew a long breath. It exploded from him again in crow laughter. "Fortunately, I have been close-mouthed," he said. "I only trust the Company will not sack me for having produced nothing all these months."

"I'll see that they don't, Wim," said Jevons. His tone was immensely gentle.

Dykstra's hands shook a little, but he tore the first sheet off his report and crumpled it in an ashtray and set fire to it.

Hawthorne flung out of the room.

The air was cool outside, at least by contrast with daytime. The squall had passed and only a mild rain fell. In the absence of the sun he could go about with no more than shorts and mask. That was a strangely light sensation, like being a boy again in a summer forest which men had since cut down. Rain washed on the decks and into the water, two distinct kinds of noise, marvelously clear; the waves themselves still ran strong, swish and boom and a joyful swirling. Through the air shone a very faint auroral trace, barely enough to tinge it with rose. But mostly the luminance came from the ocean, where combers glowed green along their backs and utter white when they foamed. Here and there a knife of blackness cut the water, as some quick animal surged.

Hawthorne went down past the machine gun to the trading pier. Heavy seas broke over it, reaching to his knees and spattering him with phosphor drops. He clung to the rail and peered into rain, hoping Oscar would come.

"The worst of it is," he said aloud, "they all mean so well."

Wings passed overhead, only a shadow and whisper.

"The proverb is wrong," babbled Hawthorne. He gripped the rail, though he knew a certain hope that a wave would sweep him loose ... and afterward the Venusians would retrieve his bones and take no payment ... "Who shall watch the watchmen? Simple, the watchmen themselves, who're no use anyway if they aren't honorable. But what about the thing watched? It's on the enemy's side. Wim and Cap and Jimmy and Shorty – and I, we can keep a secret. But nature can't. How long before someone else repeats this work? We hope to expand the station. There'll be more than one geophysicist here, and – and – Oscar! Where the hell are you, Oscar?"

The ocean gave him reply, but in no language he knew.

He shivered, teeth clapping in his jaws. There was no reason to hang around here. It was perfectly obvious what had to be done. The sight of Oscar's ugly, friendly face wouldn't necessarily make the job easier. It might even make it harder. Impossible, perhaps.

Oscar might make me sane, thought Hawthorne. Ghosts of Sinaic thunder walked in his skull. *I can't have that. Not yet. Lord God of Hosts, why must I be this fanatical? Why not register my protest when the issue arises, like any normal decent crusader, organize pressure groups, struggle by all the legal proper means – No. As well appeal to the compassion of an avalanche.*

And I am possessed.

No man, he thought in the wet blowing night, no man could foresee everything. But one could make estimates, and act on them. If Venus Station stopped being profitable, Venus would not be visited again. Not for a very long time, during which many things could happen ... a Venusian race better able to defend itself, or even a human race that had learned self-control. Perhaps men would never return. Technological civilizations might well crumble and not be rebuilt. Maybe that was best, each planet working out its own lonely fate – But all this was speculation. There were immediate facts at hand. Hawthorne's brain was as clear as glass, and about as alive, when he contemplated them.

Item: If Venus Station was maintained, not to speak of its expansion, Dykstra's discovery was sure to be repeated.

238

Item: Venus Station was economically dependent on the cooperation of the cetoids.

Item: If Venus Station suffered ruin due to the reported hostile action of the cetoids, the Company was unlikely to try rebuilding it.

Item: Even if the Company did make such an attempt, it would soon be abandoned again if the cetoids really did shun it.

Item: Venus would then be left alone.

Item: If you believed in God and sin and so forth, you could argue that the real benefactor would be humankind, saved from the grisliest burden of deeds since one day on Golgotha.

Well –

Hawthorne seemed quite remote from himself. It was another body which stole back into the station.

Which prepared the explosives and set the time fuse.

Which took a submarine and some depth bombs, and departed, and saw Venus Station go to the bottom.

Which sought out the coralite sanctuary and bombed it to ruin.

Which surfaced again and machine-gunned the cetoids that swarmed bewildered around it.

Which called the spaceship on the submarine radio, giving a well-rehearsed story of Venusian attack and one man's escape, and heard the promise of rescue by a ferry.

Hawthorne saw the vessel descend at dawn, when the sky was turning to mother-of-pearl. Oscar's corpse rolled in the water next to his boat. Small pincered crustaceans were eating it. Oscar's blood was green.

Oh, God, thought Hawthorne, *please exist. Please make a hell for me.*

ARTHUR C. CLARKE: Before Eden

"I guess," said Jerry Garfield, cutting the engines, "that this is the end of the line." With a gentle sigh, the under-jets faded out; deprived of its air cushion, the scout car *Rambling Wreck* settled down upon the twisted rocks of the Hesperian Plateau.

There was no way forward; neither on its jets nor its tractors could S.5 – to give the *Wreck* its official name – scale the escarpment that lay ahead. The South Pole of Venus was only thirty miles away, but it might have been on another planet. They would have to turn back, and re-trace their four-hundred-mile journey through this nightmare landscape.

The weather was fantastically clear, with visibility of almost a thousand yards. There was no need of radar to show the cliffs ahead; for once, the naked eye was good enough. The green auroral light, filtering down through clouds that had rolled unbroken for a million years, gave the scene an underwater appearance, and the way in which all distant objects blurred into the haze added to the impression. Sometimes it was easy to believe that they were driving across a shallow sea bed, and more than once Jerry had imagined that he had seen fish floating overhead.

"Shall I call the ship, and say we're turning back?" he asked.

"Not yet," said Dr. Hutchins. "I want to think."

Jerry shot an appealing glance at the third member of the crew, but found no moral support there. Coleman was just as bad; although the two men argued furiously half the time, they were both scientists and therefore, in the opinion of a hardheaded engineer-navigator, not wholly responsible citizens. If Cole and Hutch had bright ideas about going forward, there was nothing he could do except register a protest.

Hutchins was pacing back and forth in the tiny cabin,

studying charts and instruments. Presently he swung the car's searchlight towards the cliffs, and began to examine them carefully with binoculars. Surely, thought Jerry, he doesn't expect me to drive up there! S.5 was a hover-track. not a mountain goat . . .

Abruptly, Hutchins found something. He released his breath in a sudden explosive gasp, then turned to Coleman.

"Look!" he said, his voice full of excitement. "Just to the left of that black mark! Tell me what you see."

He handed over the glasses, and it was Coleman's turn to stare.

"Well I'm damned," he said at length. "You were right. There *are* rivers on Venus. That's a dried-up waterfall."

"So you owe me one dinner at the Bel Gourmet when we get back to Cambridge. With champagne."

"No need to remind me. Anyway, it's cheap at the price. But this still leaves your other theories strictly on the crackpot level."

"Just a minute," interjected Jerry. "What's all this about rivers and waterfalls? Everyone knows they can't exist on Venus. It never gets cold enough on this steam bath of a planet for the clouds to condense."

"Have you looked at the thermometer lately?" asked Hutchins with deceptive mildness.

"I've been slightly too busy driving."

"Then I've news for you. It's down to two hundred and thirty, and still falling. Don't forget we're almost at the Pole, it's wintertime, and we're sixty thousand feet above the lowlands. All this adds up to a distinct nip in the air. If the temperature drops a few more degrees, we'll have rain. The water will be boiling, of course – but it will be water. And though George won't admit it yet, this puts Venus in a completely different light."

"Why?" asked Jerry, though he had already guessed.

"Where there's water, there may be life. We've been in too much of a hurry to assume that Venus is sterile, merely because the average temperature's over five hundred degrees. It's a lot colder here, and that's why I've been so anxious to get to the Pole. There are lakes up here in the highlands, and I want to look at them."

"But *boiling* water!" protested Coleman. "Nothing could live in that!"

"There are algae that manage it on Earth. And if we've learned one thing since we started exploring the planets, it's this: wherever life has the slightest chance of surviving, you'll find it. This is the only chance it's ever had on Venus."

"I wish we could test your theory. But you can see for yourself – we can't go up that cliff."

"Perhaps not in the car. But it won't be too difficult to climb those rocks, even wearing thermosuits. All we need do is walk a few miles toward the Pole; according to the radar maps, it's fairly level once you're over the rim. We could manage it – oh, twelve hours at the most. Each of us has been out for longer than that, in much worse conditions."

That was perfectly true. Protective clothing that had been designed to keep men alive in the Venusian lowlands would have an easy job here, where it was only a hundred degrees hotter than Death Valley in midsummer.

"Well," said Coleman, "you know the regulations. You can't go by yourself, and someone has to stay here to keep contact with the ship. How do we settle it this time – chess or cards?"

"Chess takes too long," said Hutchins, "especially when you two play it." He reached into the chart table and produced a well-worn pack. "Cut them, Jerry."

"Ten of spades. Hope you can beat it, George."

"So do I. Damn – only five of clubs. Well, give my regards to the Venusians."

Despite Hutchins' assurance, it was hard work climbing the escarpment. The slope was not too steep, but the weight of oxygen gear, refrigerated thermosuit, and scientific equipment came to more than a hundred pounds per man. The lower gravity – thirteen per cent weaker than Earth's – gave a little help, but not much, as they toiled up screes, rested on ledges to regain breath, and then clambered on again through the submarine twilight. The emerald glow that washed around them was brighter than that of the full moon on Earth. A moon would have been wasted on Venus, Jerry told himself; it could never have been seen from the surface, there were no oceans for it to rule – and the incessant aurora was a far more constant source of light.

They had climbed more than two thousand feet before the ground leveled out into a gentle slope, scarred here and there by channels that had clearly been cut by running water. After a little searching, they came across a gulley wide and deep enough to merit the name of river bed, and started to walk along it.

"I've just thought of something," said Jerry after they had travelled a few hundred yards. "Suppose there's a storm up ahead of us? I don't feel like facing a tidal wave of boiling water."

"If there's a storm," replied Hutchins a little impatiently, "we'll hear it. There'll be plenty of time to reach high ground."

He was undoubtedly right, but Jerry felt no happier as they continued to climb the gently shelving watercourse. His uneasiness had been growing ever since they had passed over the brow of the cliff and had lost radio contact with the scout car. In this day and age, to be out of touch with one's fellow men was a unique and unsettling experience. It had never happened to Jerry before in all his life; even aboard the *Morning Star*, when they were a hundred million miles from Earth, he could always send a message to his family and get a reply back within minutes. But now, a few yards of rock had cut him off from the rest of mankind; if anything happened to them here, no one would ever know, unless some later expedition found their bodies. George would wait for the agreed number of hours; then he would head back to the ship – alone. I guess. I'm not really the pioneering type, Jerry told himself. I like running complicated machines, and that's how I got involved in space flight. But I never stopped to think where it would lead, and now it's too late to change my mind . . .

They had travelled perhaps three miles towards the Pole, following the meanders of the river bed, when Hutchins stopped to make observations and collect specimens. "Still getting colder!" he said. "The temperature's down to one hundred and ninety-nine. That's far and away the lowest ever recorded on Venus. I wish we could call George and let him know."

Jerry tried all the wave bands; he even attempted to raise the ship – the unpredictable ups and downs of the planet's ionosphere sometimes made such long-distance reception possible – but there was not a whisper of a carrier wave above the roar and crackle of the Venusian thunderstorms.

243

"This is even better," said Hutchins, and now there was real excitement in his voice. "The oxygen concentration's way up – fifteen parts in a million. It was only five back at the car, and down in the lowlands you can scarcely detect it."

"But fifteen in a *million!*" protested Jerry. "Nothing could breathe that!"

"You've got hold of the wrong end of the stick," Hutchins explained. "Nothing does breathe it. Something *makes* it. Where do you think Earth's oxygen comes from? It's all produced by life – by growing plants. Before there were plants on Earth, our atmosphere was just like this one – a mess of carbon dioxide and ammonia and methane. Then vegetation evolved, and slowly converted the atmosphere into something that animals could breathe."

"I see," said Jerry, "and you think that the same process has just started here?"

"It looks like it. *Something* not far from here is producing oxygen – and plant life is the simplest explanation."

"And where there are plants, mused Jerry, "I suppose you'll have animals, sooner or later."

"Yes," said Hutchins, packing his gear and starting up the gulley, "though it takes a few hundred million years. We may be too soon – but I hope not."

"That's all very well," Jerry answered. "But suppose we meet something that doesn't like us? We've no weapons."

Hutchins gave a snort of disgust.

"And we don't need them. Have you stopped to think what we look like? Any animal would run a mile at the sight of us."

There was some truth in that. The reflecting metal foil of their thermosuits covered them from head to foot like flexible, glittering armor. No insects had more elaborate antennas than those mounted on their helmets and back packs, and the wide lenses through which they stared out at the world looked like blank yet monstrous eyes. Yes, there were few animals on Earth that would stop to argue with such apparitions; but any Venusians might have different ideas.

Jerry was still mulling this over when they came upon the lake. Even at that first glimpse, it made him think not of the life they were seeking, but of death. Like a black

244

mirror, it lay amid a fold of the hills; its far edge was hidden in the eternal mist, and ghostly columns of vapor swirled and danced upon its surface. All it needed, Jerry told himself, was Charon's ferry waiting to take them to the other side – or the Swan of Tuonela swimming majestically back and forth as it guarded the entrance to the Underworld . . .

Yet for all this, it was a miracle – the first free water that men had ever found on Venus. Hutchins was already on his knees, almost in an attitude of prayer. But he was only collecting drops of the precious liquid to examine through his pocket microscope.

"Anything there?" asked Jerry anxiously.

Hutchins shook his head.

"If there is, it's too small to see with this instrument. I'll tell you more when we're back at the ship." He sealed a test tube and placed it in his collecting bag, as tenderly as any prospector who had just found a nugget laced with gold. It might be – probably was – nothing more than plain water. But it might also be a universe of unknown, living creatures on the first stage of their billion-year journey to intelligence.

Hutchins had walked no more than a dozen yards along the edge of the lake when he stopped again, so suddenly that Garfield nearly collided with him.

"What's the matter?" Jerry asked. "Seen something?"

"That dark patch of rock over there. I noticed it before we stopped at the lake."

"What about it? It looks ordinary enough to me."

"I think it's grown bigger."

All his life, Jerry was to remember this moment. Somehow he never doubted Hutchins' statement; by this time he could believe anything, even that rocks could grow. The sense of isolation and mystery, the presence of that dark and brooding lake, the never-ceasing rumble of distant storms and the green flickering of the aurora – all these had done something to his mind, had prepared it to face the incredible. Yet he felt no fear; that would come later.

He looked at the rock. It was about five hundred feet away, as far as he could estimate. In this dim, emerald light it was hard to judge distances or dimensions. The rock – or whatever it was – seemed to be a horizontal slab of almost black material, lying near the crest of a low ridge.

There was a second, much smaller, patch of similar material near it; Jerry tried to measure and memorize the gap between them, so that he would have some yardstick to detect any change.

Even when he saw that the gap was slowly shrinking, he still felt no alarm – only a puzzled excitement. Not until it had vanished completely, and he realized how his eyes had tricked him, did that awful feeling of helpless terror strike into his heart.

Here were no growing or moving rocks. What they were watching was a dark tide, a crawling carpet, sweeping slowly but inexorably toward them over the top of the ridge.

The moment of sheer, unreasoning panic lasted, mercifully, no more than a few seconds. Garfield's first terror began to fade as soon as he recognized its cause. For that advancing tide had reminded him, all too vividly, of a story he had read many years ago about the army ants of the Amazon, and the way in which they destroyed everything in their path . . .

But whatever this tide might be, it was moving too slowly to be a real danger, unless it cut off their line of retreat. Hutchins was staring at it intently through their only pair of binoculars; he was the biologist, and he was holding his ground. No point in making a fool of myself, thought Jerry, by running like a scalded cat, if it isn't necessary.

"For heaven's sake," he said at last, when the moving carpet was only a hundred yards away and Hutchins had not uttered a word or stirred a muscle. "What *is* it?"

Hutchins slowly unfroze, like a statue coming to life.

"Sorry," he said. "I'd forgotten all about you. It's a plant, of course. At least, I suppose we'd better call it that."

"But it's *moving*!"

"Why should that surprise you? So do terrestrial plants. Ever seen speeded-up movies of ivy in action?"

"That still stays in one place – it doesn't crawl all over the landscape."

"Then what about the plankton plants of the sea? *They* can swim when they have to."

Jerry gave up; in any case, the approaching wonder had robbed him of words.

He still thought of the thing as a carpet – a deep-pile one, raveled into tassels at the edges. It varied in thickness as it moved; in some parts it was a mere film; in others, it heaped up to a depth of a foot or more. As it came closer and he could see its texture, Jerry was reminded of black velvet. He wondered what it felt like to the touch, then remembered that it would burn his fingers even if it did nothing else to them. He found himself thinking, in the lightheaded nervous reaction that often follows a sudden shock: "If there *are* any Venusians, we'll never be able to shake hands with them. They'd burn us, and we'd give them frostbite."

So far, the thing had shown no signs that it was aware of their presence. It had merely flowed forward like the mindless tide that it almost certainly was. Apart from the fact that it climbed over small obstacles, it might have been an advancing flood of water.

And then, when it was only ten feet away, the velvet tide checked itself. On the right and the left, it still flowed forward; but dead ahead it slowed to a halt.

"We're being encircled," said Jerry anxiously. "Better fall back, until we're sure it's harmless."

To his relief, Hutchins stepped back at once. After a brief hesitation, the creature resumed its slow advance and the dent in its front line straightened out.

Then Hutchins stepped forward again – and the thing slowly withdrew. Half a dozen times the biologist advanced, only to retreat again, and each time the living tide ebbed and flowed in synchronism with his movements. I never imagined, Jerry told himself, that I'd live to see a man waltzing with a plant . . .

"Thermophobia," said Hutchins. "Purely automatic reaction. It doesn't like our heat."

"*Our* heat!" protested Jerry. "Why, we're living icicles by comparison."

"Of course – but our suits aren't, and that's all it knows about."

Stupid of me, thought Jerry. When you were snug and cool inside your thermosuit, it was easy to forget that the refrigeration unit on your back was pumping a blast of heat out into the surrounding air. No wonder the Venusian plant had shied away . . .

"Let's see how it reacts to light," said Hutchins. He
247

switched on his chest lamp, and the green auroral glow was instantly banished by the flood of pure white radiance. Until Man had come to this planet, no white light had ever shone upon the surface of Venus, even by day. As in the seas of Earth, there was only a green twilight, deepening slowly to utter darkness.

The transformation was so stunning that neither man could check a cry of astonishment. Gone in a flash was the deep, somber black of the thick-piled velvet carpet at their feet. Instead, as far as their lights carried, lay a blazing pattern of glorious, vivid reds, laced with streaks of gold. No Persian prince could ever have commanded so opulent a tapestry from his weavers, yet this was the accidental product of biological forces. Indeed, until they had switched on their flood, these superb colors had not even existed, and they would vanish once more when the alien light of Earth ceased to conjure them into being.

"Tikov was right," murmured Hutchins. "I wish he could have known."

"Right about what?" asked Jerry, though it seemed almost a sacrilege to speak in the presence of such loveliness.

"Back in Russia, fifty years ago, he found that plants living in very cold climates tended to be blue and violet, while those from hot ones were red or orange. He predicted that the Martian vegetation would be violet, and said that if there were plants on Venus they'd be red. Well, he was right on both counts. But we can't stand here all day – we've work to do."

"You're sure it's quite safe?" asked Jerry, some of his caution reasserting itself.

"Absolutely – it can't touch our suits even if it wants to. Anyway, it's moving past us."

That was true. They could see now that the entire creature – if it was a single plant, and not a colony – covered a roughly circular area about a hundred yards across. It was sweeping over the ground, as the shadow of a cloud moves before the wind – and where it had rested, the rocks were pitted with innumerable tiny holes that might have been etched by acid.

"Yes," said Hutchins, when Jerry remarked about this. "That's how some lichens feed; they secrete acids that dissolve rock. But no questions, please – not till we get back to the ship. I've several lifetimes' work here, and a couple of hours to do it in."

This was botany on the run ... The sensitive edge of the huge plant-thing could move with surprising speed when it tried to evade them. It was as if they were dealing with an animated flapjack, an acre in extent. There was no reaction – apart from the automatic avoidance of their exhaust heat – when Hutchins snipped samples or took probes. The creature flowed steadily onward over hills and valleys, guided by some strange vegetable instinct. Perhaps it was following some vein of mineral; the geologists could decide that, when they analyzed the rock samples that Hutchins had collected both before and after the passage of the living tapestry.

There was scarcely time to think or even to frame the countless questions that their discovery had raised. Presumably these creatures must be fairly common, for them to have found one so quickly. How did they reproduce? By shoots, spores, fission, or some other means? Where did they get their energy? What relatives, rivals, or parasites did they have? This could not be the only form of life on Venus – the very idea was absurd, for if you had one species, you must have thousands ...

Sheer hunger and fatigue forced them to halt at last. The creature they were studying could eat its way around Venus – though Hutchins believed that it never went very far from the lake, as from time to time it approached the water and inserted a long, tubelike tendril into it – but the animals from Earth had to rest.

It was a great relief to inflate the pressurized tent, climb in through the air lock, and strip off their thermosuits. For the first time, as they relaxed inside their tiny plastic hemisphere, the true wonder and importance of the discovery forced itself upon their minds. This world around them was no longer the same; Venus was no longer dead – it had joined Earth and Mars.

For life called to life, across the gulfs of space. Everything that grew or moved upon the face of any planet was a portent, a promise that Man was not alone in this universe of blazing suns and swirling nebulae. If as yet he had found no companions with whom he could speak, that was only to be expected, for the light-years and the ages still stretched before him, waiting to be explored. Meanwhile, he must guard and cherish the life he found, whether it be upon Earth or Mars or Venus.

So Graham Hutchins, the happiest biologist in the solar system, told himself as he helped Garfield collect their refuse and seal it into a plastic disposal bag. When they deflated the tent and started on the homeward journey, there was no sign of the creature they had been examining. That was just as well; they might have been tempted to linger for more experiments, and already it was getting uncomfortably close to their deadline.

No matter; in a few months they would be back with a team of assistants, far more adequately equipped and with the eyes of the world upon them. Evolution had labored for a billion years to make this meeting possible; it could wait a little longer.

For a while nothing moved in the greenly glimmering, fog-bound landscape; it was deserted by man and crimson carpet alike. Then, flowing over the wind-carved hills, the creature reappeared. Or perhaps it was another of the same strange species; no one would ever know.

It flowed past the little cairn of stones where Hutchins and Garfield had buried their wastes. And then it stopped.

It was not puzzled, for it had no mind. But the chemical urges that drove it relentlessly over the polar plateau were crying! Here, here: Somewhere close at hand was the most precious of all the foods it needed – phosphorous, the element without which the sparks of life could never ignite. It began to nuzzle the rocks, to ooze into the cracks and crannies, to scratch and scrabble with probing tendrils. Nothing that it did was beyond the capacity of any plant or tree on Earth – but it moved a thousand times more quickly, requiring only minutes to reach its goal and pierce through the plastic film.

And then it feasted, on food more concentrated than any it had ever known. It absorbed the carbohydrates and the proteins and the phosphates, the nicotine from the cigarette ends, the cellulose from the paper cups and spoons. All these it broke down and assimilated into its strange body, without difficulty and without harm.

Likewise it absorbed a whole microcosmos of living crea-

tures – the bacteria and viruses which, upon an older planet, had evolved into a thousand deadly strains. Though only a very few could survive in this heat and this atmosphere, they were sufficient. As the carpet crawled back to the lake, it carried contagion to all its world.

Even as the Morning Star set course for her distant home, Venus was dying. The films and photographs and specimens that Hutchins was carrying in triumph were more previous even than he knew. They were the only record that would ever exist of life's third attempt to gain a foothold in the solar system.

Beneath the clouds of Venus, the story of Creation was ended.

Section VI

The Open Question

THE story of creation was ended. So is the story of our Fantastic Venus. We are now, literally, in touch with our sister planet. It will still feature in fiction; but inevitably the accent will be different; and although a few questions have been answered, Venus remains an open question.

How did the dreamers of the past score? Well, or badly? That depends on what you require of dreams. The science fiction writers have, in the main, been fairly conservative. The wildest ideas have come from others outside the field, astronomers among them. In one of my short stories, "There Is a Tide", which first appeared in 1955, my poet-hero, returning from a tour of the Cytherean world, says: "Venus is just a clean page, waiting for man to write what he will on it. Under that CO_2 blanket, there's been no spark of life; the mountains are bare of moss, the valleys lie innocent of grass; in the geological strata, no fossils sleep; no amoebae move in the seas ..." And yet – on that clean page, several men have written who find no place here: Immanuel Velikovski, with his spectacular cosmological theories; George Adamski, visited by Venusians who were both friendly and god-like, and had hieroglyphics on their gymshoes; Desmond Leslie, who calls Venus "The Home of the Gods", commenting that from Venus in the year of 18,617,841 B.C. came the first vehicle from space to land on our planet (but he cautiously adds in a footnote, "according to the Brahmin Tables").

Earlier writers were even more venturesome. The egregious Brewster expects that on other planets "Chemistry may have new elements, new gases, new acids, new alkalis, new earths and new metals; – geology, new rocks, new classes of cataclysms, and new periods of change."

What of good old Admiral Smyth, whose *Cycle of Celestial Objects* is approvingly quoted by Brewster? He states his beliefs forthrightly in this fashion: "Thus the whole firmament, with its countless and glorious orbs, which, though sustaining apparently independent positions, are but individual constituents of one Majesty of creation, countenances the sagacity of the ancient dogma, that GOD WORKS BY GEOMETRY." Getting to work with his compasses, God, in the Admiral's mind, may have produced the perfect sphere, to roll in perpetual motion about Venus's orbit like Whewell's Witch-Ball Model!

Whatever God works by, Man clearly works by Anthropomorphy, and has clung as long as possible to the idea of life – intelligent life, human-like life – on Venus. This idea is particularly titillating if the climate there can be made out to be even worse than our own!

One of the most engaging speculations along these lines was made by Richard Proctor, who played a part in the great Plurality of Worlds debate. The distinguished author of *Half-Hours with the Telescope* tackles head-on the question of how Venus's axial inclination affects her inhabitants, and produces this thought-bubble:

"It has been said, on the authority of observers of some eminence, that her axis is inclined only 15° to the plane of her orbit. If this is really the case, a number of singular and somewhat complicated relations are exhibited, the result of which it may be interesting to present to the reader – especially as there is very little doubt that in the case of Uranus the axial peculiarity of this sort actually exists.

"In the first place, the arctic regions of Venus extend within fifteen degrees of her equator (if the axis is really bowed as supposed), while the tropics extend within fifteen degrees of her poles, – so that two zones, larger by far than the temperature zones of our earth, belong both to her arctic and her tropical regions.

"An inhabitant of the regions near either pole has to endure extremes of heat and cold, such as would suffice to destroy nearly every race of living being subsisting upon

253

the earth. During the summer, the sun circles continually close to the point overhead, so that, day after day, he pours down his rays with an intensity of heat and light exceeding nearly two-fold the mid-day light and heat of our own tropical sun.

"Only for a short time, in autumn and in spring, does the sun rise and set in those regions. A spring or autumn day, like one of our days at those seasons, lasts about twelve hours; but the sun attains at noon, in spring or autumn, a height of only a few degrees above the horizon. Then presently comes on the terrible winter, lasting about three of our months, but far more striking in its characteristics even than the long winter night of our polar regions. For, near our poles, the sun approaches the horizon at the hour corresponding to noon; and though he does not show his face, he yet lights up the southern skies with a cheering twilight glow. But during the greater part of the long night of Venus's polar regions, the sun does not appear within many degrees of the horizon.

"Nay, he is farther below the horizon than the midnight winter sun of our arctic regions.

"Thus, unless the skies are lit up with auroral splendours, an intense darkness prevails during the polar winter which must add largely to the horrors of that terrible season. Certainly, none of the human races upon our earth could bear the alterations between these more than polar terrors and an intensity of summer heat far exceeding any with which we are familiar on earth."

Warming to his theme, Proctor goes on to demonstrate how life at the equator would be even more miserable than at the poles!

From a human point of view, we now know that Venus is far more unendurable than Proctor cheerfully imagined. Indeed, it is more horrible than most writers imagined. From Proctor's point of view, more amazing is the fact that we have sent probes to scan the planet so closely, and have actually landed a probe there. Even from our own contemporary view-point, it remains amazing to think that men will one day walk on that uninviting surface. Dare we doubt that the vision embodied in Poul Anderson's *The Big Rain* will not one day be turned into unromantic fact?

Perhaps a more profound question is this: how far will

254

the forward-looking of men – exemplified, shall we say, by Proctor and Munro and Anderson and Firsoff and Clarke – have influenced that future and at present unimaginable landfall? What hidden strand will connect the imaginings of Flammarion with the eventual colonization of Venus by some yet-unborn space-merchants? The answers seem to lie deep in the complex make-up of man, the predator with a conscience, the primate with creativity.

We have dreamed of "Venusians"; they do not exist. But one thing is sure: if they had existed, under that deep and murky cloud-cover, they would never have dreamed of *us*.

So to our final section, which brings the story up to 1968 and needs little comment.

Sir Bernard Lovell, F.R.S., is the Director of Jodrell Bank Experimental Radio Astronomy Station, which co-operated with Russian scientists during the period when Russian and American space probes were nearing Venus in October, 1967. His article first appeared in the *Times* on 30th October.

The fragment, *Dream of Distance,* was written only a month later by an anonymous drug addict while under the influence of LSD. In its musings, its style, it belongs unmistakably to our times and outlook.

From that same momentous October comes John Davy's newspaper article on Venus, to carry us on beyond the narrow and nostalgic confines of this book.

What is up-to-date will be dated. What is present will be past. What is future will come. But not everything is inevitable. We may know much less of Venus than we imagine; but that, of course, is a truism, and applies equally to ourselves. We may become the sinister Venusians yet.

255

SIR BERNARD LOVELL: Some Mysteries of Venus Resolved

At 5 a.m. on October 18th I suggested to the journalists and reporters packed into the smoke-laden entrance hall of the control building at Jodrell Bank that they might step outside. The planet Venus was resplendent in the sky 48,500,000 miles distant. It was hard to believe that the bleeps emanating from a loud-speaker behind us had their origin in a ton of material dispatched from earth four months earlier which at that moment was only 10,000 miles from the planet and hurtling towards it with a speed of about 23,000 miles an hour.

A few days earlier Academician Keldysh, the President of the Soviet Academy of Sciences, had asked if we would use the radio telescope at Jodrell Bank to record the terminal phase of this enterprise. The nature of his message left little doubt that something much more than a close fly-by, or destructive impact with the planet was intended. Indeed, the signs were that the Soviet scientists were hoping to penetrate the Venus cloud cover with working instruments and possibly transmit to earth information about the surface.

In the moon experiments the Soviets and the Americans had succeeded in soft-landing instrument packages by firing retro-rockets, thereby slowing the spacecraft so that it touched down gently on the lunar surface. We considered it most unlikely that a similar direct method could be employed for Venus because of the much higher velocity of approach and the dense atmosphere. Indeed we thought that as the spacecraft approached to a few hundred miles from Venus, retro-rockets would be fired to slow the package so that it could be captured by the gravitational field of the planet and that a subsequent manoeuvre would be carried out later to make the spacecraft fall into the atmosphere of the planet.

256

At 5.30 a.m. B.S.T. our measurements showed that the probe was only about 3,000 miles from the planet, accelerating smoothly and rapidly, apparently on a collision course to an inevitable destructive impact. The rapid acceleration continued in the following minutes and at 5.38 a.m. as the terminal velocity was approached the signals ceased abruptly. We had no time to discuss this surprising end to the signals because 15 seconds later another much weaker signal appeared as far as we could tell from an instrument at rest with respect to the planet.

Indeed the Soviets had confounded our expectations by carrying out an experiment of classic elegance. By a technique which has not yet been revealed but which by any standards must be considered to be one of the most brilliant technological feats of all time, they succeeded in injecting, or separating, an instrumented canister from the main spacecraft which proceeded to descend slowly to the surface by parachute. At the moment of ejection the spacecraft was covering about seven miles every second, and the whole probe was within seconds of destruction by impact. It must be presumed that the procedure was built in as a programme to be carried out after the receipt of a signal from ground command, the actual moment of ejection being determined by measurements in the probe itself of some parameter indicative of distance from the planet. It would be impossible to command the ejection directly from the ground since radio signals take 4.3 minutes to cover the distance separating earth and planet.

The weak signals from the capsule continued for a further 90 minutes at constant strength and then ceased abruptly. Although no specific statement has yet been made by the Soviet authorities we incline to the opinion that the canister was descended slowly through the Venusian atmosphere during this period and that the instruments ceased transmitting when the payload reached the planetary surface or shortly afterwards.

During the whole period of contact with the main spacecraft and the canister, telemetry was being received. The Russian scientists alone are in a position to interpret these data, but even the preliminary announcement of the results indicates the high scientific importance of the experiment.

Although Venus is such a brilliant sight in the night sky our precise knowledge of the planet has been limited to a few data derived from a study of its orbit in the solar system. Physically it is almost a twin with the earth. The planet is slightly smaller by 3 per cent in its diameter, 9 per cent in volume and 19 per cent in mass. The surface gravity is 14 per cent less than on earth. The planet moves in an orbit closer to the sun than the earth's orbit – with a mean-distance of 67 million miles compared with the 93 million miles which separates the earth from the sun. We also know that the planet takes just under 225 earth days to complete an orbit around the sun. A few years ago the age old controversy about the rate of rotation was settled by radar measurements, and now we know that the axial period of rotation is 247 days so that the face of the planet presented to the sun changes slowly. Beyond that, exact knowledge ends and speculation begins.

Two centuries have now elapsed since the Russian astronomer M. V. Lomonosov observed the transit of Venus across the solar disc and from the haziness of the planet's appearance concluded that it was surrounded by an atmosphere "equal to, if not greater than, that which envelops our earthly sphere". The assumption that its atmosphere was similar to our own led to the emergence of the idea that Venus was a luxuriant swampy abode of primitive vegetation, probably with insects and amphibians. These fanciful ideas had to be abandoned in 1922 when C. St. John and S. B. Nicholson working at the Mt. Wilson Observatory studied the spectrum of solar light reflected from the Venusian cloud cover. They concluded that, at least to the atmospheric level penetrated by the solar light, the amount of oxygen in the planet's atmosphere must be less than a thousandth of that in the earth's atmosphere, and that there was little evidence of water vapour. Ten years later W. S. Adams and T. Dunham, using the 100-inch telescope on Mt. Wilson, confirmed these results and also discovered features in the spectrum indicating that a large amount of carbon dioxide must be present in the atmosphere of Venus.

Since those discoveries there have been many speculations about the nature of the Venusian surface. A satisfactory solution must explain the presence of the variable cloud formations observable in the ultra-violet as well as the strange constitution of the atmosphere. The problem has been exacerbated by the wide range of temperature measurements. Measurements in the infra-red indicated a temperature of $-36°F$. No one knew to which level in the atmosphere these measurements applied, but it was assumed to be at the tops of the major cloud features. Then in the last few years the radio telescopes have been able to measure the thermal emission from the planet on very short radio wavelengths which penetrate deep into the atmosphere. Apparently the temperature increased as the wavelength of observation increased, and it was concluded that at the surface the temperature must be more than $600°F$. These extreme temperatures were confirmed by the radio and infra-red measurements from the Mariner II spacecraft which passed Venus at a distance of 21,600 miles in December, 1962. Indeed the Mariner measurements suggested that the surface temperature might be even higher than $600°F$.

Now the Soviet scientists have parachuted their measuring instruments into this hostile environment and in 90 minutes seem to have settled many of the major arguments. They have confirmed that the atmosphere is more than 98 per cent carbon dioxide, that the temperature at the surface is exceedingly high, and, perhaps most significant of all, that the atmospheric pressure on the planetary surface is 15 atmospheres.

An immediate reaction to these measurements is that at least we now know *why* Venus is so hot on the surface. The conventional explanation is that the planetary surface is hot for the same basic reason that a greenhouse is hot when the sun shines on the glass. In this concept, some visible light from the sun penetrates the Venusian cloud layer and heats up the surface. The planetary surface then radiates at longer wavelengths in the infra-red, and this radiation cannot escape because of absorption and scattering in the atmosphere – so the planet's surface gets much hotter than it would in the absence of an atmosphere.

Unfortunately for this simple explanation it is known that the carbon dioxide atmosphere of Venus could not present a sufficient barrier to the escape of the infra-red radiation unless small amounts of water vapour were present – and no one has been able to detect water vapour. It has been realized though that this difficulty would disappear if there was a very high atmospheric pressure on Venus, then the carbon dioxide would be sufficiently opaque in the infra-red to produce the necessary greenhouse effect. Now from the Soviet measurements it looks very much as though this is precisely the situation.

The fanciful and exotic ideas about Venus must be abandoned. Its surface is hostile in the extreme. Hard rock or dust, probably almost featurelss, a temperature nearly three times the boiling point of water and an atmosphere 15 times denser than on earth, and of almost pure carbon dioxide.

ANONYMOUS: Dream of Distance

You are watching this film, eager to taste its first scenes. All you have ben treated to as yet, as the flimsy curtains draw back and reveal a monstrous silent sea, is a great panorama of waves and sunlight. Islands sail in the distance like ships.

No titles, no credits, fly at you over the water. There is no music. Yes, there is sound – the noise of unease, a noise that does not belong here. Someone standing outside your bedroom door, footsteps on the roof, a furry thing following you underground.

All the time, you travel over the water.

The islands show green. That and a certain quality in the atmosphere – as indefinable as the dry and melancholy-sweet flavour of life – tell you it is April, Spring is beginning again, is surely coming again, just as fools and wise men had every reason to expect it would.

And April is sacred to Venus.

Boats scatter on the water. The men with their dark faces are at home in them; they fit the boats as the boats fit the waves. In one boat, a man sings a song to himself as he looks down into the water. Nothing is still here except his regard, and even that cannot anchor the boat; it glides evasively and some feet below on the dappled bottom of the sea a clouded doppelganger moves with it. All things have counterparts.

While you are growing into a straight true lad, learning your lessons, while you decided what you would do and be in life, while the red fuses burned you into bud, you also had a counterpart, a white silent thing – perhaps a car crash, say. It lay with all the other stills on some future desk, to be glanced at sideways, not recognised. One day you would have to sit at that desk and pick it up. Stop and listen in the woods of April, as you do homage to Venus, listen to that furry thing moving underground as you move, listen to the noise of unease.

So the viewpoint moves over the water to no sound of lapping.

Caesar traced his descent from Aeneas who sprang, it is said, from the union of Mars and Venus. So great Caesar promoted the worship of Venus Victrix. This is true Mediterranean water, where vessels sailed bearing news of her verdant name. This sea too has its counterparts.

On this planet, in this place, the sea at the middle of the Earth, men worship Venus in the fourth month.

Do you see the foam on the small waves? The breeze blows sharp. And those flat breastless isles? Could they be the islands of the Cyclades, where Greek Aphrodite was born? That furred sound of unease is hushed. You never heard it go, but in its place, sweetly, sounds a honeyed voice. Ah, young lovers, lie close together tonight; breathe each other's breath, taste each other's juices, be uncurbed. Although the moon may rise here evermore, although the seas lap for ever at Naxos' shore, your loving limbs will sink below next moment's wave! All those bright carmines of your secret places, their spring is also autumn; no singer's lip can give you melody tomorrow!

You see it all on the forward-rushing screen. You take it for real. No other animal knows your happiness, no other animal can plumb your sorrows. No animal but you could carve an Aphrodite or build himself a lead grave.

Now there is another thing coming on the waves. You cannot distinguish what it is.

261

Those Romans of the classic age – they fruitfully confused Aphrodite with Venus. The common sea-faring men kissed her marble mons veneris to secure themselves from storm and shipwreck. So the goddess girls merge, so legends merge. Mistakes are made, never intentionally, but with a higher intent, creating all art, fructifying.

I too have pressed my lips there, sucked and kissed. Nothing I cared for shipwreck then! Behind that grasping body, mediterranean, garden-flowering fertile, Cytherean, furred, sourceful and resourceful, the worshipped girls, and duskier hags, Ishtar and Astarte.

It is a gate beyond the prow. A massive double gate, arched perhaps of wood, mossed, and made of dull iron or some leaden prehistoric timber, scarred, furred with lichen, spurred with seawrack.

Forward more slowly. The great gates are closed. Sea all about, silent, waiting. The sparrow the dove the swan the swallow wait there. You are crying. In the fourth month on Venus, maybe they worship some phantom Earth that in a Cytherean mind accumulated legends. The beautiful light goes underground before these prehistoric doors.

Ships wait to go in. Slowly they open, unexpectedly, great lock gates grating in a sombre gait. Beyond another world of counterparts. You go in and all you inherit is now a saga – bearded or beardless they sing it in your pristine kingdom; but because this is my story the great gates close again and the mediterranean light shines. Venus and Mars have never been so close.

Now says the audience, how characteristic that he should tell his story twice removed. But perhaps if I had gone I would not be here now. Aren't these voyages mine still? Do not verdant islands still sail like ships? What if I weep? Moisture is elemental, and silently the curtains draw together and draw together while the sea is still moon-blue. My bitch love this is your display.

You and I lie in the auditorium as the curtains draw together, hissing with the sound of waves and serpents.

JOHN DAVY: Venus Mystery for Scientists

"WHERE has all the nitrogen gone?" This is the main question astronomers are asking since the Russians landed instruments on the surface of Venus last week and found that there is no nitrogen in the planet's atmosphere.

Dr. Carl Sagan, of the Harvard Smithsonian Astrophysical Laboratory, told *The Observer* yesterday: "It beats me. It is very surprising. It means we do not understand the source of nitrogen in our own atmosphere."

The absence of nitrogen will be a major obstacle in conceiving even exotic forms of life which could exist on Venus. Dr. Sagan and his colleague, Dr. Morowitz, of Yale University, recently "designed" a theoretical organism which might be able to live a floating existence in the clouds of Venus, where it would be cooler. They suggested it could be buoyed up by a "balloon", a thin membrane filled with hydrogen, and feed on mineral dusts blown up from the planetary surface, captured on the organism's sticky lower surface.

However, Dr. Sagan's organism would need nitrogen – as does every form of life we know. Nitrogen is essential for protein and for nucleic acids which embody the "genetic code".

I have been asking one or two British scientists if they can think of exotic forms of life which might be viable on the Venus now revealed by the Russians. Dr. Pat Clarke, of University College, London, told me that some extraordinary bacteria have just been found living in hot springs in an American desert in temperatures of 92 deg. centigrade – almost hot enough to boil an egg. They have evolved a special method involving sulphur atoms to prevent their proteins being broken down. This shows what can be done – but is still a far cry from the temperatures of 280 deg.

centigrade reported by the Russians, when all water – essential to all terrestrial life – would be steam.

Thus on the Venusian surface, "life" might have to embody substances which are liquid at 280 degrees, build a strange genetic code, possibly with compounds of phosphorus or selenium, and feed on carbon dioxide and dust. It does not sound promising – but terrestrial life achieves so many surprising things in ways still poorly understood that the biochemists are not willing to rule out Venusian life altogether.

Prospects of life apart, the Russian information has prompted a whole string of still unanswered questions. One is whether the Russians intended the machine to broadcast from the surface after landing. One Moscow release says that it was designed to roll into an upright position after touching down and point a "parabolic antenna" at the earth to beam back signals.

None of this seems to have happened. The recordings at Jodrell Bank indicate that after parachuting down through the atmosphere for $1\frac{1}{2}$ hours, the probe fell abruptly silent on hitting the planetary surface. This raises further questions. One Russian statement says that "for several minutes" the probe ceased to sink through the atmosphere, and was apparently "floating".

This might indicate upcurrents in the atmosphere. There could well be considerable turbulence in the hot, dense carbon dioxide gas. But the Jodrell Bank trackers say there was no indication of an irregular descent of the probe.

Scientists would very much like to know if it has indicated the composition of the yellowish outer clouds of Venus, which hide the surface completely, and apparently contain ice crystals. Two American scientists at Lockheed's Palo Alto laboratory in California, Gerald Davidson and Albert Anderson, have recently suggested that there could be intense volcanic activity on Venus, releasing quantities of dust and gas.

But the absence of nitrogen is likely to cause most discussion (although a single measurement is a slender basis for debate). Venus used to be called the "twin" of earth, as it is much the same size, and seemed to include water in its atmosphere. But it is becoming clear that it is, in fact, a very odd planet. Existing theories of planetary evolution assume that nitrogen should be released by "outgassing," a volcanic heating action which releases gases from the interior at an early stage in planetary evolution.

Dr. Sagan said yesterday: "On earth, nitrogen is an unreactive gas and so one has always expected that it was left over from earlier stages of outgassing. Since nitrogen is cosmically abundant, we expected the atmosphere of other planets like the earth, especially Mars and Venus, to be similar." Thus either some novel processes must be conceived for Venus or ideas about the evolution of the earth must be revised. Dr. Sagan also said that the Russian report of an absence of argon gas in the Venusian atmosphere was a surprise.

This adds a further mystery to one recently established by radar studies of the planet: uniquely in the solar system, it revolves "backwards" – in the opposite direction from its motion round the sun – once every 250 days. Professor R. A. Lyttleton of Cambridge told me yesterday that this presents "a great theoretical problem." Ideas about the formation of planets suggest that they should all be spinning the same way. Possibly Venus has become turned upside down, so that its "south Pole" is near where its "north Pole" ought to be. But how this could happen is obscure.

When fuller details become available, some questions may be answered. But this will not alter the basic oddity of the planet. Thus the Russian's extraordinary feat (which to scientists is vastly more interesting than any manned moon landing is likely to prove) will pose as many new problems as it has provided answers.

STOP PRESS

SCIENTIST SAYS ICECAPS ON VENUS WOULD MAKE LIFE POSSIBLE

From *The New York Times,* 9th March, 1968
By Evert Clark

Dr. Willard F. Libby, Nobel prize-winning chemist, said today that the planet Venus might be covered with giant icecaps that made life there "distinctly possible".

He thus revived a theory generally abandoned several years ago after studies from earth and by space probes indicated Venus was too hot and dry to support oceans or icecaps.

If there were icecaps, most scientists agree, life in some form might very well exist on Venus.

In a report in *Science* magazine, and in a telephone interview, Dr. Libby pictured a cloud-covered planet of "perpetual snow" over the icefields and extremely high temperatures in the equatorial zone.

But where the hot equatorial winds strike the edges of the icecaps, "small oceans and fresh-water lakes" may be formed, he said.

In these bodies of water, "any forms of life" that could live in the high concentrations of carbon dioxide found on Venus "may well exist," he said.

Dr. Libby, a former member of the Atomic Energy Commission, is a professor of chemistry and director of the Institute of Geophysics and Planetary Physics at the University of California at Los Angeles.

He assumes that the earth and Venus are similar in chemical composition and volcanic history. He believes that the findings of America's Mariner 5 spacecraft, which passed near Venus last October, and the Soviet Union's Venera 4, which landed an instrumented capsule on the planet at the same time, can be "interpreted as evidence of giant polar icecaps holding the water that must have come out of the volcanoes", along with the carbon dioxide measured by Venera 4.

The two space probes confirmed earlier belief that temperatures on Venus – at least in the equatorial region – were extremely high compared with those on earth. But they were not found to be quite as high as scientists had estimated from the earth-based studies.

Dr. Libby's theory also assumes that the slow rotation of Venus gives the planet almost no north-to-south and east-to-west winds, leaving it only with the vertical winds rising from the hot equatorial surface.

Space agency scientists said today that if Dr. Libby were right about the winds, the rest of his theory was certainly plausible. Icecaps could form, lakes could develop at the edges of the ice sheets, and the water could support some kind of life, they said.

But they said Dr. Libby "has moved much faster than" experimenters who are still analyzing data from Mariner 5 and others who are trying to develop a new understanding of the Venusian atmosphere.

Within a few weeks, work on such an atmosphere should yield conclusions about the winds. In the meantime, Dr. Libby appears to be the first scientist in several years to publish the speculation that the icecaps could exist in view of the high equatorial temperatures.

"It is an excellent stimulus to debate about Venus and about life there," one scientist said. "Personally, I am not a biologist, but the high carbon dioxide content suggests to me yeast fermentation."

"Wouldn't it be wonderful if Venus was a floating lake of bourbon?"

Venera 4 found the Venusian atmosphere very thick and very rich in carbon dioxide.

Dr. Libby found it "extremely exciting", however, that the Soviet probe also found from one third to two thirds as much oxygen in the Venusian atmosphere as in the earth's atmosphere.

He emphasized that none of the laboratory studies of

the kinds of life than can exist in atmospheres of other planets had included attempts to support life in a high carbon dioxide atmosphere.

Dr. Libby said he was now building a room-sized "greenhouse" in which he will attempt to simulate the dense atmosphere to see if any form of life can be supported there.

Venus has long been considered the most earth-like of the planets. Thus it was only with some reluctance that many scientists discarded their notions that life might exist there as the evidence of extreme temperatures mounted.

Dr. Libby said he had been following closely the reports of the Soviet findings and had discussed his ideas with a number of American scientists.

"I haven't found a biologist who says there couldn't be life there," he said.

Bibliography
of principal non-fiction works consulted

Anon. [William Whewell]: *Of the Plurality of Worlds*, 1851.

Arrhenius, Svante: *The Destinies of the Stars*. Authorised translation from the Swedish by J. E. Fries, New York, 1918.

Ball, Sir Robert S.: *The Story of the Heavens*, 1886.

Bester, Alfred: *The Life and Death of a Satellite*. Boston, 1966.

Brewster, Sir David: *More Worlds Than One*. N.D.

Cade, C. Maxwell: *Other Worlds Than Ours*. 1966.

Firsoff, V. A.: *Exploring the Planets*. 1964.

Flammarion, Camille: *Popular Astronomy*. Translated from the French by J. Ellard Gore. 1894.

Green, Roger Lancelyn: *Into Other Worlds*. 1957.

Heuer, Kenneth: *Men of Other Planets*. N.Y., 1963.

Jackson, Francis and Moore, Patrick: *Life in the Universe*. 1962.

Leslie, Desmond and Adamski George: *Flying Saucers Have Landed*. 1953.

Moore, Patrick: *The Planets*. 1962.

Nourse, Alan E.: *Nine Planets*. N.Y., 1960.

Proctor, Richard: *Other Worlds Than Ours*. 1870.

Rudaux, Lucien, and Vancouleurs, G. de: *Larousse Encyclopaedia of Astronomy*, 1959.

Schiaparelli, G.: *Astronomy in the Old Testament*. Authorised English Translation. Oxford. 1905.

Shklovskii, I. S., and Sagan, Carl: *Intelligent Life in the Universe*. N.Y., 1966.

Thiel, Rudolf: *And There Was Light*. Translated from the German by Richard and Clara Winston. 1958.

Von Braun, Wernher, and Ordway III, Frederick I: *History of Rocketry and Space Travel*. 1967.

Index to the Science-Fiction Magazines, 1926–1950. Compiled and arranged by Donald B. Day. Portland, 1952.

The M.I.T. Science Fiction Society's Index to the S-F Magazines, 1951–1965. Compiled by Erwin S. Strauss. Cambridge, Mass., 1965.

'The future of the novel
lies in Burroughs' hands'
Books and Bookmen
'The only American novelist
living today who may conceivably
be possessed by genius'
Norman Mailer

NOVA EXPRESS 25p
William Burroughs

The free-wheeling, controversial
author of *The Naked Lunch* and
Dead Fingers Talk takes his
indubitable talents for another
walk on the wild side in
Nova Express.

The plot is simple: The Nova Police
Squad is engaged in a campaign to
destroy a mob of drug pushers and
perversion purveyors, and into
the pages of this straightforward
story Burroughs pours all his
searing knowledge and experience of
the junkie world, homosexual world,
of the submerged world of America's
affluent society

'The greatest satirist since Swift'
Jack Kerouac

SOME PANTHER AUTHORS

Norman Mailer
Jean-Paul Sartre
Len Deighton
Henry Miller
Georgette Heyer
Mordecai Richler
Gerard de Nerval
James Hadley Chase
Juvenal
Violette Leduc
Agnar Mykle
Isaac Asimov
Doris Lessing
Ivan Turgenev
Maureen Duffy
Nicholas Monsarrat
Fernando Henriques
B. S. Johnson
Edmund Wilson
Olivia Manning
Julian Mitchell
Christopher Hill

Robert Musil
Ivy Compton-Burnett
Chester Himes
Chaucer
Alan Williams
Oscar Lewis
Jean Genet
H. P. Lovecraft
Anthony Trollope
Robert van Gulik
Louis Auchincloss
Vladimir Nabokov
Colin Spencer
Alex Comfort
John Barth
Rachel Carson
Simon Raven
Roger Peyrefitte
J. G. Ballard
Mary McCarthy
Kurt Vonnegut
Alexis Lykiard

PANTHER SCIENCE FICTION
presents

THIRTY THOUSAND YEARS OF
GALACTIC HISTORY
with the uniform edition of
Isaac Asimov's
classic *Foundation* trilogy

FOUNDATION
FOUNDATION AND EMPIRE
SECOND FOUNDATION

each 25p

'At last, for the first time in Britain, all three of the
Foundation books are available at the same time.
The *Foundation* trilogy is probably the prime example
of "straight" science fiction published to date. No
other book can compare with the magnificent scope
that this series offers. For anyone who has not yet
read all three parts I heartily recommend them'

VECTOR
(*The Journal of the British
Science Fiction Association*)

Th[e]
B[ook of]
Rude Jokes
for *Older*
Girls

Zymurgy Publishing, 2006

The moral rights of authors Amanda Thomas and

Martin Ellis have been asserted.

A CIP catalogue record for this book is available from the British
library.

Cover artwork Paul Goldsmith
Cover models Andrea and Keely
Cover design Nick Ridley

Printed in the UK by CPI William Clowes Ltd,
Beccles, NR34 7TL
ISBN 1 903506 23 9
ISBN 978 1903506 23 3

Published by Zymurgy Publishing,
Newcastle upon Tyne
10 9 8 7 6 5 4 3
© Zymurgy Publishing 2006
reprinted 2008

This is a collection of jokes gathered from many people. We have often discovered several versions of the same joke – as jokes get retold they evolve.

Zymurgy Publishing is grateful to the following for their contributions:-

J. Allen, N. Allon, B. Bibby, R. Bland, P. Brettle, P. Goldsmith, D. Hiscocks, J. Lee, H. Limon and R. Northam.

"It's not the man in my life that counts - it's the life in my man."

Mae West (*I'm No Angel* 1933)

In an attempt to gee up his sex life a bloke buys some flavoured condoms and tries them out on his girlfriend.

She's up for it so he asks her to go under the covers to try and guess which flavour he's chosen.

"Mmm" she says, "smokey bacon?" – to which he replies,

"What? I haven't put it on yet!"

A man's willy is severed in an industrial accident.

His doctor tells him that it will be possible to fit an artificial willy which would be just as good as his original, if not better. The doctor tells him that it won't be cheap, it will cost £1,000 an inch, but he is due £9,000 compensation. He tells him to consider carefully what to do next, to discuss the issue with his wife, as she might be a bit put out if he decided to go for 9 inches, or perhaps she would be disappointed if he went for perhaps 5 inches."

Next day the doctor asks him if he has discussed the matter with his wife and if they have reached a decision.

He replies, "Yes, we are going to get a new kitchen."

A bloke goes to the doctor complaining that his sex life is diminishing with age.

He's 94 and the doctor reassures him that this is normal. He's not happy about this so the doctor asks him when he first noticed it was happening:

"Twice last night and once this morning."

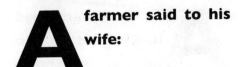

A farmer said to his wife:

"If you had bigger boobs we could get rid of the dairy cow."

She replied,

"If you had a bigger dick we could get rid of the farm hand as well."

An embarrassed bloke goes to the doctor, he shows the doctor his problem - he has a green ring around his penis.

The doctor tells him that there is nothing that he can do.

"That's hardly fair" complained the bloke,

"One of my mates came in last week with a red ring around

his member and you cured him immediately."

"Yes," said the doctor, "lipstick is hardly a medical challenge, but gangrene is a completely different matter."

A woman goes into a sex shop looking for a new vibrator. The shopkeeper is delighted with his new range and goes through half a dozen or so. Noticing that the most impressive one has been left out she enquires: "What's that big tartan one on the end there?" Gasping, he replies,

"You can't have that one, love – that's my Thermos flask."

What have a soya bean and a vibrator got in common?

They're both meat substitutes.

Why do some women choose a bloke over a vibrator?

Because a vibrator can't get the drinks in or paint the hallway.

What's the difference between a stick-up and a hold-up?

Age.

Did you hear about the stressed condom?

It was pissed off.

Why do women
have boobs?

So men will talk to them.

A guy walks into a pub with a snake on a lead.

The landlord asks him if it's poisonous and when he finds out it is, he asks what would happen if it bit someone.

"You would just get someone to suck the poison out" is the casual reply.

"But what if it bit some guy on the knob?"

"Then he would find out who his friends are."

"Love is the answer – but while you're waiting for the answer sex raises some pretty good questions."
(Woody Allen)

King Arthur was preparing to go on a quest that would take him away from Camelot for a long time.

He was worried about leaving Queen Guinevere alone with all those randy Knights of the Round Table.

So he went to Merlin for some advice. The good wizard showed him his latest invention - a chastity belt with a large hole in it.

"This is no good, Merlin!" Arthur exclaimed,

"Look at this opening. How is this supposed to protect the Queen?"

"Ah, sire, just observe," said Merlin as he selected his most worn-out wand and inserted it in the gaping aperture of the chastity belt, whereupon a small guillotine blade came down and cut it neatly in two.

"Merlin, you are a genius!" said the grateful monarch, "Now I can leave, knowing that my Queen is fully protected."

After putting Guinevere in the device, King Arthur then set out upon his quest. Several years passed until he returned to Camelot. Immediately he assembled all his knights in the courtyard and instructed them to drop their trousers for a formal inspection.

Sure enough! Each and everyone of them was either amputated or damaged in some way. All except Sir Galahad.

"Sir Galahad," exclaimed King Arthur,

"The one and only true knight! Only you among the nobles have been true to me. What is it in my power to grant you? Name it and it is yours!"

But, alas, Sir Galahad was speechless.

A couple were out celebrating their anniversary.

The husband says,

"The first time I saw you, I wanted to make love to you really badly."

She replied,

"Well, you certainly succeeded."

A woman was a keen gardener.

Every year she was disappointed with her tomatoes whilst her neighbour always had a bumper crop which ripened beautifully. One morning she asked her neighbour for his secret.

He said "Every morning I come down to my garden wearing nothing but my long grey mac and then expose myself to my tomatoes."

A few weeks later the two neighbours bumped into each other and the woman was asked how her tomatoes were doing.

She replied, "I have followed your advice, however my tomatoes are still green and tiny. Mind you, I have a bumper crop of cucumbers!"

Rugby

. . . . is a game played by men with funny shaped balls.

Two women were sitting by a river watching young men from a rowing club training.

One says to the other "It's their small cox that I fancy."

Her friend asked "Really, how can you tell?"

Buddy went round to pick up Peggy Sue.

She was not quite ready so Peggy Sue's father invited Buddy to sit with him on the veranda. Her dad asks Buddy where he intends to take his daughter.

"I thought that we would go to the pictures."

Peggy Sue's dad replies, "I wouldn't if I were you, she doesn't like the pictures, what she likes best of all is to spend the night screwing."

Buddy is staggered and says "Are you sure?"

"Oh yes, replies Peggy Sue's dad, "she loves to spend all night screwing, often she comes home on a Saturday night exhausted."

Twenty minutes after leaving home with Buddy, Peggy Sue

returns dishevelled and is in a foul mood. She greets her dad,

"Dad, why do you have to ruin everything? The dance is called the Twist!"

"A man in the house is worth two in the street." (Mae West – *Belle of the Nineties* 1934)

What does an Essex girl use for protection when having sex?

A bus shelter.

"I am a marvellous housekeeper. Every time I leave a man, I keep his house." (Zsa Zsa Gabor)

Back in the 1950s, three Italian women were working in a field on a hot summer's day.

One woman said,

"I wish I could be Sophia Loren. She is beautiful, has a glamorous life, beautiful clothes and beautiful jewellery, what could be better? Who would you wish you could be?"

The second woman said "I wish I could be Tia Maria, I hear she is the world's greatest liqueur."

The third woman says, "I wish I could be Virginia Pipalinia."

"WHO?" say the other two women in unison.

The woman puts her hand inside her bra and takes out an old newspaper cutting. She unfolds the cutting and shows it to the other women and they read the headline,

"Virginia pipeline laid by 5,000 men in 6 months."

"Love is just a system for getting someone to call you darling after sex."
(Julian Barnes)

A nurse comments to her colleague about a patient.

"The man in bed 12 has got Lado tatooed on his willy."

"I don't think so. When I gave him a bed bath this morning it clearly read Llandudno."

A man is shopping in a department store when he sees a little girl wandering about crying.

He asks her what is wrong and tries to calm her down. She replies,

"I have lost my mummy."

The man responds,

"Don't worry, I am sure we will find her. What's she like?"

The little girl responded,

"Vodka and big willies."

"Is that a gun in your pocket, or are you just pleased to see me." **(Mae West)**

Two nuns were sat on a bench and a streaker ran past.

One had a stroke, the other wasn't quick enough.

A hitch-hiking nun was picked up by a lorry driver.

He stopped for lunch, after lunch he seduced her. The lorry driver was ashamed of himself and asked the nun what she would say to her Mother Superior?

"I will tell her I was seduced twice by a lorry driver – you will be stopping for tea won't you?"

Two nuns on a tandem cycle over some cobbles on the way into town.

One says to the other "I've never come this way before."

The other replies, "Yes, I think it must be the cobbles."

Two nuns sharing a communal bath.

One says to the other, "Where's the soap?"

The other replies "Oh yes — it does, doesn't it?"

A novice nun is in the garden of the convent trying to shoo the birds off the flowers.

She's not having any luck and starts shouting at them, "Fuck off, fuck off."

The Mother Superior comes along just in time to save the soul of her pupil and says,

"Now Sister Mary, that is no way to speak. Tell the birds firmly but politely to shoo – then they'll fuck off."

Four novice nuns go to see the Mother Superior before moving to the next stage of their training.

They are asked if they have ever touched a man's penis.

The first nun says she once touched the end of a man's penis and she is told to wash her finger in the holy water. The second nun admits to giving a man a 'hand job',

Mother Superior pulls a face and tells her to scrub her hands clean.

Then one of the other nuns grabs a glass, dips it into the holy water, takes a drink and then gargles. The Mother Superior is taken aback, "What are you doing?"

The nun replies "If you think that I am going to wash my mouth out in holy water after Mary has cleaned her arse in it, you can think again!"

A nun in a bath is disturbed by a knock on the door.

"It's the blind man." says a voice on the other side.

Deciding that he would be no affront to her vow of chastity she allows him in.

On entering he says "Nice tits love – now where do you want this blind?"

To spice up their love life a man suggests to his partner that they swap positions.

She responds by saying,

"Fine, you spend the night standing by the ironing board, I will sit on the sofa drinking and farting."

A group of girlfriends go on holiday.

They see a five-storey hotel with a sign that reads "For Women Only".

Since they are without their boyfriends, they decide to go in. The Bouncer, a very attractive guy, explains to them how it works.

"We have 5 floors ... go up floor by floor, and once you find what you are looking for, you can stay there. It's easy to decide, since each floor has signs telling you what's inside."

So they start going up, and on the first floor the sign reads,

"All the men here are horrible lovers, but they are sensitive and kind" ...the friends laugh and without hesitation move on to the next floor.

The sign on the second floor reads, "All the men here are wonderful lovers, but they generally treat women badly."

This won't do, so the friends move up to the third floor where the sign reads, "All the men here are great lovers and sensitive to the needs of women."

This is good but there are still two more floors. On to the fourth floor. The sign is "Perfect, all the men here have perfect builds; are sensitive and attentive to women, and are perfect lovers. They are also single, rich and straight."

The women are pleased but they decide that they would rather see what the fifth floor has to offer.

When they reach the fifth floor, the sign reads, "There are no men here. This floor was built only to prove that it is impossible to please a woman."

A man is walking along a beach one morning and he sees an old bottle with a cork in it.

He picks up the bottle and pulls out the cork. A genie comes out and says, "Oh master, your wish is my command."

The man says "I would like a penis that reaches the ground."

54

The genie says "Oh master, your wish is my command."

There is a huge cloud of smoke and the sound of lightning.

Then the genie chops his legs off.

A man is walking along a beach one morning and he sees an old bottle with a cork in it.

He picks up the bottle and pulls out the cork. A genie comes out and says, "Oh master, your wish is my command."

The man says "I want all women to find me attractive and sensual."

The genie says "Oh master, your wish is my command."

There is a huge cloud of smoke and the sound of lightning.

Then the genie turns him into a box of chocolates.

A couple going to a fancy dress party decide to go as a cow and a bull.

They take a short cut on the way across the fields.

Unfortunately in one of the fields there is a bull which starts charging at them.

"Oh fuck, what shall we do?" screamed the woman,

"Well I am gonna run like hell, but you had better brace yourself." replies the man.

"Women need a reason to have sex. Men just need a place." (**Billy Crystal**)

Aman has been invited to a fancy dress party, he rings up a local fancy dress shop, suggests a couple of ideas and makes an appointment to pick up a costume.

His first idea is to go as Adam. He is given a plastic fig leaf to try on. It barely covers him, so the shopkeeper brings him a larger leaf which is not much better. The shopkeeper then fetches his largest fig leaf. The customer says,

"I can't go like that, I would be arrested for indecent exposure."

So the shopkeeper says,

"Let's try your other suggestion. Put your dick in your ear and go as a petrol pump."

Two nurses went for a night out on the town, had too much to drink and missed the last bus home.

By the time they get back to the nurses home the front door has been locked, so they decide to go round the back to break in. As they are climbing over the back fence, one nurse says to the other,

"I feel like one of those Royal Marine Commandos."

She replies, "Yes, but where can you find one at this time of night?"

"A hard man is good to find." (**Mae West**)

Why do men have problems making eye contact with women?

Because breasts don't have eyes.

Two women decide that for a change they will go out on the town and leave their husbands to look after the children.

They have too much to drink, spend all their money and miss the last bus home. Half way home they both desperately need to relieve themselves. They decide to nip into the cemetery, then discover that they have nothing to wipe themselves with. One woman decides to use her knickers, the other sees a piece of ribbon and uses it to wipe herself.

The next day one of the husbands rings the other husband, he is fuming,

"My wife is never going out with your wife again, she came back in a drunken state with no knickers."

The other bloke says, "Too right my wife is not going out with your wife again, she came home totally drunk with a card stuck to her backside. It said,

"From everyone at the fire station. We will never forget you!"

A female officer in the armed forces is sent to a new posting.

She doesn't arrive at the base until late. She reports to the guard and as she is hungry asks where she can get a meal.

"Mess with the men" barks the guard.

"I intend to" she replies, "but I really must have something to eat first."

"As I said, you get your meals in the mess, with the men."

A promiscuous teenager was being interviewed by the educational psychiatrist who asked her,

"Do you suffer from erotic dreams?"

"No, not at all, actually I really enjoy them."

A woman walked into a pub and asked the landlord for a double entendre.

So he gave her one.

A man checked into a hotel on a business trip and was a bit lonely, so he thought,

"I'll get one of those women you see advertised in the phone books under "Escorts and Massages." He opened the phone book to an ad for a woman calling herself Erotique, a lovely woman, bending over in the photo. She had all the right curves, in all the right places, beautiful long wavy hair, long graceful legs all the way up. You know the kind. So he is in his room, and figures what the hell, and he makes a call.

"Hello?" the woman says. 'God she sounds sexy!' the man thinks.

"Hi, I hear you give a great massage and I'd like you to come to my room and give me one. No, wait, I should be straight with you. I'm in town all alone and what I really want is sex. I want it hard, I want it hot, and I want it now. I'm talking kinky the whole night long. You name it, we'll do it. Bring implements, toys, everything you've got in your bag of tricks. We'll go hot and heavy all night. Tie me up, cover me in chocolate syrup and whipped cream, anything you want, baby. Now, how does that sound?"

She says, "That sounds fantastic, but for an outside line, you need to press 9."

Two punks were walking across Trafalgar Square and one said to the other,

"What would you do if a bird crapped on your head?"

"Don't know" said the other punk, "but I doubt if I would go out with her again."

Patrick the postman was due to retire and was on his last round.

At the first house he came to, he was invited in by the elderly couple and given a cup of coffee and a book token.

At the next house a middle aged-woman asked him in, gave him a cup of coffee and a hand-knitted jumper.

At the following house, the home of a rich businessman, with a young trophy bimbo wife, he was also asked in. She took Patrick by the hand, led him upstairs to her bedroom where she made wild, mad, passionate love to him for an hour and a half. He could not believe he wasn't dreaming, it was beyond his wildest fantasies (and Patrick the postman had some pretty wild fantasies). She then led him downstairs to the kitchen where she gave him the most magnificent breakfast that he had ever eaten: bacon, sausage, black pudding, eggs, mushrooms, tomatoes – the lot. When he finished his breakfast, the bimbo brought him a jug of freshly brewed coffee. Patrick noticed that underneath his saucer was a crisp £5 note.

Patrick asked,

"What is the £5 for?"

The bimbo replied,

"I told my husband that it was your last round before you retired and that I thought we ought to show our gratitude for all your hard work delivering the post. I suggested my five star breakfast, but my husband said, 'Patrick the postman? Fuck him - give him a fiver.'"

On hearing of a shortage at a sperm bank two London lads decide to make donations.

Unfortunately, one came on the bus and the other missed the tube.

A girl was getting rather frustrated at the slow progress she was making with her boyfriend, so she said to him,

"Would you like to see where I had my appendix out?" he replied, "No thanks, I can't stand hospitals."

A couple are at the cinema and the bloke is frustrated with the rather slow progress he is making.

So he opens his fly and guides his girlfriend's hand down to his penis.

"Stop this at once!" she snaps,

"You know you are not allowed to smoke in the cinema."

82

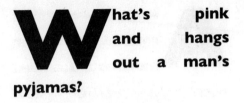

What's pink and hangs out a man's pyjamas?

His wife or his mother.

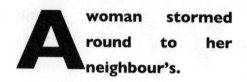

A woman stormed round to her neighbour's.

"I am disgusted, your boy has been peeing in the snow again."

"Well what is so wrong with that, lots of little boys pee in the snow?"

"He has written my daughter's name."

84

"Well what's wrong with that, they are both friends?"

"But it's in her handwriting."

"I want to tell you a terrific story about oral contraception. I asked a girl to sleep with me and she said, No."
(Woody Allen)

A young bull and an old bull are in the top field.

The young bull says to the old bull,

"Look at the bottom field, it is full of cows, why don't we run down and shag a couple of them?"

The old bull replies, "No, why don't we saunter down and shag them all?"

Why does it take one million sperm to fertilise one egg?

None of them will stop to ask directions.

When God created man,

. . . . why didn't he give him enough blood to operate his brain and the other vital organ at the same time?

A consignment of Viagra has been stolen.

The police are looking for a gang of hardened criminals.

An old man of 94 goes to the doctors and asks to be prescribed Viagra.

The doctor is rather surprised at the request and tells his patient that he is probably a 'little old' to need Viagra.

The old man replies, "I know I am too old for any of that sexual shenanigans stuff, but I am tired of peeing on my shoes."

Two women visit the zoo to look at the gorilla.

Unfortunately as his cage had not been securely locked the gorilla leaped out and dragged one of the women in. He ripped off her clothes and made mad, wild, passionate love to her. The zookeepers tried to rescue the woman, but had to retreat for their own safety. For two hours the gorilla had his filthy, dirty animal way with her, before pausing for a breather.

At this point the woman was dragged out of the cage and taken off to hospital in an ambulance.

Two days later the woman was sent home.

Her friend rang her, "I don't know what to say, you must be

distraught, distressed, you must be beside yourself."

The woman replied, "Too right I'm distraught, distressed and I am totally beside myself, I don't know what to do."

"He hasn't phoned, he hasn't written, he hasn't tried to send a message through a friend...."

A woman meets her mate for coffee because she's heard a nasty rumour.

"Jean" she says "How dare you! You've been telling everyone that my husband's got a wart on the end of his dick."

Her mate, obviously embarrassed at being found out, replies "Dolly, I'm sorry. I think you've been the victim of the rumour mill. What I actually said was it FEELS like your husband's got a wart on the end of his dick."

"My computer dating bureau came up with the perfect gentleman. Still I get another three goes." (Sally Poplin)

What do a clitoris, an anniversary and a toilet have in common?

Men usually miss them.

A little girl is playing in the garden and accidentally gets a thorn in her hand.

She runs into the house and asks her mum "Can I have a glass of cider?"

"What?" Says mum,

She replies, "When my sister gets a prick in her hand she says she has to get it in cider."

How do you titillate an ocelot?

Oscillate its tit a lot.

A pair of newlyweds arrived at the hotel where they were spending the first night of their honeymoon.

They opened the champagne and began undressing. When the bridegroom removed his socks, his new wife asked,

"Ewww what's wrong with your feet?

Your toes look all mangled and weird, why are your feet so gross?"

"I had tolio as a child," he answered.

"Don't you mean polio?" she asked.

"No, tolio, the disease only affected my toes."

Satisfied with the explanation, they continued undressing.

When the groom took off his trousers, his bride once again wrinkled up her nose.

"What's wrong with your knees?" she asked. "They're all lumpy and deformed!"

"As a child, I also had kneasles," he explained.

"Don't you mean measles?" she asked.

"No, kneasles. It was a strange

illness that only affected my knees."

The new bride had to be satisfied with this answer.

As the undressing continued, her husband at last removed his underwear.

"Don't tell me," she said. "Let me guess ... smallcox?"

An elderly couple, a middle-aged couple, and a young newly-married couple wanted to join the church.

The vicar said, "We have special requirements for new parishioners. You must abstain from sex for a four-week period."

The couples agreed and came back at the end of the four weeks.

The vicar went to the elderly couple and asked, "Were you able to abstain from sex for the four weeks?"

The old man replied, "No problem at all, vicar"

"Congratulations! Welcome to the church!" said the vicar.

The vicar then went to the middle-aged couple and asked, "Were you able to abstain?"

The man responded, "The first week was easy, the second week was not too bad, but the third and fourth weeks I had to sleep on the couch several nights."

"Congratulations! Welcome to the church!" said the vicar.

He then approached the newlywed couple and asked, "Were you able to abstain from sex for the four weeks?"

"No, vicar. We were not able to go without sex for four weeks," the young man said, sadly.

"What happened?" enquired the vicar.

"Well, we made it through three whole weeks, then my wife was reaching for a can of paint on the top shelf and dropped it. When she bent over to pick it up, I was overcome with lust and took advantage of her right there."

"Well," the vicar stated. "You realise this means you will not be welcome in our church?"

"We know," said the young man shaking his head,

"We're not welcome at *Homebase* anymore either."

At the end of the Second World War, Pierre the great French fighter pilot returns home to Paris to his lover Fifi.

Togezzer, zey retire to ze boudoir, and togezzer, zey begeen to make ze love.... ...Pierre, he take ze wine, and slowly, he pour ze wine all over ze breasts of ze lovely Mam'selle Fifi... and slowly, he lick off ze wine! Fifi ees getting a leetle excited! Pierre, he take ze *Cointreau*. Slowly, gently, he pour ze *Cointreau* into ze navel and zen slowly, gently, he lick out ze *Cointreau*! Fifi ees getting very excited! Zen, Pierre, he take ze cognac, and slowly, delicately, he treeckle ze cognac over zee *ahem! hi haw hi haw!* private parts of ze exqueeseete Fifi . . . and zen, he set light to ze cognac!!

Fifi, she cry: "Pierre!! Qu'est-ce que tu fais??!!" Ze great fighter pilot, he reply:

"Mademoiselle, when Pierre goes down, he goes down in flames!!!"

"I am the boss in our house. It's just that my wife makes all the decisions." **(Woody Allen)**

A woman asks her mate "Do you smoke after sex?"

"I dunno," she replies,

"I've never looked."

Aman was having trouble satisfying his wife.

He was only trying to stimulate her clematis by mistake.

After several years of marriage a man confides to his wife that he's not happy in the bedroom and that the spark they once shared is all but gone.

"Can you do something for me?" he asks her, "I've got an idea, why don't you moan during sex?"

So the next time they're getting down to it, it's going really well, they're relighting the fire and she says "Why don't you buy me flowers anymore? AND, you've never cleaned out the fridge!"

"How many husbands have I had? You mean apart from my own?" (**Zsa Zsa Gabor**)

What do men and tights have in common?

They either cling, run or don't fit the crotch very well.

A pub advertises for new bar staff, three women apply so the landlord decides to give them a night's trial.

Each night he leaves a ten pound note at the back of the bar.

The first barmaid carefully slides it up her sleeve when nobody is watching.

The second barmaid picks up the tenner, looks at it and then decides to put it in the till.

The third barmaid picks up the tenner, walks up to the landlord and tells him that she found ten pounds at the back of the bar.

Who got the job?

The one with the biggest boobs.

How can you tell if a man is sexually excited?

Check if he is breathing.

Why do women rub their eyes in the morning?

Because they don't have balls to scratch.

What is a man's idea of foreplay?

Pleading and begging for half an hour.

_or_

Prodding you to see if you are awake.

A new member of staff at a bakery was undergoing training on their first day.

The master baker took out his false teeth and started crimping the Cornish pasties.

"Don't you have a tool that you can use?" asked the trainee.

The master baker replied, "I save that for the doughnuts."

What is the difference between medium and rare?

Six inches is medium.

Eight inches is rare.

Two old ladies are at a dance.

One lady says to the other, "Do you remember the minuet."

She replies, "No, I can't even remember the ones I shagged."

Two Aussie travellers arrive in London after a long journey via Europe.

Keen to check out the local fellas, one says to the other: "Where d'you think all the talent is in this town? Do we go to the City, East End, West End, Notting Hill, Clapham Junction?"

"I reckon we go to the Houses

of Parliament to try and score an MP. I heard that they've got a really hot one called Big Ben — gotta meet him!"

"I dress for women, and undress for men." **(Angie Dickinson)**

A little girl runs out into the garden to her dad.

"Dad, what's sex?" she asked.

Believing that it was best to be frank and honest with his children, he sat her down and explained: sperm, eggs, conception, contraception, periods and the importance of loving relationships.

126

"Why did you ask the question?" he asked his daughter.

The little girl replied,

"Mum asked me to run out into the garden and tell you that lunch will be ready in a few secs."

Why are men like snow?

You don't know when it's coming, how much you are going to get or how long it will last.